WALTER

D1548609

Electronic Circuit Analysis

Macmillan Series in Electrical Science
Roger F. Harrington, Editor

Electronic Circuit Analysis

Couros Ghaznavi
University of Bridgeport

Arthur H. Seidman
Pratt Institute

The Macmillan Company, New York
Collier-Macmillan Limited, London

The Macmillan Company
866 Third Avenue, New York, New York 10022
Collier-Macmillan Canada, Ltd., Toronto, Ontario

Library of Congress catalog card number: 71-146618

First Printing

To our families
PARVIN and INA
and
LENORE, REBECCA,
and BEN

Contents

Electronic Circuit
Analysis

Introduction

If one were to demand a nutshell description of the tasks of an electronics engineer, the answer would have to be that his chief activities are *analysis* and *synthesis* of networks. Analysis is required in seeking information about the behavior of a circuit. For example, analysis of a network yields such data as the voltage across a branch, the current flowing through a particular element, or the power gain of an amplifier.

Synthesis is used in the design of circuits. Given a set of specifications for a network, how can the network be physically realized? This type of question is answered with the aid of synthesis, and usually there is no unique solution. It should be emphasized, however, that analysis is also employed. During the synthesis and upon its completion, the resulting circuit is analyzed to determine if the specifications are satisfied.

In using either analysis or synthesis, it becomes necessary to develop a representation, or *model*, of the device under consideration. The engineer must somehow simplify the physical device so it becomes amenable to analysis. Once the model is established, the engineer can then proceed with the analysis or synthesis of a network.

1.1 The Physical World

The engineer deals with a variety of physical components : *passive* elements such as resistors, inductors, capacitors, transformers, and diodes; and *active* devices, such as transistors. Passive elements cannot furnish power gain; active ones are capable of yielding power gain.

Values attributed to the components vary with operating conditions. For example, the value of a resistor will tend to increase with the frequency of current flowing through it; this is referred to as skin effect. Further, if the resistor is made of a carbon compound, its value will decrease as the ambient temperature rises. For a wirewound type, the opposite is true; that is, the resistance increases with increasing temperature.

1

Let us examine now the leads of a simple resistor. Because a pair of leads can act as two plates of a capacitor with the dielectric being the surrounding air, a shunting capacitance appears across the resistor. In addition, the leads themselves behave as inductors at high frequencies. At very high frequencies the resistance may even act as an antenna radiating electromagnetic energy. Taking these factors into account, one can derive a model of the "simple" resistor valid for a large range of frequencies, as illustrated in Fig. 1.1.

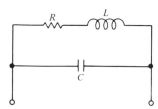

Fig. 1.1   Model of a resistor that is valid for a large range of frequencies.

At high frequencies, the models for an inductor and a capacitor also became rather complex. But to deal with relatively complex models when they can be simplified is a waste of time and effort. For example, at dc or low frequencies, the model reduces to resistance R.

The engineer, just as the physicist, is always concerned with the simplification of reality. He must, however, be on his guard not to oversimplify the problem. For a simple and effective analysis of a problem, only the non-essentials have to be stripped away.

1.2   Linearity and Nonlinearity

The preceding discussion did not indicate the manner in which resistance varies with current flow or impressed voltage. One may ask whether resistance is independent of, or increases (or decreases) directly, or as the square of, or as a higher power of, current or voltage. This leads to the following basic consideration: What is meant by linearity and nonlinearity of devices or components? Let us look at some examples that will help answer the question.

Consider a resistor in series with a dc voltage source. Suppose the resistance is a function of current I flowing through it. This can be stated as

$$R = f(I).   \tag{1.1}$$

Curves of a resistance that obeys (1.1) and one which is independent of current are shown in Fig. 1.2. The resistance given by (1.1) is said to be *nonlinear*, because its value depends on current flow; a resistance that is independent of current is called *linear*.

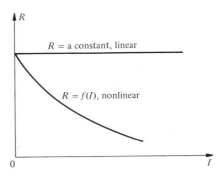

Fig. 1.2 Examples of linear and non-linear resistances.

As another example, for the magnetization curve of an iron core inductor, the slope at any point on the curve is defined as the incremental permeability μ:

$$\mu = \Delta B / N\Delta I = f(I), \tag{1.2}$$

where B = flux density; $N\Delta I$ = ampere turns/meter.

Inductance is a function of permeability, but the permeability depends on current (1.2) for an iron core inductor. Therefore, inductance is a function of current:

$$L = f(I). \tag{1.3}$$

Equation (1.3) is that of a nonlinear inductor. A coil wound on an air core is an example of a linear inductor.

Let us examine now the concepts of linearity and nonlinearity from a mathematical point of view. Consider a series RLC circuit; assuming all elements are linear, that is, independent of current or voltage, one can describe the behavior of the circuit by a differential equation:

$$Ri + L\, di/dt + (1/C) \int i\, dt = v(t). \tag{1.4}$$

Equation (1.4) is a linear differential equation with constant coefficients. It is linear because the derivatives and integrals are to the first power. Some nonlinear differential equations are

$$aL(di/dt)^2 + Ri + (1/C) \int i\, dt = v(t) \tag{1.5}$$

and

$$bLi(di/dt) + Ri + (1/C) \int i\, dt = v(t). \tag{1.6}$$

In (1.5) the derivative of i with respect to t is raised to the second power. Although no derivative or integral is raised to a power in (1.6), it is non-linear because the coefficient of (di/dt) contains i, the dependent variable; the product of a dependent variable and its derivative is a nonlinear term, like the squared derivative term in (1.5).

An analytical solution of a linear equation such as (1.4) may be realized by classical techniques or with the aid of Laplace transforms. These methods are straightforward, and an answer is usually obtained with a minimum of effort. Solutions to a nonlinear equation are generally not direct; numerical, graphical, or a combination of methods must be employed. The work in obtaining an answer, and usually only an approximate one, can be time consuming unless a library of programs and a digital or an analog computer are available.

Nature is basically nonlinear in its ways. The resistor, even at dc, is not strictly linear for all ranges of current. The diode, used in changing alternating current to a unidirectional current and in numerous other applications, is a nonlinear device. The transistor, the vacuum tube, and many other active devices are also nonlinear. In analyzing these components the engineer can either deal with nonlinearities as he finds them or develop a *linear model* that will be valid for a particular range of operation. If the first course is chosen, the effort required to effect a solution to a nonlinear problem is quite formidable. On the other hand, if the linear approach is taken, very often a solution may be realized with simple algebra.

As an example of the latter approach, consider a transistor amplifier. The transistor exhibits nonlinear characteristics. For small signals, however, the device behaves as though it were linear. This is because the signal swings over a small region of the characteristic curve, and a small region of a nonlinear curve can generally be considered linear. Hence, the engineer could treat the transistor as a linear device for small-signal operation and use linear analysis to obtain a solution. When large signals are present, the engineer's approach is different. Here, graphical analysis, piecewise-linear analysis (described later in the text), or the computer is used.

The Taylor series may be used to show why it is possible to treat a device with nonlinear characteristics as a linear one for small signals. With a function of single variable $i = f(v)$ assumed, the Taylor series may be written as

$$i = f(v)\bigg|_{v=V_q} + \frac{df(v)}{dv}\bigg|_{v=V_q}(v - V_q) + \frac{1}{2!}\frac{d^2f(v)}{dv^2}\bigg|_{v=V_q}(v - V_q)^2 + \cdots$$

$$+ \frac{1}{n!}\frac{d^nf(v)}{dv^n}\bigg|_{v=V_q}(v - V_q)^n. \tag{1.7}$$

Term $f(v)|_{v=V_q}$ denotes a fixed dc operating point for the device, and term $(v - V_q)$ denotes variation with respect to the fixed operating point. For small values, that is, $(v - V_q) \ll 1$, terms containing $(v - V_q)^2$ and higher may be neglected. Equation (1.7) therefore reduces to a linear expression:

$$i = f(v)\bigg|_{v=V_q} + \frac{df(v)}{dv}\bigg|_{v=V_q} (v - V_q). \qquad (1.8)$$

1.3 The Superposition Theorem

Briefly, the superposition theorem states that for a *linear* circuit with many input sources, the total response is equal to the sum of the responses of each source taken separately, with all other sources set to zero (voltage sources are shorted and current sources are open circuited). This theorem is useful for solving many problems in electronic circuits. It must be emphasized that the theorem can be applied only to linear circuits; it is not applicable to nonlinear circuits—as illustrated by the following example.

Example 1.1

In the circuit of Fig. 1.3, assume resistance $R(v)$ is a function of applied voltage v, as shown in Fig. 1.4. Find the current I.

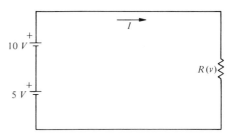

Fig. 1.3 Application of the superposition theorem.

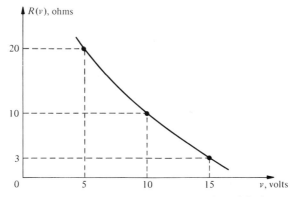

Fig. 1.4 A plot of a nonlinear resistance $R(v)$ as a function of the impressed voltage v.

Solution

(A) Incorrect Solution

Applying the superposition theorem, for the 10-V source (the 5-V source is shorted):

$$I_{10} = v/R(v) = 10/10 = 1 \text{ A}.$$

The value of $R(v) = 10$ ohms for $v = 10$ V was obtained from Fig. 1.4.

Considering the 5-V source (the 10-V battery is shorted), $R(v) = R(5 \text{ V}) = 20$ ohms, as obtained from Fig. 1.4. Hence,

$$I_5 = 5/20 = 0.25 \text{ A}.$$

The total current I is

$$I = I_{10} + I_5 = 1 + 0.25 = 1.25 \text{ A}.$$

(B) Correct Solution

By adding the 5- and 10-V sources together and referring to Fig. 1.4, one obtains the resistance for $v = 15$ V, $R(15 \text{ V}) = 3$ ohms. Therefore,

$$I = 15/3 = 5 \text{ A}.$$

Note that the answers are different. The superposition theorem cannot be applied to nonlinear circuits; in this example, the correct answer was $I = 5$ A.

1.4 Solving Nonlinear Problems

A situation often encountered in the analysis of electronic circuits containing nonlinearities is illustrated in Fig. 1.5. A dc source V, in series with

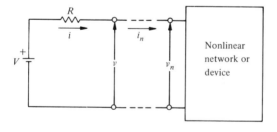

Fig. 1.5 A general problem in satisfying the condition i equals i_n and v equals v_n.

resistance R, is to be connected to a nonlinear device or network (represented by a box). The voltage-current $(v_n - i_n)$ characteristics of the nonlinear element are known. When the series circuit composed of V and R is connected to the nonlinear network, $v = v_n$ and $i = i_n$ must always be satisfied. Two methods, graphical and piecewise-linear analysis, used to advantage in the solution of problems involving nonlinear operation, will now be examined.

The piecewise-linear method is applicable to circuits containing no energy storage elements. Figure 1.6 shows a voltage source V in series with a linear

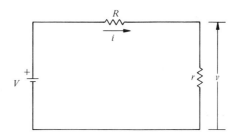

Fig. 1.6 Series circuit including a nonlinear resistance r.

resistance R and a nonlinear resistance r. A voltage-current curve of r is shown in Fig. 1.7 as curve a. The curve is nonlinear, and the value of r depends on a particular value of current i, or voltage v. Assume the curve of Fig. 1.7 can be approximated by using the first three terms of (1.7) to yield a power series:

$$i = A + Bv + Cv^2. \tag{1.9}$$

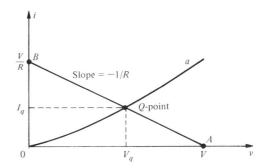

Fig. 1.7 Finding the Q-point graphically.

Representing a nonlinear curve by a power series is used often in obtaining an approximate solution.

Applying Kirchhoff's voltage law to the circuit of Fig. 1.6, one obtains

$$V = Ri + v, \tag{1.10}$$

which is an equation of a straight line with the form $y = mx + b$. Finding the values of the voltage across resistance r and the current i analytically by solving (1.9) and (1.10) is time consuming. A simple approach is to solve the problem graphically.

Equation (1.10) can be thought of as the volt-ampere characteristic of the circuit of Fig. 1.6. Consequently, if this equation is plotted or superimposed

on the characteristic curve a (Fig. 1.7) of the nonlinear resistance, the intersection of the two curves will yield a solution. Because (1.10) is an equation of
a straight line, only two points are required for its specification.

Setting $i = 0$ in (1.10) yields

$$v = V, \tag{1.11a}$$

which is plotted as point A on Fig. 1.7. Now with $v = 0$,

$$V = Ri$$

or for i,

$$i = V/R, \tag{1.11b}$$

which is point B on Fig. 1.7. A line is drawn (with slope $-1/R$) between the
two points, and the point of intersection of the line with the curve gives the
values of the voltage V_q, across r, and current I_q; the problem is solved.
Values V_q and I_q are often referred to as the dc operating, or *quiescent* (Q),
point for the circuit.

It is possible to approximate the nonlinear curve of Fig. 1.7 by linear
elements. An analysis based on this approach is called *piecewise-linear
analysis*. One possibility is illustrated in Fig. 1.8. A line is drawn between the
origin and a point on the curve to yield the best fit, or approximation, to the
actual curve. The inverse slope of the line represents an average resistance R'.

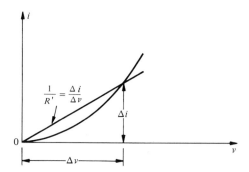

Fig. 1.8 Obtaining the average
resistance R'.

The circuit of Fig. 1.6 can now be solved analytically for V_q and I_q:

$$I_q = V/(R + R') \tag{1.12}$$

$$V_q = VR'/(R + R'). \tag{1.13}$$

The student may be disturbed by errors introduced in using piecewise-
linear analysis. To mitigate his fears, it must be pointed out that the electronics
engineer is not always seeking answers of absolute precision. He realizes that
there are tolerances on physical components. Further, once a circuit is

designed on paper, it is "breadboarded" and tested. The prime reasons for analysis are twofold:

1. To produce an optimum design. Trial and error methods cannot guarantee this.

2. To obtain component values to build his circuit. Choosing component values on a trial and error basis is inefficient and time consuming.

1.5 Incremental Analysis

If there are small variations of current or voltage about the Q-point of Fig. 1.7 incremental analysis may be employed. An incremental resistance r' is defined which has a constant value for operation near the operating point. The value of r' is equal to the inverse slope of the line tangent to the actual nonlinear $v - i$ curve at the Q-point.

This may be proven mathematically with the aid of the Taylor series. Equation (1.8) may be written as

$$i - I_q = \frac{df(v)}{dv}\bigg|_{v=V_q}(v - V_q),$$

where $I_q = f(v)|_{v=V_q}$. With $i - I_q = di$ and $v - V_q = dv$,

$$\frac{di}{dv} = \frac{df(v)}{dv}\bigg|_{v=V_q}$$

defines the slope of the tangent to the curve at the Q-point. Incremental resistance r' is equal to $1/(di/dv)$. The use of r' permits a solution based on linear circuit analysis.

Let a small magnitude ac signal v_s be introduced in series with battery V, as illustrated in Fig. 1.9. Suppose the response to the ac signal is desired.

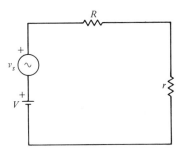

Fig. 1.9 Inserting source v_s in series with V.

Because of the small voltage swing of the ac source, operation is in the region about Q where r is approximately constant. Incremental resistance r' may therefore be used; we have now reduced the problem to a linear one. With the application of the superposition theorem and a consideration of only the ac source, the current i_s due to source v_s is

$$i_s = v_s/(R + r'). \tag{1.14}$$

Some of the preceding statements will now be illustrated with a numerical example.

Example 1.2

For the circuit of Fig. 1.6 a linear resistance $R = 100$ ohms is connected in series with a nonlinear resistance r; $V = 100$ V. Resistance r is defined by the curve of Fig. 1.10.
(a) Find the quiescent operating point for the circuit graphically and by piecewise-linear analysis.
(b) Calculate the power absorbed by the 100-ohms resistor.
(c) Assume a 1-V rms source is introduced in series with the battery. Find the incremental resistance at the Q-point, and compute the rms current due to the 1-V source.

Solution

(a) Writing Kirchhoff's voltage law for the circuit of Fig. 1.6, one obtains

$$100 = 100i + v.$$

$$\text{At } i = 0, v = 100 \text{ V.}$$

$$\text{At } v = 0, i = 100/100 = 1 \text{ A.}$$

These two points define the load line which is superimposed on the $v - i$ characteristics of the nonlinear resistance, as illustrated in Fig. 1.10. The point of intersection of the load line and nonlinear curve yields the Q-point of the circuit at 65 V and 0.4 A.

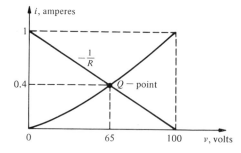

Fig. 1.10 Graphical determination of the Q-point.

By means of piecewise-linear analysis, the v-i curve is approximated by a straight line with slope $1/100 = 0.01$ mho, therefore,

$$100 = (100 + 100)I.$$

Solving for I, one obtains

$$I = 100/200 = 0.5 \text{ A},$$

$$V = 100 \times 0.5 = 50 \text{ V}.$$

A better approximation to the v-i curve could have been made by using two line segments. This will be described in the following chapter and will not be pursued here.

(b) According to the graphical analysis, $P = 100(0.4)^2 = 16$ W. From the results of the piecewise-linear analysis, $P = 100(0.5)^2 = 25$ W.

(c) The incremental resistance is equal to the inverse of the slope of a line drawn tangent to the Q-point (Fig. 1.11). The value is

$$r' = 20/0.2 = 100 \ \Omega.$$

Therefore,

$$i_s = 1/(100 + 100) = 1/200 \text{ A, rms.}$$

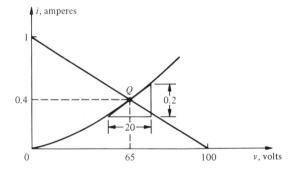

Fig. 1.11   Obtaining the incremental resistance.

1.6   Nonlinear Distortion

For a final look at the problem of nonlinearity, reference is made to the nonlinear curve of Fig. 1.7. Because the curve passes through the origin, it may be approximated by the second and third terms of (1.9):

$$i = Bv + Cv^2. \tag{1.15}$$

Let v be expressed by a sinusoidal signal:

$$v = V_m \sin \omega t. \tag{1.16}$$

Substituting (1.16) in (1.15) and solving for i, one obtains

$$i = BV_m \sin \omega t + CV_m^2 \sin^2 \omega t.$$

But $\sin^2 \omega t = (1 - \cos 2\omega t)/2$; hence,

$$i = BV_m \sin \omega t + CV_m^2/2 - (CV_m^2/2) \cos 2\omega t. \tag{1.17}$$

Equation (1.17) shows that one of the components of output current has twice the frequency of the input signal; thus, something not present at the input appears at the output. This is a property of nonlinear circuits in their behavior to sinusoidal (as well as nonsinusoidal) signals.

The appearance of a component at the output with twice the input frequency is an example of *second harmonic distortion*. Second harmonic distortion is generally a result of large-signal operation of amplifiers, as discussed later in the text. For some electronic processes, however, nonlinear operation is required. An example of this kind of operation is *modulation*, that is, adding intelligence to a carrier frequency for radio transmission, or the inverse process, *demodulation*, which extracts the intelligence signal from the radio wave.

1.7 Computer Aided Design (CAD)

A partnership between the computer and the design of electronic circuits and systems, referred to as *computer aided design* (CAD), has been formed. The alliance will be long lived and will have far-reaching consequences for the engineer. In order to write economical programs and use the computer efficiently, the engineer must have complete mastery of passive and active circuit analysis.

Besides being used for such routine tasks as calculating voltages and currents in multimesh circuits, the computer may be employed for modeling, gained insight into problems by exploring second-order effects, and optimizing networks. Complex electronic circuits and complete systems can be analyzed and designed on the computer.

To design a circuit or system on a computer, the engineer has to communicate his ideas to the computer. As yet, the computer cannot be spoken to verbally and act on voiced instructions to any great extent. Even if a light pen, which permits the engineer to draw a circuit to be analyzed or designed on the face of a cathode ray tube, is used, a program has to be written or an existing program used (examples of available programs include ECAP, NET-1 and 2, NASCAP, and CIRCUS). A chosen program may not be best for either his design or the computer available to the engineer. For example, the ECAP program is available to users of IBM computers. It is well suited for one of their larger machines, such as the IBM 7094; however, the program cannot be readily used on the smaller 1620 unless additional memory is provided.

The analog computer also has a place in the analysis and design of electronic circuits. A combination of analog and digital techniques yields the hybrid computer. The hybrid permits those parts of a problem best fitted for analog solution to be solved in an analog manner and the remaining parts to be solved in digital fashion. Examples of computer-aided analysis using ECAP are considered in the last chapter of the text.

1.8   Summary

The engineer is an inhabitant of a nonlinear world. The resistor, diode, transistor, etc., that he uses in circuits are essentially nonlinear. To analyze or synthesize circuits he derives models of these devices. In order to keep the calculations simple, a linear model is developed wherever possible. In those instances where nonlinearities cannot be ignored, graphical analysis, piecewise-linear analysis, or the computer is used.

References

CLOSE, C. M., *The Analysis of Linear Circuits*, Harcourt Brace Jovanovich, New York, 1966.

KUO, F. F., and P. K. KAISER (eds.), *System Analysis by Digital Computer*, Wiley, New York, 1966.

STERN, T. E., *Theory of Nonlinear Networks and Systems*, Addison-Wesley, Reading, Mass., 1965.

Problems

1.1   Assume that a resistor is represented by the model of Fig. 1.1. If $R = 10$ ohms, $L = 0.1\ \mu H$, and $C = 0.1\ pF$, calculate the impedance across the terminals for the following frequencies: (a) $f = 0$; (b) $f = 1\ kHz$; (c) $f = 10\ GHz$.

1.2   Repeat Prob. 1.1 for $L = 1\ \mu H$ and $C = 10\ pF$.

1.3   For the given values in Prob. 1.1, what is the resonant frequency and Q of the model?

1.4   Repeat Prob. 1.3 for the values of Prob. 1.2.

1.5   Calculate the coefficients of the power series given by (1.9) in terms of the coefficients of the Taylor series expressed by (1.7).

1.6   Using superposition, calculate and plot the output voltage v_o in the circuit of Fig. P1.6 for $v_s = 10 \sin 377t$.

1.7   Repeat Prob. 1.6 for $v_s = 10 \sin 3770t$.

1.8   If, in Prob. 1.6, the 10-volt dc source is replaced by a sinusoidal source $5 \sin 1000t$, what is the output voltage v_o?

1.9   In Fig. P1.9, resistance r_i is an incremental resistance. If $r_i = 6$ ohms, find v_o and i_o due to the sinusoidal source v_s.

1.10   Repeat Prob. 1.9 for $r_i = 16$ ohms.

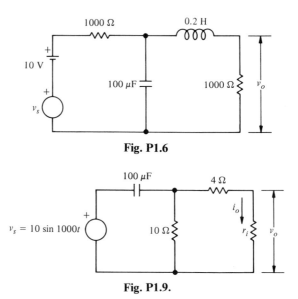

Fig. P1.6

Fig. P1.9.

1.11   Figure P1.11A shows a circuit containing a nonlinear resistance r; the i-v characteristic curve for r is given in Fig. P1.11B. (a) Determine graphically the quiescent-operating (Q) point if $V = 6$ V. (b) How much power is absorbed by r? (c) Find the incremental resistance at the Q point.

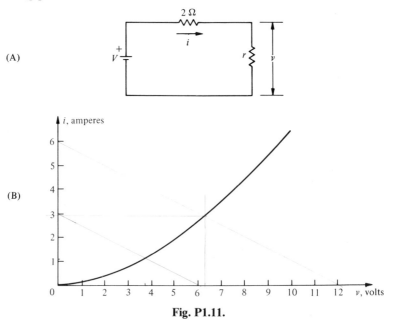

Fig. P1.11.

1.12   Repeat Prob. 1.11 for $V = 12$ V.

1.13   The characteristic curves of two nonlinear devices are approximated by linear segments in Fig. P1.13. Describe them mathematically.

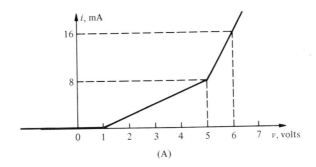

(A)

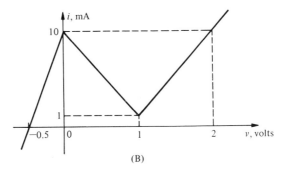

(B)

Fig. P1.13.

1.14   Assume that a nonlinear device is characterized by the following expression:

$$i = Av + Bv^2.$$

If $v = \sin \omega_1 t + \sin \omega_2 t$, determine i. What do you note in your expression for i?

1.15   A device is described by the following expression:

$$i = 2 + v + 0.5v^2.$$

If $v = 10 \sin 377t$, (a) What are the amplitudes and frequencies of the components in i? (b) If the current flows in a 1-ohm resistor, what is the average dissipated power?

The Diode

There exists a class of two-terminal devices that permit current to flow with practically no resistance in one direction and offer nearly infinite resistance to current flowing in the opposite direction. Such devices are called *diodes*. Physically, a diode may be a vacuum tube, a gaseous tube, or a semiconductor. Diodes can be applied to electronic circuits in numerous ways, including rectification of alternating current to yield a unidirectional current, detection of radio waves, wave shaping, and logic gating functions.

In this chapter, after a review of diode action, the ideal diode is defined and different kinds of physical diodes are compared. A model applicable for all types of diodes is then developed. Circuit applications of diodes will be considered in Chapter 4 and in later chapters.

2.1 Summary of Diode Action

This book assumes the reader has taken a course in physical electronics. In this section, therefore, some basic physical principles governing diode action will be highlighted.

Vacuum Tube Diode

To release electrons from a metal, a minimum amount of energy, called the *work function* of the material E_w (in electron volts), is required. The most practical method of supplying energy to the material used to emit or "boil" off electrons in a vacuum tube is to heat the emitter. This process is called *thermionic emission* and the emitter is called the *cathode*. The resulting thermionic current is expressed by the Dushman-Richardson equation:

$$J = AT^2 e^{-eE_w/kT}, \tag{2.1}$$

where J = current density, A/m^2; A = a constant that depends on the cathode material, $A(m^{-2})(°K)^{-2}$; e = charge of electron, 1.6×10^{-19}

Coulomb; E_w = work function of cathode material, eV (1 eV = 1.6×10^{-19} joule); k = Boltzmann's constant, 1.38×10^{-23} joule/°K ; T = temperature of cathode, °K.

Table 2.1   Properties of Cathode Materials

Cathode	E_w (eV)	Operating voltage (V)	Operating temp. (°K)
Tungsten	4.5	> 10,000	2500
Thoriated tungsten	3	10,000 max	1800
Oxide coated	1	1,000 max	1000

Table 2.1 lists three commonly used cathode materials and their important properties. Note that tungsten (E_w = 4.5 eV) requires a much greater operating temperature than the oxide-coated cathode (1 eV). This means that greater energy is needed to free electrons from a tungsten than from an oxide-coated cathode.

If a cathode and another electrode, called the *anode*, or *plate*, are inserted in an evacuated tube, the vacuum tube diode results. The cathode may be heated directly or heated indirectly by a filament wire placed inside the cathode and electrically insulated therefrom. In practice, the heater is not shown and the schematic diagram for the vacuum tube diode appears as shown in Fig. 2.1.

Fig. 2.1   Schematic symbol for a vacuum tube diode.

We shall consider now an experiment. As shown in Fig. 2.2, a diode is connected to a variable plate supply source V_{bb}. The voltage across the tube and the plate current flow are designated V_b and I_b, respectively. Resistor R serves to limit the plate current to a safe value. The cathode is heated to a given temperature by voltage source V_f. For a cathode temperature T_k, source V_{bb} is varied, and readings of V_b and I_b are recorded. This is repeated for different cathode temperatures. Now imagine that the connections of source V_{bb} are reversed, that is, point a is made negative with respect to point b. The diode becomes reverse biased. As the voltage is increased

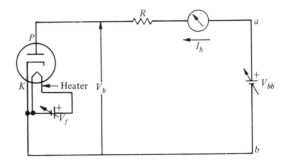

Fig. 2.2 Test circuit for obtaining the characteristics of a vacuum tube diode.

from 0 V in the negative direction, plate current I_b will fall to zero—regardless of the temperature of the cathode. When all the data is collected and plotted, the curves obtained are illustrated in Fig. 2.3. The following facts are observed from the curves:

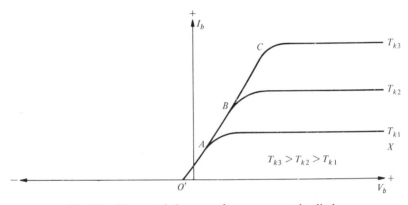

Fig. 2.3 Characteristic curves for a vacuum tube diode.

1. For a given cathode temperature, say T_{k1}, plate current I_b rises as the plate voltage V_b is increased for region $O'A$. From point A on, the plate current is fairly constant as V_b is further increased. Region $O'A$ is the *space-charge* region—the region of normal tube operation; region AX represents the *temperature-saturated* region where all electrons emitted from the cathode are attracted and collected by the plate.

2. If the cathode temperature is increased, temperature saturation occurs at a greater value of plate current.

3. At $V_b = 0$, a small current flows. This is caused by the initial velocity of electrons emitted from the cathode. Some of the electrons have sufficient energy to overcome the negative space charge surrounding the cathode, ultimately reaching the plate of the diode.

4. Current in the reverse direction is zero. The minute current near the origin owing to the initial velocity of electrons discussed previously will be neglected in further discussions.

The equation describing the behavior of an ideal vacuum tube diode containing cylindrical elements in the space-charge region, the Langmuir-Childs, or three-halves power law, is

$$J = 2.33 \times \frac{10^{-6}V_b^{3/2}}{d^2},$$ (2.2)

where J = current density, A/m^2; V_b = plate-cathode voltage, V; d = distance between cathode and plate, m.

When the plate is made positive with respect to the cathode, the tube is said to be *forward* biased. If the plate is negative with respect to the cathode, the tube is *reverse* or *back* biased.

Semiconductor Diode

The basic materials used for making a *p-n* junction diode are germanium (Ge) and silicon (Si), elements found in column IV of the Periodic Table. Both Ge and Si are tetravalent elements; that is, they have 4 valence electrons. In their pure states, the elements are said to be *intrinsic*.

Each element under column III of the Periodic Table has 3 valence electrons and is referred to as trivalent. Examples of trivalent elements include indium (In) and gallium (Ga). Elements in column V of the Table, for example, arsenic (As) and antimony (Sb), have 5 valence electrons and are called pentavalent.

The process of introducing one of the elements from column III or V into intrinsic Ge or Si is called *doping*. The doped material becomes impure or *extrinsic*. If a trivalent impurity is introduced in Ge (or Si), electron vacancies or holes are created, and the material is said to be *p*-type. Introduction of a pentavalent impurity creates free electrons, and the material is *n*-type.

Assume that a single crystal of Ge (or Si) is doped so that half the material is *p*-type and the other half *n*-type. The internal boundary between these two extrinsic regions is called a *p-n junction*. The resulting device is a junction diode (Fig. 2.4).

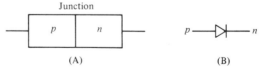

Fig. 2.4   Semiconductor junction diode. (A) Pictorial view. (B) Schematic symbol.

If, in the test circuit of Fig. 2.2, a germanium (or silicon) junction diode is substituted for the vacuum tube diode, the characteristic curve obtained for the semiconductor device appears as shown in Fig. 2.5. The curve may be expressed by the rectification equation:

$$I = I_s(e^{eV/kT} - 1), \tag{2.3}$$

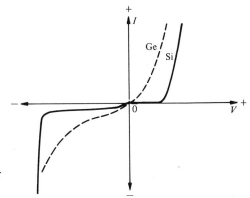

Fig. 2.5 Characteristic curves for semiconductor junction diodes.

where I = diode current, mA; I_s = reverse saturation current, mA (this current is temperature dependent); e = charge of an electron; k = Boltzmann's constant; T = temperature, °K; V = voltage across diode, V. At room temperature (300°K), and for voltages $V > 0.1$ V, (2.3) reduces to

$$I = I_s e^{39V}. \tag{2.4}$$

For $V < -0.1$ V,

$$I = -I_s. \tag{2.5}$$

The characteristic curve of a semiconductor diode differs from the vacuum tube type in three important ways:

1. Conduction in the forward direction does not begin until the *p*-side is positive with respect to the *n*-side by a fraction of a volt. For Ge, the *offset*, or *deadband*, voltage V_o is approximately 0.15–0.3 V and for Si, 0.5–0.7 V at room temperature.

2. Because of leakage current, the back resistance of semiconductor diodes is not infinite. For reverse-bias values more negative than 0.2 V, the average back resistance value is of the order of 50 K for Ge and a few megohms for Si.

3. As the reverse bias is increased, a point is reached (Zener point) at which the reverse current tends to rise rapidly. This sudden rise in reverse current is generally the result of an avalanche effect; the true Zener effect is a rupture of the covalent bonds and occurs at lower voltages. The voltage

at which the current increases rapidly is the Zener voltage, which varies from approximately 2.6 V and up and is primarily dependent on the doping of the semiconductor material. For normal operation, the maximum reverse voltage applied to the diode is kept well below the Zener voltage.

When the semiconductor diode is forward biased, the *p*-side is made positive with respect to the *n*-side. In the reverse-biased condition, the *p*-side is negative with respect to the *n*-side.

2.2   The Ideal Diode

Before analyzing the "real-world" diodes—that is, the physical diodes one would purchase and use—it is instructive to inquire about the nature of the characteristics of an ideal diode. As mentioned earlier in the chapter, the diode is a two-terminal device that offers very little resistance to current flow in one direction, but tends to prevent flow of current in the opposite direction. Based on this behavior, we shall define the ideal diode as one that offers *zero* resistance (acts as a short-circuit or closed switch) to current in one direction and offers *infinite* resistance (acts as an open switch) to current in the opposite direction.

The characteristics of an ideal diode and its electrical symbol are displayed in Fig. 2.6. When the diode is forward biased, the current is said to flow in the forward or easy direction. The voltage across the ideal diode would be zero, regardless of the amount of current flowing through the device. This is shown in Fig. 2.6 by the heavy line along the $+I$ axis at $V = 0$. When the diode is reverse or back biased, its resistance is infinite. Thus, the current flow in a reverse-biased diode is zero, regardless of the magnitude of the reverse voltage. This is indicated in Fig. 2.6 by the heavy line along the $-V$ axis at $I = 0$.

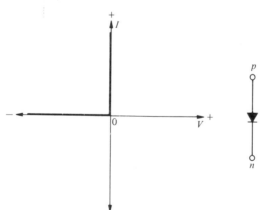

Fig. 2.6   Ideal diode characteristics and symbol.

We are now in a position to introduce a model of the ideal diode. When the diode is forward biased, the p-side is made positive with respect to the n-side, and the diode behaves as a closed switch. For the reverse-biased case (the p-side is negative with respect to the n-side), the diode acts as an open switch.

Consider the circuit of Fig. 2.7A, which shows a battery in series with an ideal diode D_i and resistor R. In this connection the diode is forward biased and can be represented by a closed switch as shown in Fig. 2.7B. The current I flowing is

$$I = V/R. \qquad (2.6a)$$

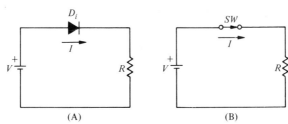

(A)　　　　　　(B)

Fig. 2.7 Ideal diode forward biased. (A) Circuit. (B) Diode represented by a closed switch.

With the polarity of V reversed, the diode is reverse biased. If the reverse-biased diode is considered an open switch, the resulting current will be zero:

$$I = 0. \qquad (2.6b)$$

In summary, the model of an ideal diode may be represented by a perfect switch which is closed when the diode is forward biased and is open when it is reverse biased.

2.3　Vacuum Tube Diode

The vacuum tube diode is normally operated in the space-charge region. A typical characteristic curve of such a diode appears in Fig. 2.8. The objective is to derive a model for the vacuum tube diode so that it can be handled

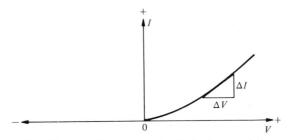

Fig. 2.8 Overall vacuum tube diode characteristics.

analytically. Compared to the ideal diode the following characteristics are observed in the vacuum tube diode:

1. When reverse biased, the vacuum tube diode is a close approximation of the ideal diode. No current flows and the open-switch model is appropriate.

2. In the forward-biased condition, the vacuum tube diode has a resistance that does not equal zero and is nonlinear. Its resistance depends on the applied forward-biased voltage V. At different points along the forward half of the curve, the ratio $\Delta I/\Delta V$ is not constant.

Assume the operating point of the diode in the forward direction is located at point A in Fig. 2.9. If a line segment is drawn connecting points A and O

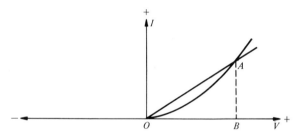

Fig. 2.9   Obtaining the average forward resistance, $r_F = OB/BA$.

(in an attempt to obtain the best "fit"), the reciprocal of the slope of the line BA/OB becomes the *average forward resistance* r_F of a forward-biased diode. We have thus "linearized" the nonlinear forward characteristic curve of the diode by a piecewise-linear construction. By the switch concept of an ideal diode, the forward resistance r_F can be thought to represent dirty switch contacts. The model of the vacuum tube diode appears as shown in Fig. 2.10. When forward biased, the diode is conducting and is shown as a closed switch in series with the forward resistance r_F. In the reverse-biased case, the switch is open. This kind of representation is called a *piecewise-linear model*, because line segments were used to approximate a nonlinear curve.

Fig. 2.10   Piecewise-linear model of a vacuum tube diode in the forward-biased state.

Consider the vacuum tube diode circuit of Fig. 2.11. By the piecewise-linear model for $V > 0$ (forward bias)

$$I = V/(r_F + R). \tag{2.7a}$$

For $V < 0$ (reverse bias),

$$I = 0. \tag{2.7b}$$

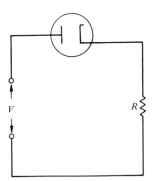

Fig. 2.11 Vacuum tube diode circuit.

2.4 Semiconductor Diodes

In developing the piecewise-linear model for a semiconductor diode, the back resistance and the deadband voltage as well as the forward resistance have to be taken into account. This is done in the manner illustrated in Fig. 2.12. Line segments OA, AB, and OC are drawn to yield the best possible

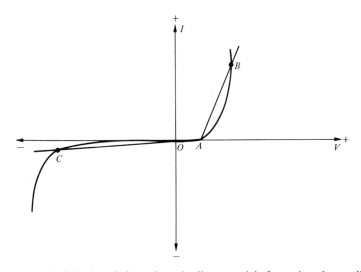

Fig. 2.12 Obtaining best fit for a piecewise-linear model of a semiconductor diode.

fit to the actual characteristic curve. Segment OA is equal to the deadband voltage V_o. The slopes of segments AB and OC are equal to the reciprocal of forward resistance r_F and back resistance r_B, respectively.

The piecewise-linear model of a semiconductor diode is shown in Fig. 2.13.

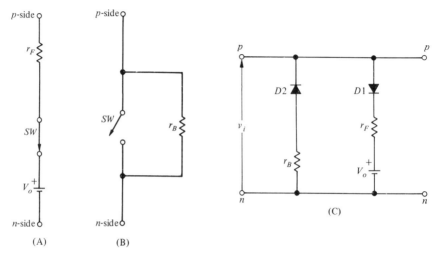

Fig. 2.13 Piecewise-linear model of a physical semiconductor diode. (A) Forward biased. (B) Reverse biased. (C) An example of a complete model.

It is noted that in the forward-bias case the model appears as a closed switch (generally shown as a connecting line) in series with the forward resistance r_F and the deadband voltage V_o. When reverse biased, the diode is represented as an open switch (generally omitted from the diagram) in parallel with the back resistance r_B. This may be thought of as being equivalent to an open manual switch with leakage across its contacts.

Example 2.1

Using ideal diodes, sources, and resistances, synthesize the piecewise-linear curves CO, OA, and AB of Fig. 2.12. Note that segment $OA = V_o$ and the slopes of segments AB and CO are equal to $1/r_F$ and $1/r_B$, respectively.

Solution

The resulting network is shown in Fig. 2.13C. For $v_i > V_o$, diode D1 is forward biased and D2 is reverse biased; this is equivalent to Fig. 2.13A where the conducting diode is represented by a closed switch. When $v_i < 0$, diode D1 is reverse biased and D2 is forward biased; this is equivalent to the model of Fig. 2.13B.

For the semiconductor diode circuit of Fig. 2.14A, taken with the piecewise-linear model for the diode in Figs. 2.14B and C, the current I is

for $0 < V < V_o$ (deadband region)

$$I = 0, \tag{2.8a}$$

for $V > V_o$ (forward bias)

$$I = (V - V_o)/(r_F + R), \tag{2.8b}$$

for $V < 0$ (reverse bias)

$$I = V/(r_B + R). \tag{2.8c}$$

In practice the back resistance r_B is so large (a few megohms for Si diodes) that the reverse current is usually neglected.

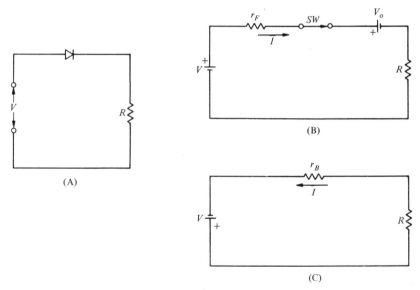

Fig. 2.14 (A) Semiconductor diode circuit. (B) Diode represented by a closed switch in series with r_F and V_o. (C) Diode represented by a back resistance, r_B.

2.5 Silicon Controlled Rectifier

The silicon controlled rectifier (SCR) is a three-terminal device. The symbol and characteristic curves for the device are given in Fig. 2.15. The anode and cathode are analogous to the p- and n-sides of a diode; gate G is the terminal to which a signal is applied to turn on the device in its conducting state. Once the SCR is on, the gate loses control over the rectifier. The SCR can be turned off only by applying a reverse bias to the device.

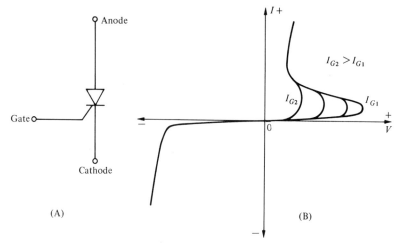

Fig. 2.15 The SCR. (A) Schematic symbol. (B) Electrical characteristic curves.

In the conducting state, the model of an SCR is similar to a conventional diode and appears as a closed switch in series with battery V_o. Voltage V_o represent the average forward drop (≈ 1 V) across the diode in its on state. The forward resistance $r_F \approx 0$. In the off state the model becomes that of a reverse-biased diode, that is, an open switch shunted with the back resistance r_B.

A general piecewise-linear model that may be applied to the devices discussed in this chapter is proposed in Fig. 2.16. Let us examine the model for each of the devices considered and see how it applies:

$$\text{Ideal diode:} \quad r_F = 0; \quad r_B = \infty; \quad V_o = 0.$$

$$\text{Vacuum tube diode:} \quad r_F \neq 0; \quad r_B = \infty; \quad V_o = 0.$$

$$\text{Semiconductor diode:} \quad r_F \neq 0; \quad r_B \neq \infty; \quad V_o \neq 0.$$

$$\text{SCR:} \quad r_F = 0; \quad r_B \neq \infty; \quad V_o \neq 0.$$

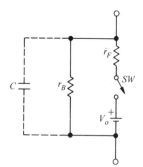

Fig. 2.16 General piecewise-linear model of a diode.

For each case in which the diode is forward biased, the switch is closed; when it is reverse biased, the switch is open. In the reverse-biased case one would simply show an open switch in parallel with r_B, or r_B alone.

One item omitted in our discussion of diodes was capacitance. Because of the physical geometry and other factors, a diode has some capacitance across its terminals. As a first approximation, one can often insert the capacitance across the terminals of the model, as illustrated by the dashed lines in Fig. 2.16. Effects of capacity become important in high-frequency operation.

2.6 Examples of Diode Applications

As mentioned earlier in the chapter, applications of diodes in electronics are numerous. In this section, we shall consider briefly the use of diodes for two important functions: rectification, that is, the conversion of alternating current to a unidirectional current, and voltage regulation. These two topics are considered in greater depth in Chapter 4.

The simplest rectifier is the single-phase half-wave rectifier circuit of Fig. 2.17. Voltage input $v(t) = V_m \sin \omega t$ is generally obtained from a transformer winding; diode D is in series with the transformer winding and load

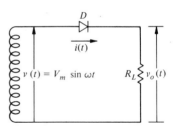

Fig. 2.17 Half-wave rectifier circuit.

R_L. From Fig. 2.18A one sees that on the positive half cycle the diode becomes forward biased and conducts. By the piecewise-linear model of the diode the current $i(t)$ is

$$i(t) = \frac{V_m \sin \omega t}{r_F + R_L}$$
$$= I_m \sin \omega t \qquad (0 < \omega t < \pi), \tag{2.9}$$

where the peak current $I_m = V_m/(r_F + R_L)$. During the negative half cycle the diode is back, or reverse, biased and the current is

$$i(t) = 0 \qquad (\pi < \omega t < 2\pi), \tag{2.10}$$

with the assumption that the back resistance r_B is infinite.

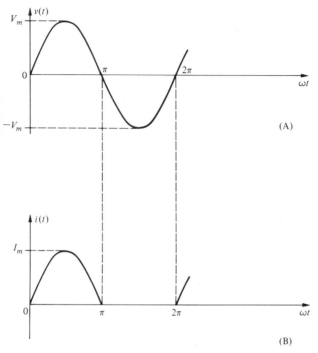

Fig. 2.18 Waveforms of interest for the half-wave rectifier. (A) Across transformer winding. (B) Rectified waveform (unidirectional current).

The resultant rectified current, illustrated in Fig. 2.18B, is *unidirectional*— something quite different from the dc obtained from a dry cell. If a dc ammeter is placed in series with resistance R_L in Fig. 2.17, the meter will read the *average* (dc) current:

$$I_{av} = I_{dc} = \frac{1}{2\pi} \int_0^{2\pi} i(\omega t)d(\omega t). \tag{2.11}$$

Substituting expressions (2.9) and (2.10) derived for the half-wave rectifier in (2.11), one obtains

$$I_{dc} = \frac{1}{2\pi}\left[\int_0^\pi I_m \sin \omega t d(\omega t) + \int_\pi^{2\pi} 0 d(\omega t) \right]$$

$$= I_m/\pi = 0.318 I_m. \tag{2.12}$$

If an ac meter is substituted for the dc meter, the *effective* or *root mean square* (rms) component of current will be read as

$$I_{rms} = \sqrt{\frac{1}{2\pi} \int_0^{2\pi} i(\omega t)^2 d(\omega t)}. \tag{2.13}$$

For the half-wave circuit,

$$I_{rms} = \sqrt{\frac{1}{2\pi} \int_0^\pi I_m^2 \sin^2(\omega t)d(\omega t)}$$

$$= 0.5 I_m.$$

(2.14)

Example 2.2

The input to the half-wave rectifier of Fig. 2.19A is the triangular waveform of Fig. 2.19B. Assuming the diode is ideal, determine (a) the average (dc) current and (b) the rms current.

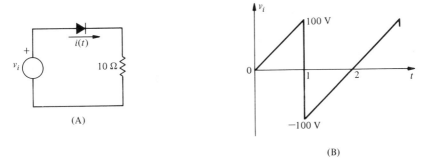

(A)

(B)

Fig. 2.19 Example 2.1. (A) Circuit. (B) Input waveform

Solution

(a) For $0 < t < 1$,

$$i(t) = 100t/10 = 10t.$$

(2.15)

For $1 < t < 2$,

$$i(t) = 0.$$

(2.16)

Substituting (2.15) and (2.16) in (2.11), one obtains

$$I_{dc} = \frac{1}{2} \int_0^1 10t\, dt = 2.5 \text{ A}.$$

(b) To find the rms value (2.15) and (2.16) are substituted into (2.13)

$$I_{rms} = \sqrt{\frac{1}{2} \int_0^1 (10t)^2\, dt} = 4.1 \text{ A}.$$

Zener Diode Regulator

The characteristics of germanium and silicon diodes were illustrated in Fig. 2.5. When either diode is reverse biased, it was noted that, in particular, the silicon diode exhibits a point (Zener point) at which the current increases rapidly in the negative direction and the voltage across the diode is nearly constant. Diodes designed with well-defined Zener voltages are referred to as Zener diodes. The characteristics of a Zener diode and its symbol are shown in Figs. 2.20A and B; a piecewise-linear model of the diode is given in Fig. 2.20C. Resistance R_z, the reciprocal of the slope of the curve in the region of increasing current, is usually of the order of a few ohms and generally can be neglected. Current I_{zo}, below the knee of the curve, is the minimum current required for operation of the Zener diode.

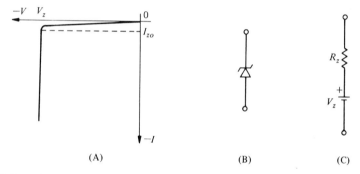

(A)   (B)   (C)

Fig. 2.20 The Zener diode. (A) Characteristics. (B) Schematic symbol. (C) Piecewise-linear model.

An important application of the Zener diode is in voltage regulating circuits, an example of which is shown in Fig. 2.21A. (Note that the Zener diode is reverse biased.) As the input voltage V_i increases or decreases, the Zener current rises and falls, respectively. From Fig. 2.20A it is seen, however, that voltage V_z is essentially constant.

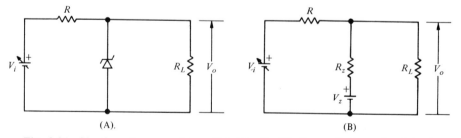

(A).   (B)

Fig. 2.21 Simple voltage regulator. (A) Circuit. (B) Zener diode replaced by its model.

To arrive at a criterion of regulation, one may define a sensitivity factor, $S_R = \partial V_o/\partial V_i$. If perfect regulation were attainable, $S_R = 0$; the larger the value of S_R, the poorer is the regulation. If the Zener diode is replaced with its model, the circuit of Fig. 2.21B is obtained. For analysis, it is convenient to replace the network to the left of R_L with its Thevenin's equivalent.

Example 2.3

For the simple voltage regulator of Fig. 2.21A, derive an expression for S_R.

Solution

The Thevenin's equivalent of the circuit is shown in Fig. 2.22, where $V_{th} = (V_i R_z + R V_z)/(R + R_z)$ and $R_{th} = R_z//R$. Resistance R is essential to the operation of the circuit. From Fig. 2.22,

$$V_o = \frac{R_L V_{th}}{R_L + R_{th}}$$

$$= \frac{R_L V_i R_z + R_L R V_z}{(R_{th} + R_L)(R + R_z)}$$

$$S_R = \frac{\partial V_o}{\partial V_i} = \frac{R_L R_z}{(R_L + R_{th})(R + R_z)}.$$

If $R_z \ll R$, $R_{th} \approx R_z$,

$$S_R \cong \frac{R_L R_z}{R(R_L + R_z)}. \tag{2.17}$$

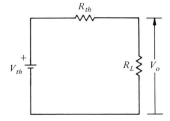

Fig. 2.22 Thevenin's model of voltage regulator.

An examination of (2.17) reveals that for best regulation R_z should approach zero or R approach infinity. In practice, R_z can be of the order of a few ohms; resistance R, however, cannot be too large because it would dissipate excessive power.

Example 2.4

For the voltage regulator of Fig. 2.21, assume that $V_o = 20$ V, $R = 20$ ohms, $R_z = 0$, and $R_L = 200$ ohms. Voltage V_i varies between 24 and 30 V.

(a) Specify the maximum and minimum current ratings for the Zener diode.

(b) Determine the maximum power dissipated in resistance R and in the Zener diode.

Solution

(a) Load current $I_L = 20/200 = 0.1$ A. The total current flowing in R for $V_i = 30$ V is:

$$I_{R(max)} = (30 - 20)/20 = 0.5 \text{ A.}$$

Therefore the maximum Zener current $I_{z(max)} = 0.5 - 0.1 = 0.4$ A. When $V_i = 24$ V,

$$I_{R(min)} = (24 - 20)/20 = 0.2 \text{A.}$$

Therefore $I_{z(min)} = 0.2 - 0.1 = 0.1$ A.

(b) $P_{R(max)} = 20(0.5)^2 = 5$ W and $P_{z(max)} = 20(0.4) = 8$ W.

Diode Specifications

In choosing a diode for a particular application, the user must check the manufacturer's data sheet and make certain that the listed specifications are not exceeded. Some of the important specifications are

1. Maximum peak forward current, not to be exceeded because of energy dissipation considerations.

2. Maximum average forward current.

3. Peak inverse voltage (PIV), which is the maximum reverse voltage the diode can withstand.

4. Ambient temperature of operation. For semiconductor devices, the junction temperature is significant.

2.7   Summary

A diode is a two-terminal device that offers very little resistance to current flow in one direction of applied voltage and practically infinite resistance in the opposite direction of applied voltage. These refer to the forward- and reverse- (or back-) biased conditions, respectively. Diodes may be represented by a piecewise-linear model composed of a closed switch in series with the forward resistance r_F and the deadband voltage V_o for the forward-biased state. When reverse biased, the model is an open switch in parallel with the back resistance r_B. At high frequencies, the capacitance across the diode has to be considered. In each application the user should check the manufacturer's specifications and make certain they are not exceeded.

References

GE Transistor Manual, 7th ed., 1964.
GE Silicon Controlled Rectifier Manual, 2nd ed., 1961.
Motorola Silicon Rectifier Handbook, 1966.
The Semiconductor Data Book, Motorola, 1966.
RCA Receiving Tube Manual RC–25, 1966.
RCA Transistor Manual SC–10, 1962.

Problems

2.1 Using ideal diodes, sources, and resistances, synthesize the networks whose *i–v* curves are given in Fig. P2.1.

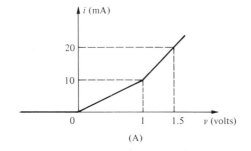

(A)

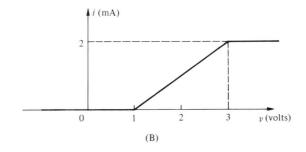

(B)

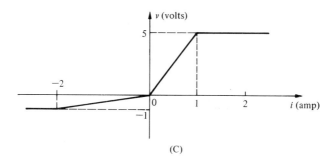

(C)

Fig. P2.1

2.2 For the circuit of Fig. P2.2A, assume that when the diode conducts
it may be represented by a 1-V dc source in series with 100 ohms;
when nonconducting, it acts like a 2 K resistance. Plot and dimension
$v_o(t)$ if the input voltage is that of Fig. P2.2B.

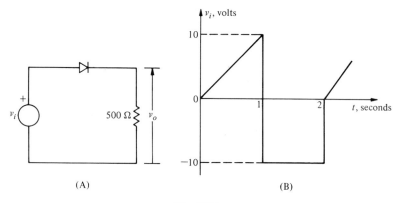

(A)   (B)

Fig. P2.2.

2.3 Repeat Prob. 2.2 assuming that when the diode is nonconducting it
acts like an open circuit.

2.4 Figure P2.4 shows a half-wave rectifier; $v_s = 100 \sin 377t$. Assume
that a conducting diode may be represented by a 0.7-V dc source in
series with 100 ohms; when nonconducting, the diode is represented
by a 50 K resistance. (a) Plot and dimension $v_o(t)$. (b) Calculate the
dc and rms values of $v_o(t)$.

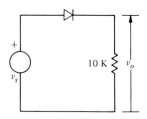

Fig. P2.4.

2.5 Assuming the diode is ideal, repeat Prob. 2.4. Compare the results
with those obtained in Prob. 2.4.

2.6 The input to the circuit of Fig. P2.6 is $v_i = 100 \sin 1000t$. Assuming
$V_1 = 50$ V and $V_2 = -50$ V, plot and dimension $v_o(t)$.

2.7 Repeat Prob. 2.6 for $V_1 = 50$ V and $V_2 = -20$ V.

2.8 Repeat Prob. 2.6 for $V_1 = 20$ V and $V_2 = 50$ V.

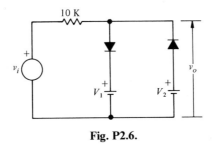

Fig. P2.6.

2.9 The input v_i to the rectifier of Fig. P2.9A is given in Fig. P2.9B. Assume that $V = 50$ V. (a) Sketch and dimension $v_o(t)$. (b) Calculate the average value of $v_o(t)$.

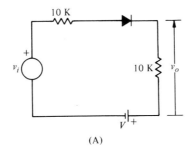

(A)

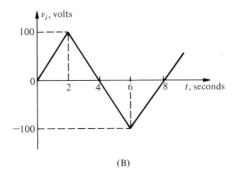

(B)

Fig. P2.9.

2.10 Repeat Prob. 2.9 for $V = 75$ V.
2.11 For the circuit of Fig. P2.11, $V = 1$ V. Plot and dimension the voltages across the resistance and diode. What is the PIV of the diode?
2.12 Repeat Prob. 2.11 for $V = 2$ V.
2.13 Referring to Fig. P2.13, plot v_o for one cycle of the smaller frequency.

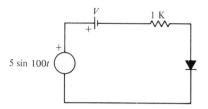

Fig. P2.11.

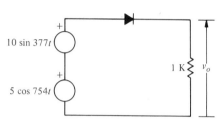

Fig. P2.13.

2.14 Referring to Fig. P2.14, the Zener diode voltage drop is 20 V if the Zener current is in the range of 100 mA and 1 A; assume $R_z = 0$ and $R_L = 20$ ohms. (a) If V_{dc} varies between 26 and 30 V, what value of R is required to ensure that the output voltage is regulated at 20 V? (b) Find the maximum power dissipated in R and the Zener diode. (c) Find S_R.

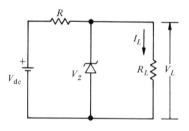

Fig. P2.14.

2.15 Using the same circuit of Prob. 2.14, assume that the input voltage varies between 12 and 15 V and the load current between 10 and 60 mA. The Zener voltage $= 10$ V; minimum Zener current for regulation is 5 mA; $R_z = 0$. (a) Find the maximum values for R. (b) What is the maximum power dissipated in the Zener diode? (c) Determine S_R.

2.16 For the value of R determined in Prob. 2.14, answer the following questions: (a) What happens if V_{dc} becomes greater than 30 V or less than 26 V? (b) Assume that V_{dc} remains in the range of 26–30 V and load resistance R_L varies. Is regulation still obtained? Why?

2.17 In Fig. P2.14, the dc source is replaced by a sinusoidal source $30 \sin 377t$. Plot and dimension the voltage across R_L. Assume that $R_L = 20$ ohms and $R = 3$ ohms. $V_z = 20$ V.

The Basic
Amplifier

In this chapter the study of amplifiers is initiated. An amplifier may be considered a four-terminal device that amplifies or "magnifies" a signal applied to its input terminals and is therefore said to exhibit gain. Based on whether it is designed for voltage, current, or power gain, the circuit is designated as a voltage amplifier, current amplifier, or power amplifier, respectively.

The *ideal* amplifier will be defined first. In this manner the essential properties of amplification can be studied in very basic terms. The physical or "real world" amplifier and its characteristics will then be investigated. It will be found that devices such as transistors and vacuum tubes are nonlinear. In large-signal applications these nonlinearities cannot be ignored; hence, the graphical methods and piecewise-linear techniques considered in Chapter 1 are used for their analysis.

3.1 The Ideal Voltage Amplifier

One form of an ideal amplifier, the voltage amplifier, and its output volt-ampere characteristics are shown in Fig. 3.1. Looking across the output terminals (2-2) of the amplifier, one sees a voltage source γv_1, where γ is the *voltage amplification factor* of the device and v_1 is the input signal voltage. Voltage source γv_1 is a *dependent* (voltage-controlled) voltage source. The output voltage v_2 is at every instant equal to the input signal v_1 multiplied by γ:

$$v_2 = \gamma v_1. \tag{3.1}$$

The output volt-ampere characteristics consist of a family of equally spaced vertical straight lines for each equal increment of input voltage (Fig. 3.1B). The ideal curves are useful because they define optimum characteristics of physical devices that are employed as amplifiers.

The impedance across the input terminals, referred to as the *input impedance*,

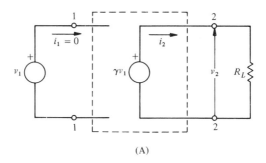

(A)

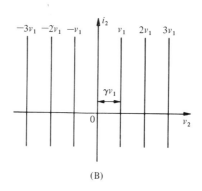

(B)

Fig. 3.1   An ideal voltage amplifier. (A) Model. (B) Output characteristics.

for the ideal voltage amplifier is infinite; therefore, the input current is zero regardless of the value of the input voltage v_1. The input power is zero under all conditions and the power gain (output power/input power) is infinite. The output power P_2 is

$$P_2 = (\gamma v_1)^2 / R_L, \tag{3.2}$$

where R_L = load resistance.

Equation (3.2) merits some discussion. Assume γv_1 is constant; as R_L is increased, the output power decreases. For very large values of load resistance R_L, the output power is of no consequence; the amplifier produces voltage gain and is classified as a *voltage amplifier*. When R_L is small, appreciable output power is obtained. In this mode of operation, the amplifier is said to be a *power amplifier*.

For given values of γ and R_L, the output power will be proportional to the input signal squared v_1^2. In order to increase the output power, a greater input voltage is needed. This can be realized by amplifying the signal voltage before applying it to the power amplifier stage, as shown in Fig. 3.2. This is an example of *cascading* amplifier stages. For n cascaded *ideal* voltage amplifiers, that is, as defined by the model of Fig. 3.1A, the output voltage v_n is

$$v_n = \gamma_1 \gamma_2 \cdots \gamma_n v_1, \tag{3.3}$$

where $\gamma_1, \gamma_2, \ldots$, are voltage amplification factors for each stage.

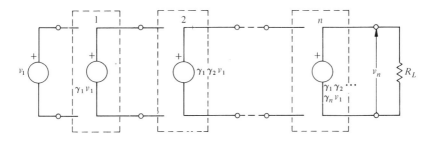

Fig. 3.2 Cascading n amplifier stages.

3.2 The Ideal Current Amplifier

The dual of a voltage source is a current source; the dual of the ideal voltage amplifier is the ideal current amplifier. This is illustrated in Fig. 3.3, along with its output volt-ampere characteristics. For each value of input signal current i_1, the output current i_2 has a value of

$$i_2 = hi_1, \tag{3.4}$$

where h is the current amplification factor. Current gain is independent of the load voltage.

Consideration of input terminals (1-1) shows a short circuit. Therefore, the input power is zero, and the power gain is infinite (as for the ideal voltage amplifier). Consideration of output terminals (2-2) shows a current source hi_1. Current source hi_1 is another example of a *dependent* source; in this case it is referred to as a current-controlled current source.

The output power is:

$$P_2 = (hi_1)^2 R_L. \tag{3.5}$$

An examination of (3.5) shows that the greater the value of R_L, the greater is the output power. This behavior is the exact opposite to that of the voltage amplifier [see (3.2)].

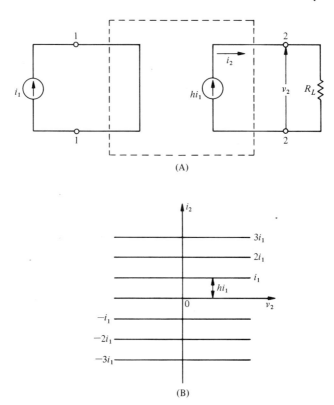

Fig. 3.3   An ideal current amplifier. (A) Model, (B) output characteristics.

3.3   Gain in Decibels

A voltage or current amplifier that is not ideal will have a finite power gain. The gain may be written as a ratio of output power P_2 to input power P_1, P_2/P_1, where $P_2 = v_2^2/R_L$ and $P_1 = v_1^2/R_1$ (R_1 is the input resistance). Another measure that proves very useful in expressing voltage, current, or power gain is obtained by taking logarithms of ratios to form decibels (dB). The gain G in dB is defined as

$$G = 10 \log(P_2/P_1) \, \text{dB}, \tag{3.6}$$

where log is the common logarithm to base 10. Thus if $P_2 = 100$ W and $P_1 = 1$ W, the power gain is 20 dB.

The power gain of the amplifier may be also written as

$$G = 10 \log \frac{v_2^2/R_L}{v_1^2/R_1} = 20 \log \frac{v_2}{v_1} + 10 \log \frac{R_1}{R_L}.$$

If $R_1 = R_L$, then

$$G = 20 \log(v_2/v_1).$$

By convention, the voltage gain in dB is defined as $20 \log(v_2/v_1)$, *regardless* of the values of R_1 and R_L. If $R_1 = R_L$, one can then say that the power gain is equal to the voltage gain.

If the power gain is written in terms of current,

$$G = 10 \log(i_2^2 R_L/i_1^2 R_1) = 20 \log i_2/i_1 + 10 \log R_L/R_1.$$

The current gain in dB is defined as $20 \log i_2/i_1$; if $R_1 = R_L$, the power gain and current gain are equal.

3.4 The Transistor as an Amplifier

A semiconductor junction diode is made by forming a junction between p- and n-type germanium or silicon. A junction transistor is made by sandwiching one layer of p-type material between two layers of n-type material to form an n-p-n transistor, or sandwiching one layer of n-type material between two layers of p-material to form a p-n-p transistor. An amplifier circuit showing an n-p-n transistor is given in Fig. 3.4A; the circuit for a p-n-p transistor is shown in Fig. 3.4B. Because current flow can be due to electrons or holes, the junction transistor is also referred to as a *bipolar junction transistor* (BJT).

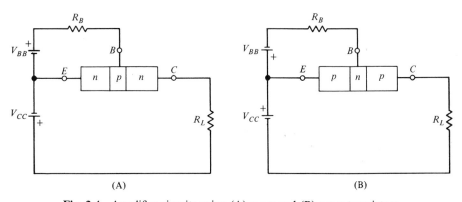

(A)   (B)

Fig. 3.4 Amplifier circuits using (A) *n-p-n* and (B) *p-n-p* transistors.

Schematic symbols for *n-p-n* and *p-n-p* transistors are provided in Figs. 3.5A and B. The three terminals marked by letters *C*, *B*, and *E* are the collector, base, and emitter, respectively. The collector and base regions form the collector-base junction; the emitter and base regions result in a second junction, the emitter-base junction.

(A)   (B)

Fig. 3.5   Transistor schematic symbols. (A) *n-p-n* type. (B) *p-n-p* type.

For normal amplifier operation the collector-base junction must be reverse biased and the emitter-base junction must be forward biased, as illustrated in Fig. 3.4. If the signal is applied to the base of an *n-p-n* device, current amplification is obtained because nearly all the carriers (electrons) in the semiconductor passing through the forward-biased emitter-base junction reach the reverse-biased collector terminal, which attracts the electrons, rather than the emitter terminal. A similar statement can be made for a *p-n-p* device if the term "holes" is substituted for electrons.

Figure 3.6 shows a transitor amplifier circuit with the emitter common to the base and collector circuits; this is called a *common-emitter* (CE) amplifier.

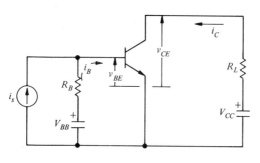

Fig. 3.6   Common-emitter (CE) amplifier.

The first step in the analysis or design of an amplifier is to find the quiescent operating, or *Q*-point. Before proceeding further, however, we must define carefully the symbols used in describing transistor amplifier circuits. For transistor circuits the following conventions are used:

V_{BB} = base circuit dc bias voltage.
V_{CC} = collector circuit dc supply voltage.
I_B = average value of base current.
i_b = instantaneous value of signal base current.
i_B = instantaneous total value of base current.
v_{CE} = instantaneous total value of collector-emitter voltage.
i_C, i_E = instantaneous total values of collector and emitter currents, respectively.

v_{BE} = instantaneous total value of base-emitter voltage.
v_{be} = instantaneous value of signal base-emitter voltage.
V_{BE} = average value of base-emitter voltage.
V_{CE} = average value of collector-emitter voltage.
v_{ce} = instantaneous value of signal collector-emitter voltage.
I_C, I_E = average values of collector and emitter currents, respectively.
i_c, i_e = instantaneous values of signal collector and emitter currents, respectively.

Finding the Transistor Q-Point Graphically

Because of the nonlinear characteristics of a transistor, a graphical solution for finding the Q-point provides an alternative to the piecewise-linear method. The output and input characteristics for the transistor amplifier of Fig. 3.6 in the *CE* configuration are given in Fig. 3.7. These characteristics bear a closer resemblance to those of the ideal current amplifier of Fig. 3.3 than to those of the ideal voltage amplifier of Fig. 3.1.

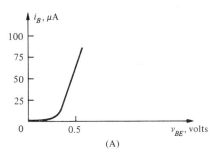

(A)

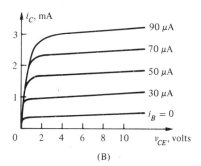

Fig. 3.7 Common-emitter transistor characteristics. (A) Base (input) and (B) collector (output) characteristics.

(B)

The equation for the output load line (i_C vs. v_{CE}) may be obtained by writing an equation for the collector-emitter circuit. With reference to Fig. 3.6:

$$V_{CC} = i_C R_L + v_{CE}.$$

If one solves for i_C,

$$i_C = V_{CC}/R_L - (1/R_L)v_{CE}. \tag{3.7}$$

Equation (3.7) is that of a straight line, $y = b + mx$. Because two points determine a line, the two points for drawing the load line are obtained by solving (3.7) for v_{CE} set to zero and i_C set to zero. For $v_{CE} = 0$,

$$i_C = V_{CC}/R_L;$$

and for $i_C = 0$,

$$v_{CE} = V_{CC}.$$

The same procedure is used for finding i_B and v_{BE}. The dc loop equation for the input side of Fig. 3.6 ($I_s = 0$) is

$$V_{BB} = i_B R_B + v_{BE}.$$

If one solves for i_B,

$$i_B = V_{BB}/R_B - (1/R_B)v_{BE}. \tag{3.8}$$

The intersection of the load line defined by (3.8) with the input characteristic curve yield I_B and V_{BE}.

Example 3.1

The common emitter (CE) characteristics for the transistor used in the circuit of Fig. 3.8 are given in Fig. 3.7. Find the Q-point.

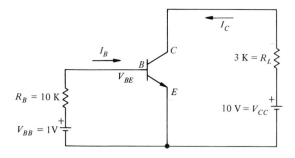

Fig. 3.8 Transistor amplifier circuit for Example 3.1.

Solution

For the input side from (3.8), when $i_B = 0$, $v_{BE} = 1$ V. With $v_{BE} = 0$, $i_B = (1 \text{ V})/(10 \text{ K}) = 100 \, \mu\text{A}$. The load line is then superimposed on the input (base) characteristics of Fig. 3.9B. At their point of intersection, it is found that $I_B = 50 \, \mu\text{A}$ and $V_{BE} = 0.5$ V.

On the output side and with reference to (3.7), setting $i_C = 0$ yields $V_{CC} = 10$ V. For $v_{CE} = 0$, $i_C = (10 \text{ V})/3 \text{ K} = 3.3 \text{ mA}$. With the load line superimposed on the collector characteristics of Fig. 3.9A, the line intersects the base curve $I_B = 50\,\mu A$, and the Q-point is $I_C = 2\,mA$ and $V_{CE} = 4\,V$. The emitter current is given by

$$I_E = I_C + I_B. \tag{3.9}$$

Therefore, $I_E = 2 + 0.05 = 2.05\,mA$.

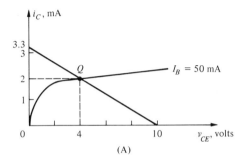

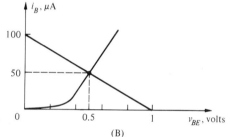

Fig. 3.9 Determining the quiescent operating point for the circuit of Example 3.1. (A) Collector characteristics. (B) Base characteristics.

Piecewise-Linear Model for the Transistor

The piecewise-linear transistor model often simplifies the calculation of the Q-point for the device. The linearization of the output characteristics can result in a set of curves corresponding to those of the ideal current amplifier. The output characteristics are approximated by straight, horizontal lines, which are equally spaced for equal increments of base current, as shown in Fig. 3.10. This is reflected in the piecewise-linear transistor model by a *current-controlled current source* ($h_{FE}I_B$) in parallel with an ideal diode. The base-emitter junction behaves in a manner similar to that of a junction diode and can therefore be represented by a diode.

Figures 3.11A and B show the piecewise-linear models for *n-p-n* and *p-n-p* transistors, respectively. In normal transistor amplifier operation, the emitter-base diode is forward biased, and the collector-base diode is reverse biased.

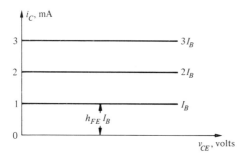

Fig. 3.10 Piecewise-linear characteristics for a transistor in the common-emitter configuration.

This results in the simplified model where the base-emitter diode is shorted and the collector-base diode is open.

The only parameter to be determined for the idealized piecewise-linear model of the transistor is h_{FE}, the dc current amplification factor. Parameter h_{FE} is obtained from the collector characteristic curves and is expressed by

$$h_{FE} = (\Delta I_C / \Delta I_B)_{V_{CE} = \text{constant}}. \tag{3.10}$$

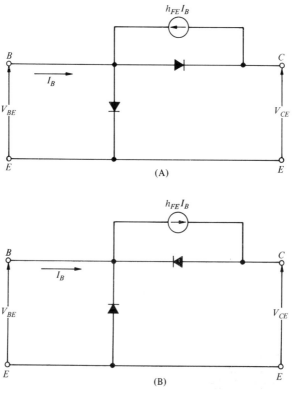

Fig. 3.11 Piecewise-linear models for (A) *n-p-n* and (B) *p-n-p* transistors.

Example 3.2

The circuit shown in Fig. 3.12A is sometimes used as an elementary voltage regulator. The purpose of the Zener diode in the base circuit is to maintain a constant voltage between points A and B. The power supplied by the Zener diode is, however, limited; for this reason the transistor is used and the output voltage V_L is taken across R_L. Assume $R_B \gg R_L$.

(a) Draw a piecewise-linear model for this circuit, and show that the voltage across R_L remains constant and equal to V_L regardless of the values of V_{CC} and R_L.

(b) Calculate and compare the power supplied by the Zener diode with that consumed by load resistor R_L.

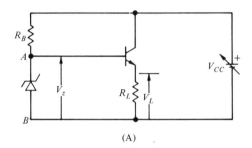

(A)

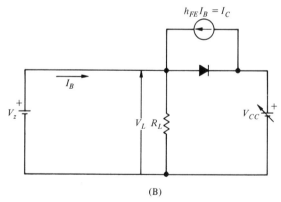

(B)

Fig. 3.12 Example 3.2. (A) Circuit of a simple voltage regulator. (B) Its piecewise-linear model.

Solution

(a) The piecewise-linear model is given in Fig. 3.12B, where the Zener diode is represented by a battery V_z. Because $R_B \gg R_L$, R_B is neglected in the analysis. From this idealized circuit it is seen that $V_L = V_z$ and is therefore independent of either V_{CC} or R_L.

(b) Power supplied by the Zener diode is $V_z I_B$. The power delivered to the load is $V_z I_E = V_z(1 + h_{FE})I_B$ since $I_E = I_B + I_C = I_B(1 + h_{FE})$. Therefore,

$$\text{(load power)/(Zener power)} = 1 + h_{FE}.$$

Other Transistor Configurations

The common-emitter (*CE*) configuration of Fig. 3.6 is the most widely used transistor amplifier. There are, however, two other configurations called *common-base* (*CB*) and *common-collector* (*CC*), or *emitter follower*. The reasons for their use are considered in detail in later chapters.

An example of the common-collector amplifier (emitter follower) was given Fig. 3.12A of Example 3.2. For the *Q*-point, the emitter follower may be considered a practical common-emitter circuit with $R_L = 0$ and emitter resistance R_E inserted between emitter and ground. The emitter follower has a voltage gain of less than unity, high input impedance, and low output impedance.

The circuit of Fig. 3.13 is a common-base (*CB*) amplifier. If a graphical method is used to analyze the circuit, the input and output characteristics of the common-base transistor as shown in Fig. 3.14A and B are required.

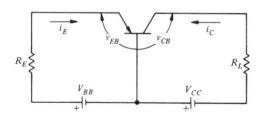

Fig. 3.13   Common-base (CB) amplifier circuit.

Again the loop equation at the output provides the load line: $V_{CC} = R_L i_C + v_{CB}$, and the load line is drawn as in Fig. 3.14A. The load line for the input circuit may be obtained by writing the loop equation at the input: $V_{BB} = R_E i_E + v_{EB}$, drawn in Fig. 3.14B. The *CB* amplifier has a current gain of less than unity, low input impedance, and high output impedance.

Of all the possible collector families of curves, the family for the common-emitter (*CE*) configuration is the most useful. It can be used for the emitter follower because $I_C \approx I_E$. The common-base curves are in a sense trivial because they are basically horizontal-parallel lines. They can be generated by the user by drawing horizontal lines, remembering that $I_E \approx I_C$.

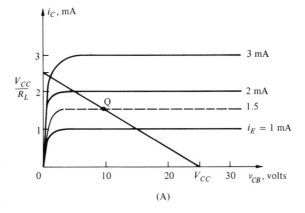

(A)

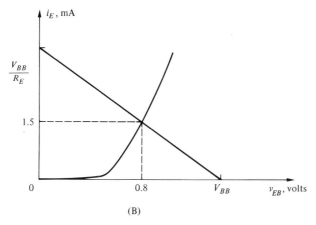

(B)

Fig. 3.14 Obtaining the Q point for a common-base amplifier. (A) Output characteristics. (B) Input characteristics.

3.5 Field-Effect Transistor Amplifier

The field-effect transistor (FET) is a voltage-controlled semiconductor device that has a high input impedance. There are two kinds of field-effect transistors; the junction FET (JFET) and the insulated-gate FET (IGFET), which is also called the metal-oxide semiconductor FET (MOSFET). A schematic representation of a JFET is shown in Fig. 3.15; Fig. 3.15A shows that a narrow semiconductor channel provides a conducting path between two terminals called the source S and the drain D. The channel may be either n- or p-type; the n-type is illustrated in Fig. 3.15.

With no bias applied to the transistor, the channel has a certain conductance G_c. If a reverse bias is applied between the gate terminal G and the source S, the depletion region width is increased, the thickness of the channel is reduced, and the conductivity therefore decreases. The gate bias V_{GS} just required to reduce the channel thickness to zero is called the pinch-off voltage V_p; Fig. 3.15B shows this condition.

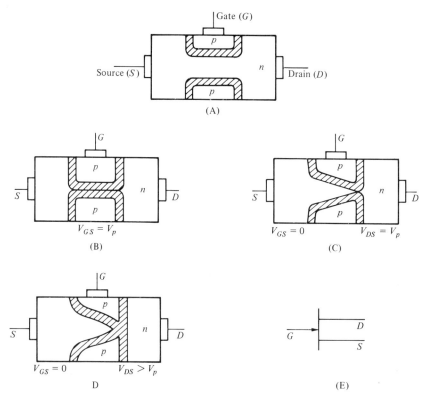

Fig. 3.15 The *n*-channel junction field-effect transistor (JFET). (A) Basic structure. (B) Pinch-off condition. (C) Reduction of channel thickness near the drain end. (D) The drain-source voltage V_{DS}, greater than the pinch-off voltage, V_p. (E) Schematic symbol for the *n*-channel FET.

If the gate-source voltage V_{GS} is zero, and the drain D is made positive with respect to the source, the drain current I_D is equal to the drain-source voltage V_{DS} times the channel conductance G_c. The positive drain-source voltage, however, reverse biases the p-n junction near the drain end of the channel; when the drain voltage is increased to the pinch-off voltage, the channel thickness is reduced to zero near the end of the channel (Fig. 3.15C). As the drain voltage is increased beyond V_p, the depletion region thickness is increased between the gate and the drain, but is nearly unchanged between the pinch-off point and the source (Fig. 3.15D). The source current remains essentially constant as the drain voltage increases beyond V_p because the additional voltage appears across the depletion region. This current is called the saturation current I_{DSS}. For $V_{GS} < 0$, I_{DSS} decreases as V_{GS} is made more negative. The first two subscripts denote the drain and source; the third indicates the gate is shorted to the source.

The JFET operates normally with the drain voltage V_{DS} greater than V_p and a reverse bias applied to the gate. If the gate is forward biased with respect to the source, the channel conductance will increase. Above a few tenths of a volt the gate-to-channel current begins to rise exponentially; hence, forward gate bias is avoided in the JFET.

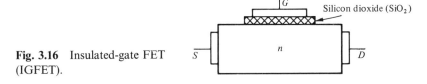

Fig. 3.16 Insulated-gate FET (IGFET).

In the IGFET, also referred to as the MOSFET (Fig. 3.16), the depletion region is replaced by a layer of silicon dioxide, which is a good insulator. In contrast to the JFET, the gate may be forward biased to increase the channel conductance as well as reverse biased to decrease the conductance. When the IGFET is forward biased, the operation is called *enchancement* mode; if reverse biased, it is called *depletion* mode. The depletion-mode device operates in the same way as the JFET; its characteristics are also similar to JFET as shown in Fig. 3.17A. Characteristic curves for the enhancement-mode device are given in Fig. 3.17C.

For the IGFET, the gate voltage is limited by the destruction of the diode dielectric under the gate. The reverse-biased gate voltage of the JFET is limited by avalanche breakdown.

An amplifier circuit employing the field-effect transistor is given in Fig. 3.18; the operation of this amplifier is similar to a vacuum tube amplifier (considered in the latter part of this chapter) where the drain is analogous to the plate, the gate to the grid, and the source to the cathode. Some commonly used symbol conventions for field-effect transistors are

V_{DD} = drain-supply voltage.
V_{GG} = gate supply voltage.
V_p = pinch-off voltage.
v_{ds} = instantaneous value of signal drain-to-source voltage.
v_{gs} = instantaneous value of signal gate-to-source voltage.
i_d = instantaneous value of signal drain current.
i_g = instantaneous value of signal gate current.
I_D, I_G = dc values of drain and gate currents, respectively.

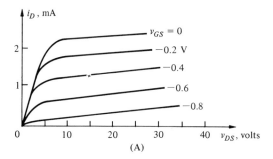

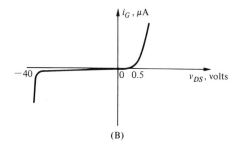

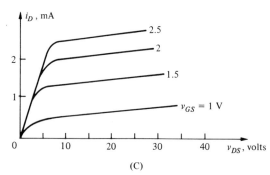

Fig. 3.17 Characteristic curves for a field-effect transistor. (A) Depletion mode. (B) Input. (C) Enchancement mode.

The Q-Point of a FET Amplifier

The same graphical method used to find the Q-point for a junction transistor may be used here. From Fig. 3.18 the loop equation for the drain-source circuit is

$$V_{DD} = i_D R_L + v_{DS}.$$

If one solves for i_D,

$$i_D = (V_{DD}/R_L) - (v_{DS}/R_L). \tag{3.11}$$

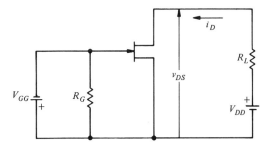

Fig. 3.18 Common-source (CS) field-effect transistor amplifier.

Again, (3.11) is an equation of a straight line. The two points for drawing the line are

$$v_{DS} = 0, \qquad i_D = V_{DD}/R_L;$$

$$i_D = 0, \qquad v_{DS} = V_{DD}.$$

For a JFET or IGFET operating in the depletion mode, the gate current is zero and the output load line is drawn as shown in Fig. 3.19; at the value of $-V_{GG} = v_{GS}$, the quiescent point is obtained.

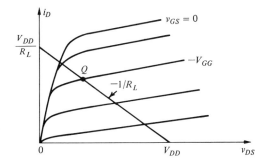

Fig. 3.19 Graphical determination of the Q-point for a FET amplifier.

3.6 Triode Vacuum Tube Amplifier

The simplest vacuum tube used for amplification is the triode; Fig. 3.20 shows its electrical symbol. Like the vacuum tube diode, the cathode emits electrons that are attracted to the plate. The grid is usually a spiral of wire

Fig. 3.20 Schematic symbol for triode vacuum tube.

concentric with the cathode and placed in the space between the cathode and plate. Because the grid structure is located very close to the cathode, the grid exerts more influence on the flow of electrons to the plate than does the plate itself. Less of a grid voltage change than plate voltage change is therefore required for a given variation in plate current. This kind of behavior results in a voltage gain for the triode.

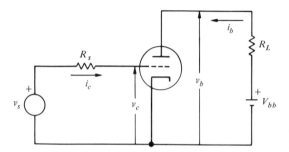

Fig. 3.21   Basic triode common-cathode amplifier.

A simple triode amplifier stage is shown in Fig. 3.21. Input voltage and current to the tube are labeled v_c and i_c, respectively; corresponding output quantities are designated v_b and i_b. Typical sets of measured triode character-istics are shown in Figs. 3.22A and B. By comparing the actual triode

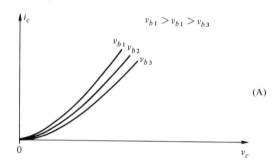

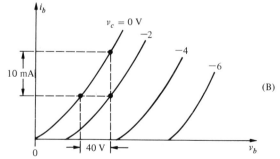

Fig. 3.22   Triode characteristics. (A) Input. (B) Output.

characteristics with those of the ideal voltage amplifier (see Fig. 3.1), we observe two significant differences:

1. The input impedance has a finite value for positive values of v_c.
2. The output impedance is not zero.

From Fig. 3.22B it is seen that, if the grid is made more negative, the plate voltage must be made more positive to yield the same plate current. The characteristics of Fig. 3.22B also show that the grid is more effective than the plate in controlling the plate current. For example, with the plate voltage fixed, a plate current change of 10 mA may correspond to a 2-V change in grid voltage. To provide the same variation in plate current by changing the plate voltage and keeping the grid voltage fixed, a plate voltage change of 40 V would be required. Under these conditions, we can say the voltage amplification factor μ for the triode is

$$\Delta V_b / \Delta V_c = 40/2 = 20.$$

The characteristics shown in Fig. 3.22B are not linear. The plate current is a function of v_c and v_b and is approximately given by the three-halves power law.

$$i_b = K(v_b + \mu v_c)^{3/2}, \tag{3.12}$$

where K is a constant. It is not practical to use this type of function to solve circuit problems analytically. In order to facilitate the solution, graphical analysis and piecewise-linear analysis may be used as for the junction and the field-effect transistors in determining the quiescent operating point.

For vacuum tube circuits the following conventions are used:

V_{cc} = grid circuit supply (bias) voltage.
v_c = instantaneous value of the grid potential relative to the cathode.
v_g = instantaneous value of the signal (ac) potential relative to the cathode.
V_c = average value of grid-cathode voltage.
i_c = instantaneous value of grid current.
I_c = average value of grid current.
V_{bb} = plate (anode) supply voltage.
v_b = instantaneous value of the total plate potential with respect to the cathode.
v_p = instantaneous value of the ac component of the plate potential with respect to the cathode.
V_b = average plate (anode) voltage.
i_b = instantaneous value of plate current.
i_p = instantaneous value of the ac component of plate current.
I_b = average value of plate current.

Because of the superiority of solid-state devices, such as the junction and field-effect transistors, vacuum tubes are seldom used in new circuit designs except in very high-power circuits. Vacuum tube circuits, however, can be analyzed by the same procedures used for transistors; this is illustrated by the following examples.

Example 3.3

The output and input characteristics of a triode are given in Fig. 3.23; the circuit is shown in Fig. 3.24A. Using the graphical method, find (a) the quiescent point of operation and (b) for an input signal $v_s = 4 \sin \omega t$, calculate the peak value of the output voltage v_o. Sketch v_o as a function of time.

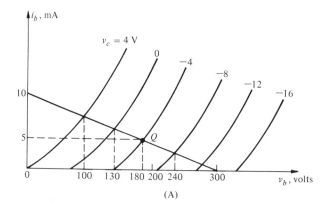

(A)

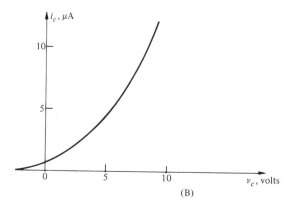

(B)

Fig. 3.23 Determining the Q-point for the amplifier of example 3.3. (A) Output characteristics. (B) Input characteristics.

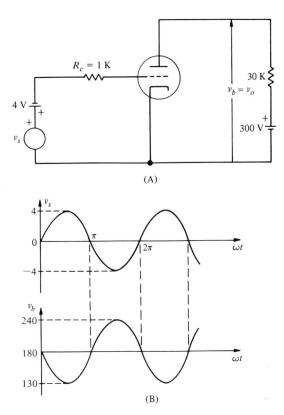

Fig. 3.24 Example 3.3. (A) Circuit. (B) Output and input phase relations.

Solution

(a) The equation for the load line is $V_{bb} = R_L i_b + v_b$. For $v_b = 0$, $i_b = V_{bb}/R_L = 300\text{ V}/30\text{ K} = 10\text{ mA}$. With $i_b = 0$, $v_b = V_{bb} = 300\text{ V}$. The load line is drawn as shown in Fig. 3.23A. Because the grid is negative with respect to the cathode, no grid current flows; therefore, $v_c = V_{cc} = -4\text{ V}$. The Q-point is then $I_b = 5\text{ mA}$ and $V_b = 180\text{ V}$.

(b) With $v_s = 4\sin\omega t$, v_c varies from $v_{c(min)} = -4 - 4 = -8$ (for $\sin\omega t = -1$) to $v_{c(max)} = -4 + 4 = 0$ (for $\sin\omega t = 1$). The corresponding values of $v_b = v_o$ are located on Fig. 3.23A; $v_{b(min)} = 130\text{ V}$ and $v_{b(max)} = 240\text{ V}$. The maximum value of plate voltage $= 240\text{ V}$ occurs when the input signal is at its minimum, -4 V; there is a 180° phase reversal between the input and output voltage. Figure 3.24B shows the phase relationship between the input and output voltages. There is also a 180° phase reversal for the common-emitter and common-source amplifiers.

Example 3.4

For the triode used in Example 3.3, (a) draw the piecewise-linear characteristics and calculate the amplification factor μ and the average plate resistance r_B. (b) Draw the piecewise-linear model for the circuit and calculate the quiescent operating point.

Solution

(a) The piecewise-linear characteristics are drawn in Fig. 3.25. The value of μ is calculated by

$$\mu = -(\Delta V_b/\Delta V_c)_{I_b=\text{constant}} = -80/(-4) = 20.$$

The value of r_B is obtained by

$$r_B = (\Delta V_b/\Delta I_b)_{V_c=\text{constant}} = 40/0.006 = 6600 \text{ ohms}.$$

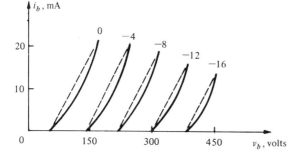

Fig. 3.25 Piecewise-linear characteristics used in Example 3.4.

(b) The piecewise-linear model of the circuit is drawn in Fig. 3.26. By writing a loop equation for the output or plate circuit, the quiescent point is obtained:

$$300 - 80 = (6.6 + 30)10^3 I_b.$$

If one solves for I_b,

$$I_b = 6 \text{ mA}$$

and

$$V_b = 80 + 6.6 \times 6 = 120 \text{ V}.$$

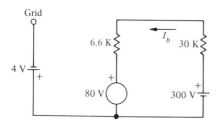

Fig. 3.26 Piecewise-linear model for Example 3.4.

The triode is the simplest vacuum tube used as an amplifier. It should be mentioned, however, that a small interelectrode capacitance exists between each pair of the three electrodes of the triode; that is, grid-to-cathode, grid-to-plate, and plate-to-cathode. At low-frequency operation these capacitances do not enter into the calculation because their value is of the order of 10 pF and hence they have high impendances. These capacitances are not negligible at high frequencies and may become troublesome; this is especially true of the grid-to-plate capacitance.

The grid-to-plate capacitance may be reduced to a negligible value by adding a fourth electrode placed between the grid (now called the *control grid*) and the plate. This new electrode is called the *screen grid* and is held at a fixed dc potential. It acts as an electrostatic shield or screen between the control grid and plate. The grid-to-plate capacitance can be reduced by a factor of 100 or more by the addition of a screen grid. A vacuum tube with the above four electrodes is called a *tetrode.*

Although tetrodes are used in some applications, their characteristics are not desirable for the majority of applications. The output characteristic for a typical tetrode is shown in Fig. 3.27. For normal operation the screen current is approximately 20 % of the plate current. When the plate voltage is less than the screen-grid voltage, electrons from the cathode strike the plate with sufficient kinetic energy to release one or more electrons from the plate.

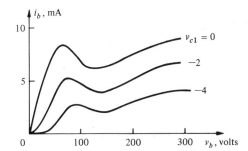

Fig. 3.27   Plate characteristics for a tetrode vacuum tube.

These *secondary* electrons are accelerated toward the screen grid and the plate current is reduced, as shown in the characteristics of Fig. 3.27. In this region of operation, as the plate voltage is increased, the plate current decreases. This phenomenon is an example of *negative resistance*; negative resistance is generally undesirable because it can lead to unstable amplifier operation.

To prevent this phenomenon, another electrode, called the *suppressor grid*, is placed between the screen grid and plate and generally connected to the cathode. The resulting structure is called a *pentode.* Another method used for preventing secondary electrons from reaching the screen grid is the placement of deflecting plates in the vicinity of the plate and screen grid. The resulting device is called a *beam-power* tube and is intended for power applications.

The schematic of a pentode and its output characteristics is shown in Fig. 3.28; a basic amplifier circuit using a pentode is illustrated in Fig. 3.29. The graphical and piecewise solutions for a tetrode or pentode are basically the same as for a triode.

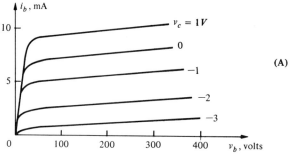

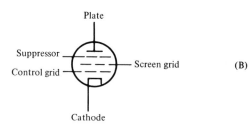

Fig. 3.28 Pentode vacuum tube. (A) Plate characteristics. (B) Schematic symbol.

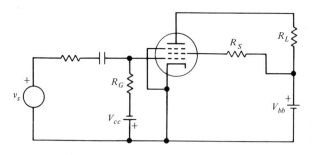

Fig. 3.29 Basic pentode amplifier circuit.

3.7 Classes of Amplifier Operation

Besides defining amplifiers as voltage, current, or power amplifiers, an amplifier can also be defined in terms of its biasing. If the excitation is a sinusoidal signal and the amplifier is so biased that the output (or load) current flows for 360 degrees, the operation is said to be *class A*. Biasing the amplifier such that output current flows for 180 degrees yields *class B* operation. In the situation where the output current flows for greater than 180 degrees but less than 360 degrees, we have class *AB* operation. Finally, if the amplifier is biased such that output current flows for less than 180 degrees, this results in *class C* operation.

The amplifiers considered in this chapter were so biased that class A operation was obtained (the output current flow was for 360 degrees). Class A is used when "linear" operation is required. Class B and AB are used often in power amplifiers; class C operation finds application in some power amplifiers and in tuned amplifiers. These topics will be considered later in the text.

3.8   Summary

In this chapter the ideal voltage and current amplifiers are dicussed. Physical devices such as the vacuum tube, the junction transistor, and the field-effect transistor are used in basic amplifier circuits. A vacuum tube has good voltage amplification, however, its life is short and requires additional power for heating. For these reasons it has been replaced mostly by semiconductor devices. The junction transistor is basically a current amplifier but may also be used as a voltage amplifier. Its input resistance, however, is less than that of the vacuum tube. The FET has an input resistance of the order of that for vacuum tubes. For the IGFET the input resistance could be as high as 10^{15} ohms. The following table shows the corresponding terminals of the above devices used in electronic circuits.

Terminal no.	Vacuum tube	Junction transistor	FET
1	Cathode	Emitter	Source
2	Grid	Base	Gate
3	Plate	Collector	Drain

Each of these devices may be used with terminal 1, 2, or 3 as common to ac signals.

References

ANGELO, JR., E. J., *Electronic Circuits*, 2nd ed., McGraw-Hill, New York, 1964.

COCHRUN, B. L., *Transistor Circuit Engineering*, Macmillan, New York, 1967.

COMER, D. J., *Introduction to Semiconductor Circuit Design*, Addison-Wesley, Reading, Mass, 1968.

SEIDMAN, A. H., and S. L. MARSHALL, *Semiconductor Fundamentals: Devices and Circuits*, Wiley, New York, 1963.

Problems

NOTE: Characteristic curves for the specified device types are found in the Appendix.

3.1 An ideal 3-stage voltage amplifier is given in Fig. P3.1. (a) If $R_L = 100$ ohms, find the overall voltage gain v_4/v_1. (b) If $v_1 = 0.1$ V rms, determine the output voltage v_4, current i_4, and the power absorbed by R_L.

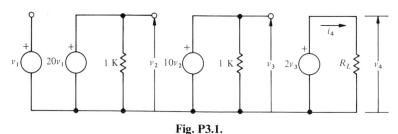

Fig. P3.1.

3.2 Repeat Prob. 3.1 for $R_L = 10$ ohms. Compare results.

3.3 A small-signal model of an amplifier using a voltage-operated device, such as a field-effect transistor or vacuum tube, operating at low frequencies is illustrated in Fig. P3.3. What is the output voltage v_o?

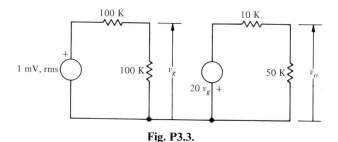

Fig. P3.3.

3.4 An ideal 2-stage current amplifier is shown in Fig. P3.4. (a) Determine the overall current gain i_3/i_1. If $i_1 = 0.1$ mA rms, find the current i_3, voltage v_3, and the power absorbed by R_L. Assume that $R_L = 1$ K.

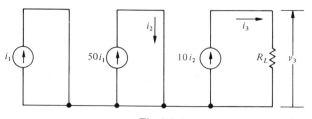

Fig. P3.4.

3.5 Repeat Prob. 3.4 for $R_L = 100$ ohms. Compare results.

3.6 A small-signal model of an amplifier using a current-operated device, such as a junction transistor, operating at low frequencies is shown in Fig. P3.6. Neglecting the dependent source $10^{-4}v_o$, calculate the output current i_o and voltage v_o.

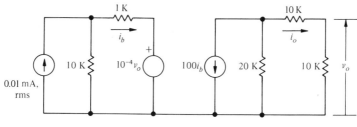

Fig. P3.6.

3.7 Repeat Prob. 3.6 without neglecting the dependent source $10^{-4}v_o$. Compare results.

3.8 Express the following ratios in decibels (dB): (a) $P_2/P_1 = 250$; (b) $V_2/V_1 = 60$; (c) $I_2/I_1 = 150$; (d) $V_2/V_1 = 0.1$.

3.9 For the common-emitter amplifier of Fig. P3.9, determine graphically (a) base current and (b) Q-point. Assume that $V_{BB} = 2$ V, $V_{CC} = 15$ V, and $V_{BE} = -0.25$ V.

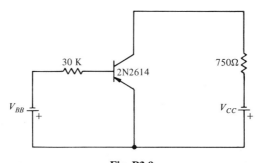

Fig. P3.9

3.10 Repeat Prob. 3.9 for $V_{BB} = 1.5$ V and $V_{CC} = 10$ V.

3.11 Referring to the common-base amplifier of Fig. 3.13, calculate the emitter current and Q-point. Assume that $V_{BE} = 0.7$ V, $R_E = 1$ K, $V_{BB} = 2.7$ V, $V_{CC} = 40$ V, and $R_L = 10$ K.

3.12 Repeat Prob. 3.11 for $V_{BB} = 3.7$ V and $V_{CC} = 50$ V.

3.13 Using graphical methods, find the Q-point for the common-source FET amplifier of Fig. 3.18. Assume that the FET used is a type E300, $V_{GG} = 1.5$ V, $V_{DD} = 16$ V, and $R_L = 2$ K.

3.14 Repeat Prob. 3.13 for $V_{DD} = 24$ V.

3.15 Draw a piecewise-linear model for the FET amplifier of Fig. 3.18 and repeat Prob. 3.13.

3.16 Determine the Q-point for the amplifier of Fig. P3.16.

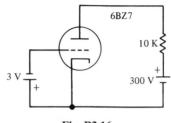

Fig. P3.16.

3.17 Calculate the average values of μ and r_B at the Q-point found in Prob. 3.16.

3.18 A 6AU6A pentode is used in the amplifier of Fig. 3.29. If $R_L = 40$ K, $V_{CC} = 1.5$ V, and $V_{bb} = 300$ V. (a) Determine the Q-point. (b) If the screen (grid 2) current is 2.1 mA, what is the value of R_S? $V_{C2} = 150$ V.

3.19 Calculate the average value of μ and r_B at the Q-point found in Prob. 3.18.

3.20 A piecewise-linear model of a 2-stage amplifier is shown in Fig. P3.20. For the signal, find (a) the overall voltage gain in dB and (b) the power gain of the second stage in dB. Assume that the capacitors act as shorts to the signal.

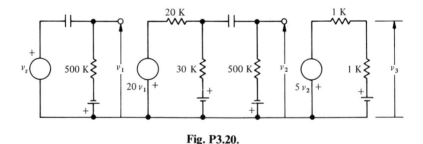

Fig. P3.20.

3.21 In the transistor amplifier of Fig. P3.21, source V_{BB} is made variable in order to obtain different values of base current I_B. If the base signal current is 0.5 sin ωt mA, draw curves of collector signal current as a function of ωt and specify the class of operation for (a) $I_B = 0.5$ mA; (b) $I_B = 0.2$ mA; (c) $I_B = 0$ mA; (d) the polarity of V_{BB} is reversed and base current flows for only 90 degrees of its positive half cycle.

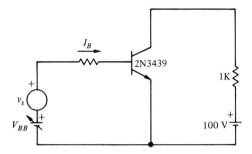

Fig. P3.21.

Diode
Rectifiers
and Filters

Because of the great economy and efficiency realized, electric power is transmitted to the consumer in ac rather than in dc form. There are many useful applications for ac: they range from running machinery in industrial plants to running the washing machine in the home. In electronics, however, most circuits require dc for their operation. There is thus a need of changing or *rectifying* ac to dc. This conversion is done generally in two steps. In the first, the ac is changed to a unidirectional current. The second step is concerned with smoothing, or filtering, the undirectional current to a direct current. As indicated in Chapter 2, diodes are used for rectification; combinations of inductors (and occasionally resistors) with capacitors are used for filtering.

In the first part of this chapter a number of single-phase and polyphase rectifier networks will be studied. The piecewise-linear model of the diode developed in Chapter 2 will be used in the analysis of these circuits. Filter networks and electronic regulation will be our concern in the remainder of the chapter.

4.1 Ratings and Characteristics

When faced with the problem of choosing a rectifier diode, one may consult the manufacturer's data sheet to make certain the correct device for the application is selected. On the sheet, the prospective user will find data under two general headings: *ratings* and *characteristics*. A rating refers to a maximum value of voltage, or temperature, or current that a component can withstand without catastrophic failure or gradual degradation of its performance; these values should never be exceeded. Examples of ratings are peak inverse (or reverse) voltage (PIV, PRV) and average rectified forward current (I_{dc}).

A characteristic refers to a measurable quantity, determined under specified test conditions, that is common or inherent to the device. Examples are dc forward voltage drop (V_F) and dc reverse leakage current (I_R). A complete

listing of definitions for various device ratings and characteristics will be found
in the literature. (See references at the end of chapter.)

4.2   Half-wave Rectifier

In this and ensuing discussions, the analysis will assume semiconductor
rectifiers are used; the methods developed, however, apply to other rectifying
devices as well. The back or reverse resistance of a semiconductor diode r_B will
be considered infinite in value, and the offset voltage V_o will be ignored.

As was indicated in Chapter 2, the simplest rectifier is the single-phase
half-wave rectifier of Fig. 2.17. General expressions for the average, or direct,
current (I_{dc}) and the root-mean square current (I_{rms}) were derived; these
expressions were denoted by (2.11) and (2.13), respectively, and are repeated
here:

$$I_{dc} = \frac{1}{2\pi} \int_0^{2\pi} i \, d(\omega t), \tag{2.11}$$

$$I_{rms} = \sqrt{\frac{1}{2\pi} \int_0^{2\pi} i^2 \, d(\omega t)}. \tag{2.13}$$

To simplify the analysis for sinusoidal excitation, it is often advantageous
to replace the argument ωt by $\omega t = \theta$; (2.11) and (2.13) therefore become

$$I_{dc} = \frac{1}{2\pi} \int_0^{2\pi} i \, d\theta \tag{4.1}$$

and

$$I_{rms} = \sqrt{\frac{1}{2\pi} \int_0^{2\pi} i^2 \, d\theta}. \tag{4.2}$$

For the half-wave rectifier it was shown that $I_{dc} = 0.318 I_m$ and $I_{rms} = 0.5 I_m$,
where I_m is the peak current.

Ripple Factor

A figure of merit for rectifiers mentioned often in the literature is the
ripple factor r. By definition, the ripple factor is the ratio of the rms value of
the ac component of current (or voltage) to the dc component of current (or
voltage). By means of current the ac component $i(t)_{ac}$ is defined as the total
instantaneous current $i(t)$ minus the dc component, I_{dc}:

$$i(t)_{ac} = i(t) - I_{dc}. \tag{4.3}$$

In terms or rms and dc quantities, (4.3) may be expressed as

$$RI^2_{ac(rms)} = RI^2_{rms} - RI^2_{dc}$$

or

$$I_{ac(rms)} = \sqrt{I^2_{rms} - I^2_{dc}}. \tag{4.4}$$

Therefore,

$$r = I_{ac(rms)}/I_{dc} = \sqrt{(I_{rms}/I_{dc})^2 - 1}. \tag{4.5}$$

$$r = \sqrt{(I_{rms}/I_{DC})^2 - 1}$$

Rectifier Efficiency

Another figure of merit for rectifier circuits is the *rectifier efficiency* η_r. This is defined as the dc power absorbed by the load resistance P_{dc} to the total average power supplied to the circuit P_i:

$$\eta_r = P_{dc}/P_i. \tag{4.6}$$

The average input power P_i is

$$\eta_r = P_{DC}/P_i$$

$$P_i = \frac{1}{2\pi} \int_0^{2\pi} vi \, d\theta \tag{4.7}$$

or

$$P_i = \frac{1}{2\pi} \int_0^{\pi} \frac{V_m^2}{r_F + R_L} \sin^2 \theta \, d\theta. \tag{4.8}$$

Substituting $V_{rms} = I_{rms}(r_F + R_L)$ and $V_{rms} = \sqrt{2}V_m$ in (4.8) and simplifying, one obtains

$$P_i = I^2_{rms}(r_F + R_L). \tag{4.9}$$

$$P_i = I^2_{RMS}(r_F + R_L)$$

The dc power P_{dc} is

$$P_{dc} = I^2_{dc}R_L. \tag{4.10}$$

$$P_{DC} = I^2_{DC}R_L$$

Hence,

$$\eta_r = \frac{I^2_{dc}R_L}{I^2_{rms}(r_F + R_L)}. \tag{4.11}$$

For the half-wave rectifier,

$$\eta_r = \frac{(0.318)^2 R_L}{(0.5)^2(r_F + R_L)} = \frac{0.406 R_L}{r_F + R_L}.$$

$$\eta_r = \frac{P_{DC}}{P_i} = \frac{I^2_{DC}R_L}{I^2_{RMS}(r_F + R_L)}$$

Dividing the numerator and denominator by R_L and multiplying the result by 100%, one obtains a convenient expression for the half-wave rectifier:

$$\eta_r = \frac{40.6\%}{r_F/R_L + 1}. \tag{4.12}$$

According to (4.12), the maximum rectification efficiency for a single-phase half-wave rectifier reaches 40.6% and occurs when an ideal diode rectifier ($r_F = 0$) is used.

Peak Inverse Voltage

PEAK REVERSE VOLTAGE

A very important consideration is the maximum, or peak, inverse (reverse) voltage PIV (PRV) that the diode sees when nonconducting. To determine this quantity for the half-wave rectifier, imagine a peak-reading voltmeter V_p is placed across the diode during the time it is reverse biased. One can see that the PIV $= V_m$, the maximum transformer winding voltage for a resistive load.

4.3   Voltage Regulation

An ideal constant voltage source, that is, one with *no* internal source resistance, maintains its output voltage regardless of the magnitude of load current. This is illustrated by the solid curve of Fig. 4.1. A physical source, however, has some internal resistance; consequently, when load current flows, a voltage drop exists across the internal resistance and the output voltage decreases. This is indicated by the dashed curve of Fig. 4.1.

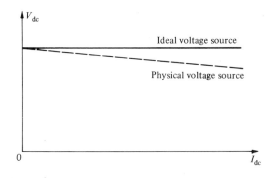

Fig. 4.1 Regulation (voltage) curves for ideal and physical voltage sources.

The effectiveness of a voltage source in maintaining its output voltage constant with load current is termed the *voltage regulation* of the source. A figure of merit, percent regulation (%Reg), is defined as

$$\% \text{ Reg} = [V_{NL} - V_{FL})/V_{FL}] \times 100\%, \tag{4.13}$$

ideal source $V_{NL} = V_{FL}$ & %Reg $= 0$

where V_{NL} = voltage output with zero or a small value of load current and V_{FL} = output voltage at a specified full-load current. For an ideal voltage source, $V_{NL} = V_{FL}$ and %Reg = 0. The poorer the regulation, the greater is the %Reg figure.

4.4 Transformer Winding Ratings

Once a rectifier circuit has been chosen and analyzed, the next step is the specification of power ratings for the input power transformer. A knowledge of these ratings can serve also as another figure of merit for comparing the effectiveness of various rectifier circuits. The following analysis will be concerned with the *single-phase half-wave* rectifier; the procedure developed, however, is also applicable to other rectifier configurations (see Table 4.1 for summary of results).

The secondary rms voltage is $V_s = V_m/\sqrt{2}$. To express this value in terms of the dc output voltage, $V_{dc}/0.318$ is substituted for V_m, and

$$V_s = V_{dc}/(\sqrt{2} \times 0.318) = 2.22 V_{dc}.$$

Similarly, for the secondary rms current I_s:

$$I_s = I_m/2 = 1.57 I_{dc}.$$

Secondary power rating, P_s, is

$$P_s = V_s I_s = 3.49 V_{dc} I_{dc} \text{ volt-amperes (VA)}. \tag{4.14}$$

From (4.4), the secondary ac component is

$$I_{ac} = \sqrt{I_s^2 - I_{dc}^2} = 1.21 I_{dc}.$$

Considering the transformer turns ratio N_s/N_p (where N_s is the number of secondary turns and N_p the number of primary turns), one obtains the primary rms current I_p

$$I_p = 1.21 I_{dc}(N_s/N_p).$$

The primary voltage, V_p is $(N_p/N_s)V_s$, or

$$V_p = 2.22 V_{dc}(N_p/N_s).$$

The primary power rating P_p is, therefore,

$$P_p = V_p I_p = 2.7 V_{dc} I_{dc} \text{(VA)}. \tag{4.15}$$

Example 4.1

For the half-wave rectifier circuit of Fig. 4.2, determine (a) I_{dc}, (b) I_{rms}, (c) r, (d) η_r, (e) PIV, (f) %Reg, and (g) power rating of transformer.

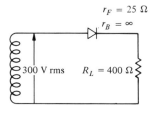

$r_F = 25\ \Omega$

$r_B = \infty$

300 V rms $R_L = 400\ \Omega$

Fig. 4.2 Circuit for Example 4.1.

Solution

(a) $V_m = 300/0.707 = 425$ V,
$\quad I_m = V_m/(r_F + R_L) = 425/425 = 1$ A; therefore,
$\quad I_{dc} = 0.318 \times 1 = 0.32$ A.

(b) $I_{rms} = I_m/2 = 1/2 = 0.5$ A.

(c) From (4.5), $r = \sqrt{(0.5/0.32)^2 - 1} = 1.21$.
(For the half-wave circuit, the ac or ripple component is greater than the desired dc output; as will be explained later in the chapter, the ripple factor can be reduced by using an appropriate filter network following the rectifier.)

(d) $\eta_r = 40.6\%/(1 + 25/400) = 38\%$.

(e) PIV $= V_m = 425$ V.

(f) $V_{NL} = 0.318V_m = 0.318 \times 425 = 135$ V,
$\quad V_{FL} = R_L I_{dc} = 400 \times 0.32 = 128$ V,
$\quad \%\text{Reg} = (135 - 128)/128 \times 100\% = 5.45\%$.

(g) $P_s = 3.49V_{dc}I_{dc} = 3.49 \times 135 \times 0.32 = 150$ VA.
$\quad P_p = 2.7V_{dc}I_{dc} = 2.7 \times 135 \times 0.32 = 117$ VA.

4.5   Full-wave Rectifier

A single-phase full-wave rectifier circuit is illustrated in Fig. 4.3. The transformer secondary winding has a center tap (CT), and voltage $v(t) = V_m \sin \omega t$ appears across each half of the winding with the shown polarity, that is, series aiding. During the positive half cycle diode *D*1 conducts; diode *D*2 is nonconducting. By the piecewise-linear model for the ideal

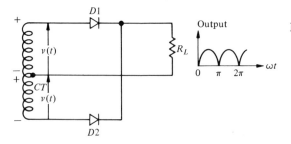

Fig. 4.3 Full-wave rectifier.

Table 4.1 Comparison of Some Rectifier Circuits

Circuit	I_{dc} (or V_{dc})	I_{rms} (or V_{rms})	r	η_r(max)	PIV	P_s (VA)	P_P (VA)
Single-phase							
Half-wave	$0.318\,I_m$	$0.5\,I_m$	1.21	40.6 %	V_m	$3.49\,V_{dc}I_{dc}$	$2.7\,V_{dc}I_{dc}$
Full-wave	$0.636\,I_m$	$0.707\,I_m$	0.48	81.2 %	$2\,V_m$	$1.74\,V_{dc}I_{dc}$ [a]	$1.23\,V_{dc}I_{dc}$
Bridge	$0.636\,I_m$	$0.707\,I_m$	0.48	81.2 %	V_m	$1.23\,V_{dc}I_{dc}$	$1.23\,V_{dc}I_{dc}$
Three-phase							
Half-wave	$0.827\,I_m$	$0.840\,I_m$	0.177	97 %	$1.73\,V_m$	$1.5\,V_{dc}I_{dc}$ [b]	$1.24\,V_{dc}I_{dc}$ [b]

[a] Total secondary rating.
[b] Total transformer (three windings) rating.

diode (Fig. 4.4A), the current i_{D1} is

$$i_{D1} = V_m \sin \omega t/(r_F + R_L) = I_m \sin \omega t. \tag{4.16a}$$

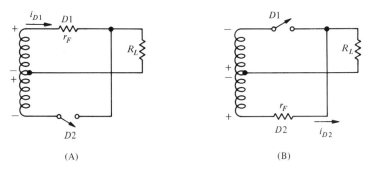

(A)   (B)

Fig. 4.4 Piecewise-linear model of full-wave rectifier. (A) Diode $D1$ conducting. (B) Diode $D2$ conducting.

For the negative half cycle, diode $D2$ conducts while $D1$ is nonconducting

$$i_{D2} = I_m \sin \omega t. \tag{4.16b}$$

Substituting (4.16a, b) in the expressions for average and rms values of current (4.1) and (4.2), one obtains for the full-wave rectifier

$$I_{dc} = 2I_m/\pi = 0.636 I_m, \tag{4.17}$$

$$I_{rms} = I_m/\sqrt{2} = 0.707 I_m. \tag{4.18}$$

(Similar expressions hold for voltages.)

The average value of current for the full-wave circuit is twice that of the half-wave rectifier; the rms component is approximately only 40% greater; the ripple factor r is 0.48. A lower value of ripple factor for the full-wave circuit should not be too surprising. A comparison of output waveforms for half- and full-wave rectifiers shows that the full-wave waveform is smoother. One can therefore expect a somewhat smaller ripple factor for the full-wave circuit.

By the analysis procedure used for the half-wave rectifier, the rectification efficiency for the full-wave circuit is

$$\eta_r = 81.2\%/(1 + r_F/R_L). \tag{4.19}$$

The peak-inverse voltage (PIV) across a nonconducting diode in a full-wave rectifier is twice that for the half-wave case, or $2V_m$. Referring to Fig. 4.4A or B, imagine a voltmeter is placed across the open switch. (As you recall, the open switch can be used as a model for a nonconducting diode whose back resistance is neglected.) Since both halves of the transformer windings are series aiding, the maximum voltage read by the voltmeter will be $2V_m$.

Example 4.2

The rms voltage for each half winding of a transformer for a full-wave rectifier is 300 V. Assume $r_F = 25$ ohms and r_B is infinite; let $R_L = 400$ ohms. Find (a) I_{dc}, (b) I_{rms}, (c) η_r, (d) PIV, (e) %Reg, (f) r, and (g) power rating of transformer.

Solution

(a) $V_m = 300/0.707 = 425$ V,
          $I_m = V_m/(r_F + R_L) = 1$ A,
          $I_{dc} = 0.636 I_m = 0.636 \times 1 = 0.636$ A.
(b) $I_{rms} = 0.707 I_m = 0.707$ A.
(c) $\eta_r = 81.2\%/(1 + 25/400) = 76\%.$
(d)   PIV $= 2V_m = 2 \times 425 = 850$ V.
(e) $V_{NL} = 0.636 \times 425 = 270$ V,
          $V_{FL} = 400 \times 0.636 = 254$ V,
    %Reg $= (270 - 254)/254 \times 100\% = 6.3\%.$
(f) $r = \sqrt{(I_{rms}/I_{dc})^2 - 1} = \sqrt{(0.707/0.636)^2 - 1} = 0.48.$
(g) From Table 4.1,

$$P_s = 1.74 V_{dc} I_{dc} = 1.74 \times 270 \times 0.636 = 298 \text{ VA},$$

$$P_p = 1.23 V_{dc} I_{dc} = 211 \text{ VA}.$$

The effects of back resistance, which has been assumed infinite in the preceding analysis, will now be examined. For convenience, the half-wave rectifier is considered. The forward resistance is r_F, and the back resistance is r_B. The current flowing during the positive half-cycle is $i_F(t) = I_m \sin \omega t$; during the negative half-cycle, the current is $i_B(t) = I'_m \sin \omega t$, where $I'_m = V_m/(r_B + R_L)$. With $\omega t = \theta$, substitution of these terms in (4.1) yields

$$I_{dc} = \frac{1}{2\pi}\left[\int_0^\pi I_m \sin \theta \, d\theta + \int_\pi^{2\pi} I'_m \sin \theta \, d\theta \right]. \tag{4.20}$$

Theoretically, the reverse saturation current of a semiconductor diode remains constant for all back, or negative, voltages greater than about -0.1 V. Because of surface leakage at higher voltages, however, the reverse current increases. For a high-quality silicon rectifier diode, the back resistance may be of the order of many megohms. For all practical purposes, the value I'_m for physical circuits is zero; the second integrand in (4.20) vanishes, and the result reduces to $0.318 I_m$. The same kinds of conclusions are reached when considering rms values. If diodes with a lower back resistance than that of silicon are used (for example, germanium or selenium), it may become necessary to consider the diode back resistance.

Although the examples considered so far assumed a sine-wave source, which is the most common excitation for rectifier circuits, rectification of nonsinusoidal waveforms is of course also possible. This will be illustrated by the following example.

Example 4.3

Assume a square-wave excitation of 200 V peak-to-peak and a period of 2 seconds is impressed across a half-wave rectifier where $r_F = 25$ ohms, $R_L = 400$ ohms, and r_B is infinite. Determine (a) I_{dc}, (b) I_{rms}, (c) r, (d) η_r, (e) PIV, and (f) %Reg.

Solution

(a) $V_{dc} = \frac{1}{2} \int_0^1 100 \, dt = 50$ V.

Therefore, $I_{dc} = 50/425 = 0.118$ A.

(b) $V_{rms} = \sqrt{\frac{1}{2} \int_0^1 (100)^2 \, dt} = 70.7$ V,

$I_{rms} = 70.7/425 = 0.167$ A.

(c) $r = \sqrt{(0.167/0.118)^2 - 1} = \sqrt{2 - 1} = 1$.

(d) $\eta_r = \dfrac{I_{dc}^2 R_L}{I_{rms}^2 (r_F + R_L)} = \dfrac{(0.118)^2 \times 400}{(0.166)^2 \times 425} \times 100\% = 40.2\%$.

(e) PIV $= 100$ V.

(f) $V_{NL} = V_{dc} = 50$ V,

$V_{FL} = 0.118 \times 400 = 47.3$ V,

%Reg $= (50 - 47.3)/47.3 \times 100\% = 5.7\%$.

4.6   Bridge Rectifiers

Two features of the full-wave rectifier that may be undesirable for certain applications are

1. The need of a transformer with a center tap.
2. The peak-inverse voltage (PIV) across a nonconducting diode is twice the maximum voltage across half a transformer winding.

The full-wave bridge rectifier of Fig. 4.5 overcomes these two objections; however, four diodes are required instead of two, and load R_L does not have a connection, referred to as *ground*, common to the ac excitation source.

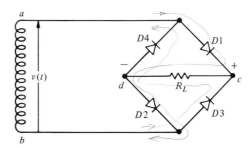

Fig. 4.5 Full-wave bridge rectifier.

A smaller transformer is required (see Table 4.1). Because the PIV across a nonconducting diode is only V_m, the bridge rectifier is well suited for high-voltage applications.

For this analysis, ideal diodes will be assumed. From Fig. 4.5, when point a is positive with respect to b, diodes $D1$ and $D2$ conduct while diodes $D3$ and $D4$ do not conduct. On the other half cycle diodes $D3$ and $D4$ are conducting; $D1$ and $D2$ are reverse biased. The resultant is a full-wave output with point c positive with respect to point d. The maximum reading of a voltmeter placed across a nonconducting diode would be V_m, the maximum voltage across the transformer winding. All other relationships derived for the full-wave circuit apply to the bridge rectifier, as summarized in Table 4.1.

4.7 Polyphase Rectifiers

Alternating current power is distributed often to industrial plants as three-phase power. For applications requiring large amounts of dc power, *polyphase rectifiers* are employed instead of single-phase units. Besides having greater power capability than a single-phase circuit, a polyphase rectifier offers additional advantages in that:

1. The ripple factor is less.
2. The first sinusoidal term in the Fourier series that represents the rectified output has a greater frequency; thus it permits the use of smaller components for the filter network.
3. The rectifier efficiency is higher.

A three-phase half-wave rectifier is illustrated in Fig. 4.6. The secondary Y-connected transformer has a diode in each leg, labeled D_A, D_B, D_C. The polarity of the resultant voltage across the load resistance R_L is such that the resistance side connected to point a is positive with respect to neutral point n. The three phasor voltages V_A, V_B, and V_C are 120 degrees apart; their resultant sinusoidal waveforms are shown in Fig. 4.7. The sinusoidal voltages may be expressed as follows:

$$v_A(t) = V_m \sin \omega t, \tag{4.21a}$$

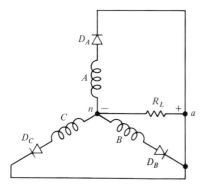

Fig. 4.6 Three-phase half-wave rectifier.

$$v_B(t) = V_m \sin(\omega t - 120°), \tag{4.21b}$$

$$v_C(t) = V_m \sin(\omega t - 240°). \tag{4.21c}$$

Figure 4.7A shows that during the interval between $\omega t_1 = \pi/6$ rad (30°) and $\omega t_2 = 5\pi/6$ rad (150°), $v_A(t)$ is more positive than either $v_B(t)$ or $v_C(t)$; consequently only diode D_A conducts and diodes D_B and D_C are reverse biased. For the interval $\omega t_2 - \omega t_3$, $v_B(t)$ is most positive, and only diode D_B conducts. Likewise, during $\omega t_3 - \omega t_4$, diode D_C conducts. The angle of conduction in each instance is 120 degrees.

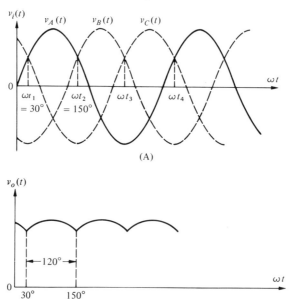

Fig. 4.7 Process of rectification in a three-phase, half-wave rectifier. (A) Sinusoidal input voltages. (B) Output rectified voltage.

The resultant rectified output is shown in Fig. 4.7B. According to the basic definition of average current expressed by (4.1), I_{dc} is

$$I_{dc} = \frac{3I_m}{2\pi} \int_{\pi/6}^{5\pi/6} \sin\theta \, d\theta = 0.827 I_m, \tag{4.22}$$

where $I_m = V_m/(r_F + R_L)$.
The effective, or rms value, from (4.2) is

$$I_{rms} = I_m \sqrt{\frac{3}{2\pi} \int_{\pi/6}^{5\pi/6} \sin^2\theta \, d\theta} = 0.840 I_m. \tag{4.23}$$

By (4.5), the ripple factor is found to be

$$r = \sqrt{(0.840 I_m/0.827 I_m)^2 - 1} = 0.177. \tag{4.24}$$

The rectifier efficiency (4.11) is

$$\eta_r = 97\%/(1 + r_F/R_L). \tag{4.25}$$

To determine the PIV of a nonconducting diode, assume diode D_A is conducting and diodes D_B and D_C are nonconducting (Fig. 4.6). The voltage across a nonconducting diode, such as diode D_B, is found to be

$$\text{PIV} = V_m - V_m \angle{-120°} = 1.73 V_m. \tag{4.26}$$

The above values are tabulated in Table 4.1; a comparison of the data shows the superiority of a polyphase rectifier. Another polyphase rectifier, the three-phase full-wave bridge, is given in Fig. 4.8. The analysis of this circuit is left to the student.

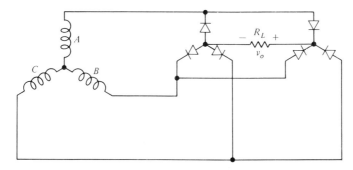

Fig. 4.8   Three-phase, full-wave bridge rectifier.

4.8   Filter Networks

In examining the output waveforms obtained from the half- and full-wave and bridge rectifiers, one observes a unidirectional current or voltage instead of the flat and constant output of a dc source, such as a battery. To realize a smooth, or dc output, a filter is needed. The first to be considered is the pure capacitor (C) filter. Based on an understanding of the operation of the capacitor filter, voltage multiplying circuits, such as the voltage doubler, will be analyzed. Other filter configurations to be considered include the pure L, L-section, and pi filters.

Capacitor Filter

One of the simplest methods for obtaining filtering is to place a capacitor C across a load resistance R_L (see Fig. 4.9). To understand the operation

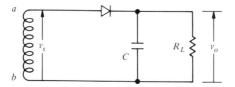

Fig. 4.9 Simple Capacitor (C) filter.

and limitations of this circuit, we shall first assume that R_L is infinite, that is, no load current flows. When point a is positive with respect to b, the diode conducts and capacitor C charges to V_m volts. The charging of the capacitor takes place during the first quarter-cycle ($\pi/2$ radians or 90°) of the input waveform, as illustrated in Fig. 4.10. Thereafter, the voltage across capacitor C (output voltage) will be constant and always equal to V_m volts. Since the voltage across the output is now equal to V_m, the diode remains always reverse biased and does not conduct after the first quarter-cycle.

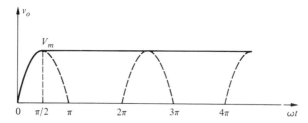

Fig. 4.10 The output of a C filter when R_L is infinite. Diode conducts during first-quarter cycle of the input voltage.

As mentioned previously, after the first quarter-cycle the diode remains reverse biased. Consequently, when v_s forces point a to become negative with respect to b, the maximum voltage across the transformer winding is $-V_m$. This adds in series to the output voltage V_m across C; the maximum inverse, or reverse, voltage across the diode is therefore equal to $2V_m$.

The preceding discussion was simplified for the sake of illustrating some basic operating principles of the pure capacitor filter. We now embark on an analysis of a more realistic nature where R_L is not infinite and load current therefore flows. Refer to Fig. 4.11 which shows the output waveform across capacitor C and load R_L. From 0 to ωt_1, the diode conducts and the output follows the sinusoidal waveform (neglecting the transformer winding and forward diode resistances). The output voltage is

$$v_o = V_m \sin \omega t \qquad \text{for } 0 < \omega t < \omega t_1. \tag{4.27}$$

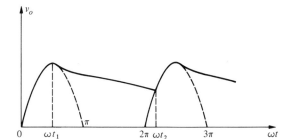

Fig. 4.11 The output voltage across C for finite R_L.

At $\omega t = \omega t_1^+$ (the superscript $+$ denotes "just after ωt_1"), the output voltage is more positive than the source voltage v_s; the diode therefore becomes back biased. Time t_1 is called the *cutout* time. The diode is reverse biased and at time t_1 the voltage across capacitor C is $V_o = V_m \sin \omega t_1$. (Note: The value of ωt_1 is not necessarily equal to $\pi/2$ radians, or 90°, as will be explained later.) Writing the differential equation for the network one obtains

$$R_L C \frac{dv_o}{dt} + v_o = 0. \tag{4.28}$$

Solving (4.28) and using the initial condition $v_o(t_1) = V_o$ results in

$$v_o = V_o \exp[-(t - t_1)/R_L C]. \tag{4.29}$$

To determine time t_2, the *cutin* time where $v_s = v_o$ and the diode begins conducting once again, the following must hold:

$$V_m \sin \omega t_2 = V_o \exp[-(t_2 - t_1)/R_L C]. \tag{4.30}$$

Equation (4.30) is transcendental and cannot be solved by analytical methods. By a trial and error solution on a digital computer, the value of t_2 can be found to a great degree of accuracy if one is interested. Another procedure is to plot (4.30) and determine graphically the cutin point at t_2.

The cutout point can be determined analytically. During the time the diode conducts (neglecting transformer winding and forward diode resistances), it is seen from (4.27) that the source voltage is impressed across C and R_L. The current flowing through the diode is

$$i = \frac{v_s}{R_L} + C\frac{dv_s}{dt}. \tag{4.31}$$

Substituting for $v_s = V_m \sin \omega t$ in (4.31) and simplifying one obtains

$$i(t) = V_m\sqrt{(1/R_L)^2 + (\omega C)^2}\,\sin(\omega t + \theta) \tag{4.32}$$

where phasor angle $\theta = \tan^{-1}(\omega C R_L)$. The surge current I_s is defined by

$$I_s = V_m(1/R_L^2 + \omega^2 C^2)^{1/2}. \tag{4.33}$$

From (4.32) $i(t)$ will be zero when $\omega t + \theta$ equals π or some multiple of π. Therefore,

$$\omega t + \theta = n\pi. \tag{4.34}$$

For $n = 1$, $\omega t_1 = \pi - \theta$. Note that, in general, ωt_1 does not equal 90 degrees.

Figure 4.12 shows the output voltage waveshapes for different values of R_L.

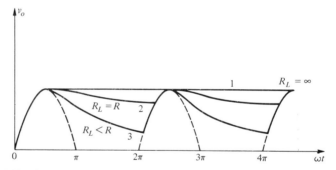

Fig. 4.12   Output voltage as a function of ωt for three different values of R_L.

As R_L decreases in value, the output voltage departs greatly from something resembling a dc source. This is also borne out by (4.29) which applies while the diode is back biased. As R_L decreases, $1/R_L C$ increases and the output decays rapidly to cutin.

It should be clear from the foregoing analysis that a simple capacitor filter is inadequate for a load (small R_L) drawing appreciable current. For moderate current, however, the decay may be tolerable, as illustrated by exponential decay curve 2 of Fig. 4.12. To simplify the analysis for this condition, exponential curve 2 will be approximated by a straight line, as illustrated in Fig. 4.13. Voltage V_R is the peak-to-peak value of ripple voltage and may be obtained from the fundamental relationship that the charge q lost by capacitor C is $q = CV_R$. With constant current assumed, the charge q lost in time T is equal to $I_{dc}T$ where $I_{dc} \approx V_m/R_L$; therefore,

$$I_{dc}T = CV_R,$$

or

$$V_R = I_{dc}T/C.$$

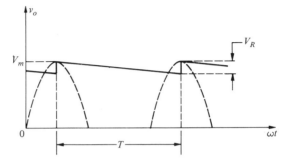

Fig. 4.13 Approximation of an exponential curve.

But $T = 1/f$; hence,

$$V_R = I_{dc}/fC. \tag{4.35}$$

It is seen from (4.35) that the ripple voltage V_R increases with I_{dc} and decreases with f and C.

From Fig. 4.13, the average, or dc, output voltage V_{dc} is

$$\begin{aligned} V_{dc} &= V_m - V_R/2 \\ &= V_m - I_{dc}/2fC. \end{aligned} \tag{4.36}$$

From (4.33), at cutin the surge current I_s is a function of C for a given value of load resistance R_L. This value can be much greater than I_{dc}, possibly destroying the diode rectifier. If the surge current exceeds the maximum rating supplied by the manufacturer of the diode, a series resistance R_s, called a *surge resistor*, is inserted in series with the diode. (The surge resistor will also reduce the output voltage.)

Voltage Multiplying Circuits

It is sometimes necessary to provide a relatively high voltage at a very small current drain. In these cases a high load resistance is used. An example of such an application is the high voltage needed for the anode circuit of a cathode-ray tube. The current drain may be in the order of only a few hundred microamperes. A simple way of obtaining such a supply is by using a voltage multiplying circuit, for example, a *voltage doubler*.

Consider the bridge voltage doubler circuit of Fig. 4.14. Note the similarity of this circuit to the bridge rectifier of Fig. 4.5; two diodes have been replaced by two capacitors. When point a is positive with respect to b, diode $D1$ conducts and capacitor C_1 charges to V_m volts with the indicated polarity. On the negative half cycle, C_2 charges to V_m volts and its polarity is such that it adds in series with the nearly constant voltage across C_1. The total voltage across R_L is therefore equal to $2V_m$ volts.

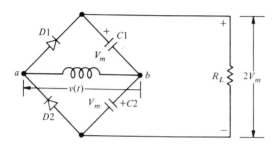

Fig. 4.14 Full-wave bridge doubler.

Assume that R_L is infinite. The voltage across C_1 is v_{C1}; across C_2, v_{C2}; and across R_L $v_{C1} + v_{C2}$. When R_L is finite, the effect of drawing load current on the output voltage is illustrated in Fig. 4.15, which shows a plot of the normalized dc output voltage as a function of $\omega R_L C$ for different values of the average dc resistance R_{dc} (which is the sum of the forward diode resistance r_F and the source resistance) to the load resistance R_L. There are some interesting points to note:

1. For a given value of ω and C, $V_{dc} = 2V_m$ only when load resistance R_L is infinite and the average dc resistance is zero.

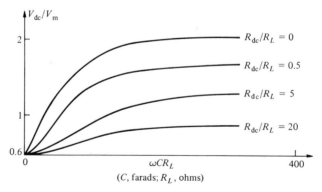

Fig. 4.15 Plots of V_{dc}/V_m as a function of $\omega C R_L$ for different values of R_{dc}/R_L for the bridge doubler.

2. As R_L decreases or R_{dc}/R_L increases, V_{dc} becomes less than $2V_m$. This demonstrates that a voltage doubler (or for that matter any voltage multiplying circuit) is most useful for small load currents, that is, high values of load resistance R_L.

One can, at least in theory, design an *n*-voltage multiplier, where *n* is 2, 3, 4, 5, ... ; the circuit is illustrated in Fig. 4.16 where ideal and identical components are assumed. Suppose *b* is the terminal common to the input and output voltages. When *b* is positive with respect to *a*, capacitor C_1 charges through diode *D1* to V_m volts, with the indicated polarity shown in Fig. 4.16. During the next half cycle, *a* becomes positive with respect to *b*; diode *D1* is reverse biased and diode *D2* forward biased. Capacitor C_2 will now charge to a maximum value of (V_m volts across C_1) + (V_m volts owing to the source which is in series with C_1) = $2V_m$. The process continues along the line so that voltages of $4V_m$ (quadrupler), $6V_m$ (sextupler), etc. are possible.

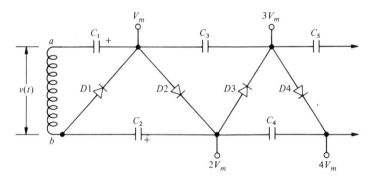

Fig. 4.16   An *n*-voltage multiplier.

If terminal *a* is the common terminal, values of V_m (which is obtained from a simple half-wave rectifier) $3V_m$ (tripler), $5V_m$ (quintupler), etc. are realized. One advantage of this circuit over the bridge multiplier is that a common terminal exists for the input and output voltages.

The output voltage decreases rapidly with load current for a quadrupler. This is a common property of all voltage multiplying circuits. They are useful only if the load current drain is small and constant.

Pure Inductance (L) *Filter*

The Fourier series of the output of a full-wave rectifier is

$$v(t) = \frac{2V_m}{\pi} - \frac{4V_m}{\pi} \left(\frac{\cos 2\omega t}{3} + \frac{\cos 4\omega t}{15} + \cdots \right). \tag{4.37}$$

The average, or dc, value is $2V_m/\pi = 0.638V_m$; the first ac term of the series has a frequency equal to *twice* the source frequency. The coefficients of the higher order frequency terms are much less than the first, or fundamental, term and will therefore be ignored in the analysis.

A full-wave rectifier with an L filter is shown in Fig. 4.17. By means of the first two terms of the Fourier series, the model of Fig. 4.18 is obtained. The dc term is represented by a battery of $0.636V_m$ volts and the fundamental term is represented by an ac source $(4V_m/3\pi)\cos 2\omega t$ volts. Resistance R_{dc} is the sum of the transformer winding and forward diode resistance.

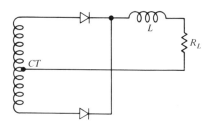

Fig. 4.17 Full-wave rectifier using a pure *L* filter.

A steady-state analysis of the model of Fig. 4.18 is now undertaken. Components L, R_{dc}, and R_L are generally considered to be linear and, therefore, superposition may be employed in the analysis. With the ac source at zero, the dc output voltage V_{dc} is

$$V_{dc} = \frac{2V_m R_L}{\pi(R_{dc} + R_L)}. \tag{4.38}$$

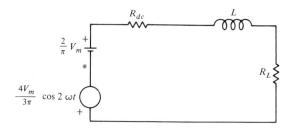

Fig. 4.18 Model for analyzing the circuit of Fig. 4.30.

With the dc source at zero, the rms magnitude of the ripple voltage V_R is

$$V_R = \frac{4V_m R_L}{(3\pi\sqrt{2})\sqrt{(R_{dc} + R_L)^2 + 4\omega^2 L^2}}. \tag{4.39}$$

The ripple factor r may be obtained by taking the ratio of the ripple voltage to the dc voltage:

$$r = \frac{2(R_L + R_{dc})}{(3\sqrt{2})\sqrt{(R_{dc} + R_L)^2 + 4\omega^2 L^2}}. \tag{4.40}$$

In practice, L is chosen so that $2\omega L \gg (R_{dc} + R_L)$. With this approximation, (4.40) reduces to

$$r = \frac{R_L + R_{dc}}{3\sqrt{2}\omega L}. \tag{4.41}$$

Example 4.4

A full-wave rectifier operating at a line frequency of 60 Hz uses an L filter. The given component values are $R_{dc} = 100$ ohms, $R_L = 500$ ohms, and $L = 10$ henrys. Find (a) the dc voltage V_{dc} and (b) the ripple factor r. Assume $V_m = 500$ V.

Solution

(a) From (4.38),

$$V_{dc} = \frac{2 \times 500}{\pi} \times \frac{500}{600} = 265 \text{ V.}$$

(b) For $f = 60$ Hz, $\omega = 120\pi = 377$ rad/sec. Therefore, $2\omega L = 2 \times 377 \times 10 = 7540$ ohms. The sum $R_{dc} + R_L = 600$ ohms; $7540 > 600$ and (4.41) may be used instead of (4.40). Hence,

$$r = \frac{600}{3\sqrt{2} \times 3770} \approx 0.038.$$

Compare this value of ripple factor with those listed in Table 4.1.

L-Section (Choke-Input) Filter

The ripple voltage can be further attenuated by placing a capacitor C across the load R_L, as illustrated in Fig. 4.19. The resulting filter is called an L-section, or choke-input, filter; a model of the circuit is given in Fig. 4.20.

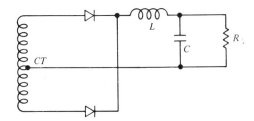

Fig. 4.19 Full-wave rectifier with L-section filter.

With the ac source set to zero, (4.38) for the dc output still applies. The ripple output is obtained by setting the dc source to zero. (This assumes that current flows for at least 2π radians in steady state, which may not always be true.

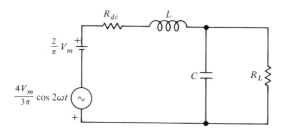

Fig. 4.20 Model for the circuit of Fig. 4.19.

This case will be considered after Example 4.5.) If C is chosen so that $X_C \ll R_L$, the ripple voltage V_R is expressed by

$$V_R = \frac{-4V_m(-jX_C)}{3\pi\sqrt{2}[R_{dc} + j(X_L - X_C)]}.$$ (4.42)

In practice it is usual for X_L to be much greater than X_C and R_{dc}. With these approximations, (4.42) reduces to

$$V_R \approx \frac{4V_m}{(3\pi\sqrt{2})4\omega^2 LC}.$$ (4.43)

The ripple factor r is

$$r = \frac{1 + R_{dc}/R_L}{6\sqrt{2}\omega^2 LC}.$$ (4.44)

Example 4.5

Repeat Example 4.4 for an L-section filter. Use the same component values, and let $C = 20 \ \mu F$.

Solution

(a) The dc output voltage will be the same, that is $V_{dc} = 265$ V.
(b) The ripple factor is

$$r = \frac{1 + 100/500}{6\sqrt{2(377)^2 10 \times 20 \times 10^{-6}}} = 0.005.$$

A comparison of this result with the ripple factor of Example 4.4 shows that the ripple factor has been reduced by a factor of approximately eight.

Our analysis of the full-wave rectifier with an L-section filter assumed continuous current flow for every 2π radians of input voltage. Is this always a valid assumption? Assume R_L is infinite; for this condition no current flows and capacitor C charges to the peak voltage V_m of the secondary transformer half winding. As R_L becomes finite, current begins to flow. For small currents, however, the filter behaves as though it was a pure capacitor filter; in other words, the inductor is not effective, and cutout occurs. At a critical value of dc load current I_{dc}', the inductance takes over its role and the diodes never cut out. The dc output voltage as a function of dc load current is plotted in Fig. 4.21.

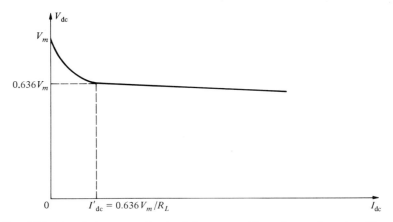

Fig. 4.21 Regulation curve for the full-wave rectifier using an L-section filter.

The value of the minimum, or *critical*, inductance L_c needed to ensure the condition in which the diodes always conduct and never cut out is determined by equating the critical dc current to the peak value of the ripple current (see Fig. 4.22):

$$\frac{2V_m}{\pi R_L} \geq \frac{4V_m}{3\pi(2\omega L_c)}.$$

Solving for L_c and simplifying, one obtains

$$L_c = R_L/3\omega. \hspace{2cm} (4.45)$$

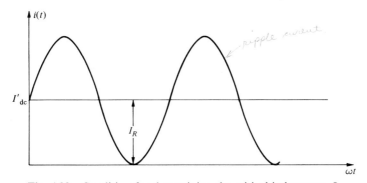

Fig. 4.22 Condition for determining the critical inductance, L_c.

The preceding result was based on using the fundamental term of the Fourier series for the full-wave rectifier output waveform. In practice, the value of L_c found by (4.45) should therefore be increased by approximately 20%. To avoid the region of operation between V_m and $0.636 V_m$ of Fig. 4.21, which results in very poor regulation, a resistance placed across the capacitor, called a *bleeder*, is commonly used. The value of the bleeder resistance R_B is determined from

$$R_B = 0.636 V_m / I_{dc}. \tag{4.46}$$

In addition to improving regulation, the bleeder resistor also provides safety. When a load is removed from the power supply, capacitor C has a discharge path through the bleeder resistance R_B.

The inductance of an iron-core inductor, or choke, can be made to depend on the dc current flowing through it. A choke designed specifically for this purpose is called a *swinging choke*. For example, a swinging choke may have a value of 25 H for some minute current and 5 H at, say, 200 mA. The use of a swinging choke permits a large value of bleeder resistance. In practice, however, the cost of a swinging choke is seldom warranted except for very high output power supplies.

A variation of the L-section filter is the replacement of the inductance with a resistance, as illustrated in Fig. 4.23. With superposition in the analysis, as was done previously, the dc output voltage V_{dc} is

$$V_{dc} = \frac{2V_m}{\pi} \frac{R_L}{R_{dc} + R_A + R_L}. \tag{4.47}$$

Again with $X_C \ll R_L$ assumed, the ripple voltage V_R is

$$V_R = \frac{4V_m}{3\pi\sqrt{2}} \frac{-jX_C}{(R_{dc} + R_A) - jX_C}. \tag{4.48}$$

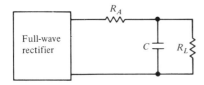

Fig. 4.23 The inductance of an *L*-section filter replaced by resistance R_A.

Also with $X_C \ll (R_{dc} + R_A)$ and taking magnitudes, the ripple factor is

$$r = \frac{\sqrt{2}}{3} \frac{1 + R_L/(R_{dc} + R_A)}{\omega C R_L}. \tag{4.49}$$

Example 4.6

In Example 4.5, the 10-H choke is replaced by a resistance. What is the minimum value of R_L required to obtain the same dc output voltage of 263 V?

Solution

The inductive reactance $X_L = 2\omega L = 7540$ ohms. Let us replace this reactance by resistance $R_A = 7540$ ohms. Solving (4.47) for R_L, one obtains

$$263 = 0.636 \times 500 R_L/(7540 + 100 + R_L)$$

$$R_L = 37 \text{ K}.$$

The value of $R_L = 37$ K is much greater than the 500 ohms used in Example 4.5 where a choke-input filter was employed. This demonstrates that when a resistance is used in place of a choke, the supply is limited to low output current. If greater ripple is tolerated, a smaller value of R_A can be used and therefore more load current drawn from the supply.

Half-Wave Rectifiers with L and L-Section Filters

Consider a half-wave rectifier with an inductance L in series with a diode and load R_L. The inductance used in this manner is called a pure L filter. Plots of iR_L/V_m versus ωt and ripple factor versus $\omega L/R_L$ are given in Fig. 4.24 and 4.25, respectively. An examination of these curves indicates that filtering action is quite nil and not very practical except for very large currents; for this reason, the circuit will not be analyzed.

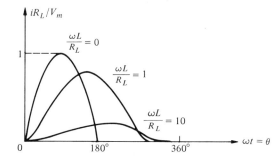

Fig. 4.24 Performance of a pure *L*-filter. (Courtesy of Motorola.)

A practical version of an L-section filter in a half-wave rectifier circuit is shown in Fig. 4.26. Resistance R permits the capacitor to discharge during the negative half-cycle. If the inductance is sufficiently large, continuous

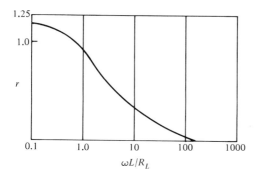

Fig. 4.25   Ripple as a function of $\omega L/R_L$. (Courtesy of Motorola.)

current will flow and no cutout occurs. The addition of R, however, lowers the efficiency of the circuit. One may conclude that, when an L-section filter is used, the rectifier will generally be a full-wave circuit.

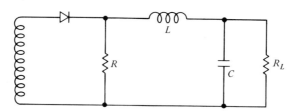

Fig. 4.26   Practical half-wave rectifier with *L*-section filter. Resistance R serves as a discharge path for L when the diode is reverse biased.

Pi-Section Filter

Figure 4.27 shows an example of a pi-section filter used with a full-wave rectifier. The circuit may be viewed as an L-section filter that filters the

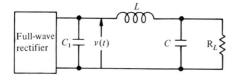

Fig. 4.27   Pi-section filter.

triangular output waveform of Fig. 4.28. The triangular waveform, a good approximation to the decaying discharge curve, is similar to that used for analyzing the half-wave rectifier with a pure-C filter. The Fourier series for the triangular waveform is

$$v(t) = V_{dc} - \frac{V_R}{\pi}(\sin 2\omega t - \tfrac{1}{2}\sin 4\omega t + \tfrac{1}{3}\sin 6\omega t \mp \cdots). \qquad (4.50)$$

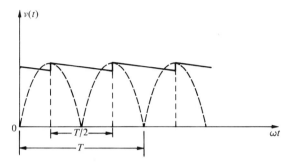

Fig. 4.28 Approximated triangular waveform across C_1 of Fig. 4.27.

For a full-wave output, with constant I_{dc} assumed, ripple voltage V_R is

$$V_R = I_{dc}T/2C_1 = I_{dc}/2fC_1. \qquad (4.51)$$

With only the fundamental term of (4.50) considered, the rms value V'_R is

$$V'_R = \frac{I_{dc}}{2fC_1\sqrt{2\pi}} = \frac{2I_{dc}}{4\pi fC_1\sqrt{2}} = \sqrt{2}I_{dc}X_{c1}. \qquad (4.52)$$

For simplicity, let $R_{dc} = 0$ and $X_C \ll R_L$; therefore the output ripple voltage V_{RO} is

$$V_{RO} = 2I_{dc}X_{c1}X_c/X_L. \qquad (4.53)$$

The ripple factor is equal to

$$r = \frac{V_{RO}}{V_{dc}} = \frac{\sqrt{2}}{8R_L\omega^3CC_1L}. \qquad (4.54)$$

In comparison with the L-section filter, the pi filter has the following advantages:
1. Higher dc output voltage.
2. Lower ripple factor can be attained.

Its disadvantages are
1. Poorer voltage regulation.
2. Higher diode forward peak current.

Multiple-Section Filters

To achieve very low ripple, one can cascade two or more L-section filters as illustrated in Fig. 4.29. Since each inductance has dc resistance, the penalty one pays for this arrangement is a decrease in dc output voltage under load. To compensate for the IR drop(s) across the additional inductor(s), a larger power transformer is required.

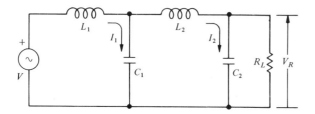

Fig. 4.29   Cascading two *L*-section filters.

In Fig. 4.29, voltage V is an rms ripple voltage that may be the output of a full-wave rectifier or the triangular voltage across a capacitor output. Two practical assumptions will be made in analyzing this circuit: (1) $X_{C2} \ll R_L$ and (2) X_{C1}, X_{C2} are much less than X_{L1} and X_{L2}. The rms current I_1 flowing through C_1 is, therefore,

$$I_1 \approx V/X_{L1}. \tag{4.55}$$

The voltage drop across C_1 is

$$V_1 = I_1 X_{C1} = V X_{C1}/X_{L1}. \tag{4.56}$$

Voltage V_1 appears across the second L-section filter. Current I_2 is

$$I_2 = V_1/X_{L2} = V X_{C1}/(X_{L1} X_{L2}). \tag{4.57}$$

Finally, the ripple voltage V_R is

$$V_R = I_2 X_{C2} = V X_{C1} X_{C2}/(X_{L1} X_{L2}) \tag{4.58}$$

$$= \frac{V}{16\omega^4 C_1 C_2 L_1 L_2}.$$

With equal-value *L*'s and *C*'s assumed, for *n*-sections,

$$V_R = V/(4\omega^2 CL)^n. \tag{4.59}$$

4.9   Electronic Voltage Regulator

Examples of elementary voltage regulators were examined in Chapters 2 and 3. Examples 2.3 and 2.4 considered a simple Zener diode circuit; an emitter follower and a Zener diode were elements of a more sophisticated regulator covered by Example 3.2. In both cases, however, ideal components were assumed. With physical elements that are not ideal, these simple circuits do not provide the degree of regulation needed for many applications. To achieve superior regulation a circuit that monitors the output voltage is required. As the output voltage changes because, for example, of a change in line voltage or in load current, it produces a signal that is processed in such a manner as to maintain the output voltage essentially constant. The circuit that accomplishes this is called an *electronic voltage regulator*.

A schematic diagram of a basic electronic voltage regulator connected to an unregulated supply, like a full-wave rectifier with an L-section filter, is shown in Fig. 4.30. Zener diode D_z provides a reference voltage V_z for transistor $Q2$. Resistance R_D limits the current to the diode to a small value in its Zener region of operation. Resistances R_1 and R_2 form a voltage divider, providing an operating bias and presenting to the base of $Q2$ voltage V_2, which is a fraction of the output voltage V_o. Transistor $Q2$ serves as the *control amplifier*, monitoring the voltage across resistance R_2; $Q1$, the *series transistor*, is connected as an emitter follower to provide a low output resistance. Load current I_L is approximately equal to the emitter current of $Q1$. Resistance R limits the collector current of $Q2$ and the base current of $Q1$.

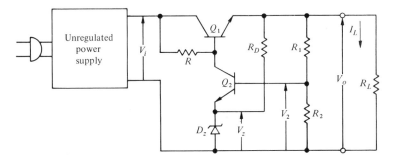

Fig. 4.30 Basic circuit of an electronic voltage regulator.

To understand the regulating action assume, for example, that the voltage of the unregulated supply, V_i rises because of a rise in the line voltage. This will tend to cause output voltage V_o to increase, as well as voltage V_2 across the input circuit of $Q2$. Greater collector current in $Q2$ therefore flows and reduces the available base current to $Q1$. A reduction in base current in $Q1$ results in an increase in voltage across the collector-emitter circuit of the series transistor. This forces a reduction in V_o and thereby tends to cancel the initial rise in output voltage. For a properly designed circuit, the output voltage will remain essentially constant. This will also be true for a falling line voltage or for load current changes.

To determine how effective the regulation is, we shall adopt the following approach. Output voltage V_o, besides being a function of input voltage, depends also on load current, Zener voltage, temperature, etc. Limiting our analysis to changes in input voltage V_i and load current I_L, we can write a functional relationship for these quantities:

$$V_o = f(V_i, I_L).$$

A change in V_o, designated as dV_o, is

$$dV_o = \frac{\partial V_o}{\partial V_i}\bigg|_{I_L} dV_i + \frac{\partial V_o}{\partial I_L}\bigg|_{V_i} dI_L. \tag{4.60}$$

For small changes, linear operation can be assumed; therefore, (4.60) can be
expressed in terms of increments:

$$\Delta V_o = \frac{\Delta V_o}{\Delta V_i}\bigg|_{\Delta I_L = 0} \Delta V_i + \frac{\Delta V_o}{\Delta I_L}\bigg|_{\Delta V_i = 0} \Delta I_L. \tag{4.61}$$

With

$$-\frac{\Delta V_o}{\Delta I_L}\bigg|_{\Delta V_i = 0} = S_L \quad \text{(the output resistance of the regulator)} \tag{4.62a}$$

and

$$\frac{\Delta V_o}{\Delta V_i}\bigg|_{\Delta I_L = 0} = S_R \quad \text{(the voltage regulation),} \tag{4.62b}$$

(4.61) reduces to

$$V_o = S_R \Delta V_i - S_L \Delta I_L, \tag{4.63}$$

where S_R and S_L are the *sensitivity*, or *stability*, factors.

Sensitivity factors will now be derived for the regulator of Fig. 4.30. The
analysis will be simplified by assuming the changes in base-emitter voltage
of each transistor and the Zener diode voltage are negligible; our results
will therefore be approximate. For this purpose we can replace transistors
$Q1$ and $Q2$ by the piecewise-linear model derived in Chapter 3. Because the
base and emitter terminals are common in this model, we let $R_A = R_D//R_1$
and $R_B = r_z//R_2$, where r_z is the average Zener diode resistance. Furthermore, since we are interested in varying quantities, incremental values of
current and voltage will be used. The resulting model appears in Fig. 4.31,
where the unregulated supply is replaced by ΔV_i in series with source
resistance R_s.

From Fig. 4.31,

$$\Delta I_{B2} = \frac{\Delta V_o}{R_A + R_B(1 + h_{FE2})} \tag{4.64}$$

and

$$\Delta I_{B1} = \Delta I - \Delta I_{C2}$$

$$= \Delta I - \frac{h_{FE2}\Delta V_o}{R_A + R_B(1 + h_{FE2})}. \tag{4.65}$$

Also,

$$\Delta I = \frac{\Delta V_i' - \Delta V_o}{R} \tag{4.66}$$

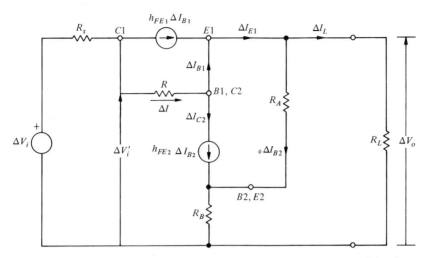

Fig. 4.31 Analysis of the voltage regulator using piecewise-linear models of transistors.

and

$$\Delta V_i' = \Delta V_i - R_s(\Delta I + h_{FE1}\Delta I_{B1}). \tag{4.67}$$

Substitution of (4.67) for $\Delta V_i'$ in (4.66) yields

$$\Delta I = \frac{\Delta V_i - R_s h_{FE1}\Delta I_{B1} - \Delta V_o}{R + R_s}. \tag{4.68}$$

Replacing (4.68) in (4.65) and solving for ΔI_{B1}, one obtains

$$\Delta I_{B1} = \frac{\Delta V_i}{R + R_s(1 + h_{FE1})} - \Delta V_o \left[\frac{1}{R + R_s(1 + h_{FE1})} \right.$$

$$\left. + \frac{h_{FE2}(R + R_s)}{[R + R_s(1 + h_{FE1})][R_A + R_B(1 + h_{FE2})]} \right]. \tag{4.69}$$

The variation in load current is approximately equal to the variation in emitter current of $Q1$. Further, h_{FE1} and h_{FE2} in (4.69) are much greater than one. Hence,

$$\Delta I_L \approx \Delta I_{E1} = (1 + h_{FE1})\Delta I_{B1}$$

$$\approx \frac{h_{FE1}\Delta V_i}{R + h_{FE1}R_s} - \Delta V_o \left[\frac{h_{FE1}}{R + h_{FE1}R_s} \right.$$

$$\left. + \frac{h_{FE1}h_{FE2}(R + R_s)}{(R + h_{FE1}R_s)(R_A + h_{FE2}R_B)} \right]. \tag{4.70}$$

Application of (4.62a,b) yields

$$S_L = -\frac{\Delta V_o}{\Delta I_L}\bigg|_{\Delta V_i = 0}$$

$$= \cfrac{1}{\cfrac{h_{FE1}}{R + h_{FE1}R_s} + \cfrac{h_{FE1}h_{FE2}(R + R_s)}{(R + h_{FE1}R_s)(R_A + R_B h_{FE2})}}$$

(4.71)

and

$$S_R = \frac{\Delta V_o}{\Delta V_i}\bigg|_{\Delta I_L = 0}$$

$$= \cfrac{1}{1 + h_{FE2}(R + R_s)/(R_A + h_{FE1}R_B)}.$$

(4.72)

Example 4.7

For the electronic voltage regulator of Fig. 4.30, $h_{FE1} = 100$, $h_{FE2} = 200$, $R_1 = R_D = 1$ K, $r_z = 10$ ohms, $R_2 = 1$ K, $R = 1.5$ K, and $R_s = 10$ ohms. Based on the equations derived for the approximate model of Fig. 4.31, determine the output resistance R_o and the voltage regulation S_R.

Solution

$$R_A = 1 \text{ K}//1 \text{ K} = 500 \text{ ohms.}$$
$$R_B = 10 \text{ ohms}//1 \text{ K} \approx 10 \text{ ohms.}$$

From (4.71), $S_L = R_o$; therefore,

$$R_o = \cfrac{1}{\cfrac{100}{1500 + 100 \times 10} + \cfrac{100 \times 200 \times 1510}{(1500 + 100 \times 10)(500 + 10 \times 200)}}$$

$$\approx 0.21 \text{ ohms.}$$

From (4.22),

$$S_R = \cfrac{1}{1 + \cfrac{200(1510)}{500 + 100 \times 10}} \approx \frac{1}{200} = 0.005.$$

In general, the current gains of the transistors should be high, and for good voltage regulation R should have a large value.

The preceding analysis and example were primarily intended for illustrative purposes. Many versions of practical electronic voltage regulators are described in the literature.

4.10 Summary

A number of basic rectifiers and filter networks were analyzed in the chapter. It was seen that for small load current, a half-wave rectifier with a capacitor filter is generally suitable. Voltage doublers and higher order multipliers are generally limited to only minute currents since their regulation deteriorates rapidly with appreciable load current. The best general-purpose rectifier and filter for relatively large load current is the full-wave rectifier with either an L-section or pi filter. The L-section filter provides better regulation than the pi filter; the dc voltage output, however, is greater for the pi filter circuit. Where a high degree of voltage regulation is needed, an electronic voltage regulator is used.

References

GENERAL ELECTRIC CO., *Transistor Manual*, Syracuse, N.Y., 1964.
MOTOROLA, INC., *Silicon Rectifier Handbook*, Phoenix, Ariz., 1966.
MOTOROLA, INC., *Silicon Zener Diode Handbook*, Phoenix, Ariz., 1959.

Problems

4.1 A single-phase half-wave rectifier is supplying power to a 500-ohm load. The supply source is 120-V rms and $f = 60$ Hz; the forward diode resistance is 20 ohms and the back resistance is infinite. Determine (a) I_m, (b) I_{dc}, (c) I_{rms}, (d) r, (e) η_r, and (f) percent regulation.

4.2 Repeat Prob. 4.1 for a supply source of 208-V rms.

4.3 The input v_i to the diode rectifier circuit of Fig. P4.3A is the triangular waveform of Fig. P4.3B. Find (a) I_{dc}, (b) I_{rms}, (c) PIV, (d) r, and (e) η_r.

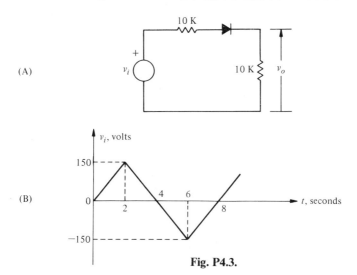

Fig. P4.3.

4.4   Prove that for a single-phase half-wave rectifier, maximum dc output
power occurs when the load resistance R_L is equal to the diode forward
resistance r_F.

4.5   Verify the values given in Table 4.1 for the full-wave rectifier.

4.6   Each half-secondary transformer winding used in a full-wave rectifier
is rated at 400 V rms at 60 Hz; the transformer is ideal. Assume that
the forward resistance of each diode is 20 ohms and the back resistance
is infinite. The load resistance is 1000 ohms. Calculate (a) I_{dc}, (b) I_{rms},
(c)PIV, (d) η_r, (e) r, (f) P_s, (g) P_p, and (h) percent regulation.

4.7   Repeat Prob. 4.6 for a load resistance of 100 ohms.

4.8   Repeat Prob. 4.6 for a half-secondary winding rated at 600 V rms.

4.9   The full-wave rectifier of Fig. P4.9 is used as a battery charger. The
peak diode current is rated at 1 A. Assume that the transformer is ideal
and the turns ratio $N_1/N_2 = 10$. Neglecting the forward drops across
the diodes, calculate (a) the value of the current limiting resistance R_s
and (b) the average power absorbed by the battery.

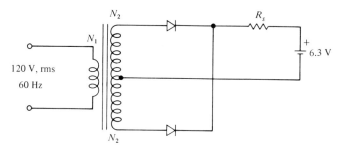

Fig. P4.9.

4.10 Repeat Prob. 4.9 for a turns ratio $N_1/N_2 = 5$. Compare results. Which
is a better choice of turns ratio? Why?

4.11 A 0–200 μA dc meter is connected to the bridge rectifier of Fig. P4.11.
The meter is calibrated to read the rms voltage of the applied sinusoid,
v_s. Assume that the resistance of the meter is 50 ohms and the diodes

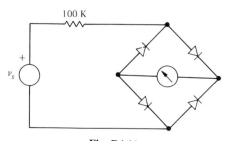

Fig. P4.11.

area ideal. For what value of v_s, in rms volts, will the meter read full scale?

4.12 Verify the values given in Table 4.1 for the three-phase half-wave rectifier.

4.13 Plot and dimension $v_o(t)$ for the three-phase full-wave rectifier of Fig. 4.8 and derive expressions for I_{dc}, I_{rms}, and r. Assume ideal diodes.

4.14 A half-wave rectifier is used with a pure C filter. The transformer voltage is 150 V rms at 60 Hz; the sum of the diode and dc transformer winding resistance is 100 ohms; the load resistance is 20,000 ohms. Determine the approximate peak-to-peak ripple voltage and the dc output voltage if $C = 100 \mu F$.

4.15 Repeat Prob. 4.14 for $C = 10 \mu F$. Compare results.

4.16 Verify equation (4.37).

4.17 Verify equation (4.50).

4.18 Given a full-wave rectifier with an L-section filter. The dc output voltage is 200 V; dc load current is 100 mA; ripple voltage should not exceed 0.1 V rms. Assume ideal diodes; each secondary-half of the transformer winding has a dc resistance of 100 ohms; the dc resistance of the choke is 100 ohms. Specify the values of the secondary power rating P_s, L, and C. The line frequency is 60 Hz.

4.19 Repeat Prob. 4.18 for a line frequency of 400 Hz. Compare results.

4.20 A full-wave rectifier uses a transformer with a 400–0–400 V rms secondary winding. The forward diode resistance is 50 ohms and the back resistance may be taken as being infinite. Assume that all other components are ideal. Determine (a) no-load dc voltage; (b) ripple voltage; (c) percent regulation for a dc load current of 200 mA for (1) pure C, (2) pure L, (3) L-section, and (4) pi filters. Value of $C = 20$ μF and $L = 30$ H. The line frequency is 400 Hz.

4.21 Repeat Prob. 4.20 for a 600–0–600 V rms secondary winding.

4.22 Repeat Prob. 4.20 for a line frequency of 60 Hz. Compare results.

4.23 In Prob. 4.20 (3), by mistake, the capacitor of the L-section filter is connected across the output of the rectifier instead of across the load. Calculate (a) the no-load dc voltage; (b) ripple voltage; (c) percent regulation. Compare results.

4.24 Suppose you have available two equal capacitors C and two equal inductors L. Under what conditions is it advantageous to use the 2 inductors in series and the 2 capacitors in parallel as an L-section filter or, instead, to use them in two cascaded L-section filters?

4.25 For the circuit of Fig. P4.25, the output of the full-wave rectifier may be approximated by the first two terms of a Fourier series:

$$v \approx \frac{2V_s}{\pi} - \frac{4V_s}{3\pi} \cos 2\omega t.$$

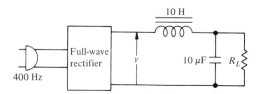

Fig. P4.25.

Let $V_s = 1000$ V and the resistance of the 10-H inductor equal 100 ohms. Find (a) the ripple voltage across R_L and (b) the dc output voltage for a load current of 250 mA dc. (c) Is the filter effective and why?

4.26   Repeat Prob. 4.25 for the cascaded filter of Fig. P4.26.

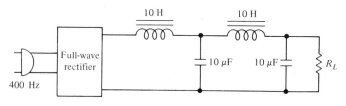

Fig. P4.26.

4.27   For the circuit of Fig. P4.27, design an L-section filter such that L has the smallest practical value and the ripple voltage is 1% of the load voltage. The load resistance $R_L = 5$ K. (a) Find the values for L, C, and V_{dc}. (b) If R_L varies from 5 K to infinity, what value of bleeder resistance, R_B, is needed to maintain good regulation? (c) What is the percent regulation if this value of R_B is used? (Use for reference V_{dc} for $R_L = 5$ K.)

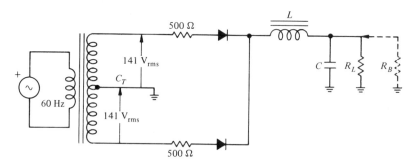

Fig. P4.27.

4.28   Referring to Fig. P4.28, the rms ripple voltage across the output of the full-wave rectifier, V'_R, may be expressed by

$$V'_R = \sqrt{2}\,I_{dc}X_C$$

where I_{dc} is the dc load current. Find the value of L so the ripple voltage across the 5 K load resistance is 0.1 V rms. The line frequency is 400 Hz.

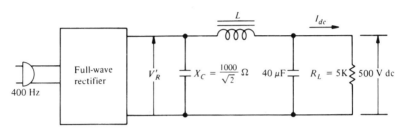

Fig. P4.28.

4.29   Repeat Prob. 4.28 for a line frequency of 60 Hz. Compare results.
4.30   Verify equation (4.70).
4.31   Component values for the electronic voltage regulator of Fig. 4.30 are $h_{FE1} = h_{FE2} = 100$, $R_1 = R_2 = R_D = 2\,\mathrm{K}$, $R_L = 5\,\mathrm{K}$, $R = 3\,\mathrm{K}$, $R_s = 20$ ohms, and $r_z = 5$ ohms. Based on the equation derived for the approximate model of Fig. 4.31, calculate the values of R_o and S_R.

Biasing and Stabilization

The simple amplifier circuits studied in Chapter 3 required two bias sources: one in the output circuit and one in the input circuit. A reasonable question is: Can a single bias source do the work of two? Another question has to do with the stability of the quiescent, or Q, point: Does the Q-point shift its position, for example, with temperature changes? If the answer is yes, how can the point be stabilized?

The objective of this chapter is to provide answers to these questions. The biasing of junction and field-effect transistors and vacuum tubes from single bias supplies will be studied; techniques used for stabilizing the operating point will be considered in detail.

5.1 The Junction Transistor

An n–p–n transistor amplifier using two separate, or *fixed*, bias sources is shown in Fig. 5.1A. As explained in Chapter 3, the necessary base current I_B is found from the intersection of the load line and collector family of curves, or from the piecewise-linear model, to yield the quiescent operating point.

Fig. 5.1 Biasing a CE amplifier. (A) Two-bias circuit. (B) Single-bias circuit.

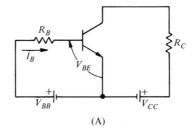

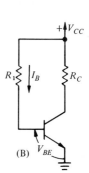

(A)

(B)

The value of the input bias source V_{BB} is either specified or selected. From Fig. 5.1A, the value of R_B is

$$R_B = (V_{BB} - V_{BE})/I_B, \tag{5.1}$$

where V_{BE} is the base-emitter voltage (approximately 0.7 V for silicon and 0.3 V for germanium at room temperature). Note that the polarities of the bias sources V_{CC} (V_{CC} is chosen to be greater than V_{BE}) and V_{BB} are such that the collector–base junction is reverse biased and the base–emitter junction forward biased—as required for amplifier operation. If a p–n–p transistor is used, the polarities of the two bias sources are reversed.

The circuit of Fig. 5.1B provides the required base current from one source, the collector–supply voltage V_{CC}. For $V_{CC} > V_{BE}$ it is seen that the base–emitter junction is forward biased and the collector–base junction reverse biased, as for the two-bias circuit. From the figure, the value of R_1 is found to be

$$R_1 = (V_{CC} - V_{BE})/I_B. \tag{5.2}$$

A more practical single-biasing circuit for the common-emitter amplifier, one necessary when stabilizing the transistor's operating point, is shown in Fig. 5.2A. Taking a Thevenin's equivalent between base and ground results in the circuit of Fig. 5.2B, where the Thevenin resistance R_B and voltage V_B are

$$R_B = R_1 R_2/(R_1 + R_2) \tag{5.3}$$

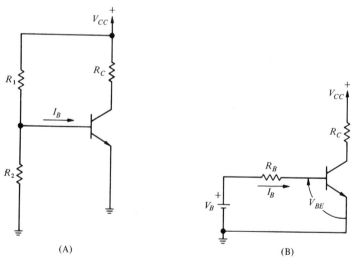

(A)   (B)

Fig. 5.2   Practical single-bias circuit for a CE amplifier. (A) Actual circuit. (B) Thevenin equivalent drawn for the biasing circuit.

and

$$V_B = R_2 V_{CC}/(R_1 + R_2). \qquad (5.4)$$

Knowing the values of I_B and R_B and referring to Fig. 5.2B, one can write

$$V_B = I_B R_B + V_{BE}. \qquad (5.5)$$

With V_B known, (5.4) can be solved for $R_1 + R_2$ and substituted in (5.3) to yield R_1

$$R_1 = R_B V_{CC}/V_B. \qquad (5.6)$$

Having obtained R_1, one can find the value of R_2 from either (5.3) or (5.4). Resistance R_B is generally determined from stability considerations; it should be as high as possible in order not to reduce the amplifier gain. If the value of R_B is comparable with the input impedance of the transistor, resistance R_B shunts some of the input signal current and the transistor receives less base current. The result is a lower signal output and a reduction in gain. In practice, a tradeoff is usually made in the value of R_B to ensure reasonable voltage gain and good stability.

A transistor in the common-base configuration with two bias sources is illustrated in Fig. 3.13; it is seen that the base-emitter junction is forward biased and the collector-base junction reverse biased. If one attempts to forward bias the base-emitter junction from the single source V_{CC}, the base-emitter junction becomes reverse, instead of forward, biased.

A method for using a single source for biasing both junctions is illustrated in Fig. 5.3. Resistance R_{ab} represents the equivalent dc resistance present

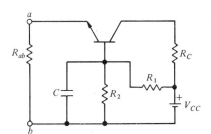

Fig. 5.3 Practical method of obtaining bias from a single source for a *CB* amplifier.

across input terminals *a–b*. Capacitance C is chosen so that its reactance is much less than the value of R_2 at the lowest signal frequency the amplifier will amplify. This condition ensures that, as far as the signal is concerned, the base is *common* to the input and output circuits; at the same time, the dc biasing requirement is satisfied. Because the common-base configuration is not often used, the single-bias circuit for this connection will not be analyzed further.

An example of biasing the emitter follower (common-collector) amplifier from a single-bias source is given in Fig. 5.4. Because $I_E \approx I_C$ for small-signal transistors, the collector family of curves can be used. A voltage equation for the input circuit, with $I_E = I_C$, is

$$V_{CC} = R_1 I_B + V_{BE} + I_C R_E.$$

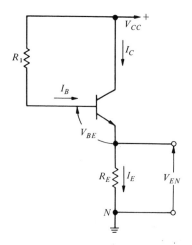

Fig. 5.4 Biasing the emitter follower (*CC*) amplifier.

Solving for R_1, one obtains

$$R_1 = (V_{CC} - V_{BE} - I_C R_E)/I_B. \tag{5.7}$$

The equation of the load line is

$$V_{CC} = i_C R_E + v_{CE}. \tag{5.8}$$

After superimposing (5.8) on the collector characteristics, the most practical procedure is to select I_B for a desired Q-point. The value of R_1 can then be solved by substituting the chosen value of I_B in (5.7).

Example 5.1

The collector characteristics of an *n-p-n* transistor are shown in Fig. 5.5A; the emitter follower with $R_E = 500$ ohms and $V_{CC} = 20$ V is given in Fig. 5.5B. Assuming $V_{BE} = 0.7$ V and $I_C = I_E$, find (a) the quiescent operating point and (b) the value of R_1. Let $I_B = 0.15$ mA.

Solution

(a) The load line with a slope equal to $-1/R_E = -1/500$ is plotted in Fig. 5.6. With $I_B = 0.15$ mA, the Q-point is $I_C = 17$ mA and $V_{CE} = 11$ V. The dc voltage across the emitter resistance is $V_{CC} - V_{CE} = 20 - 11 = 9$ V.

(b) From (5.7),

$$R_1 = (20 - 0.7 - 17 \times 0.5)/(0.15 \times 10^{-3}) = 72 \text{ K}.$$

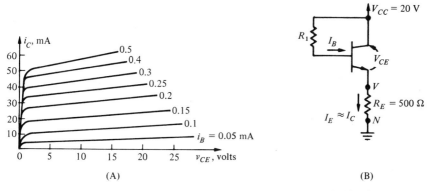

Fig. 5.5 Example 5.1. (A) Transistor characteristics. (B) Circuit.

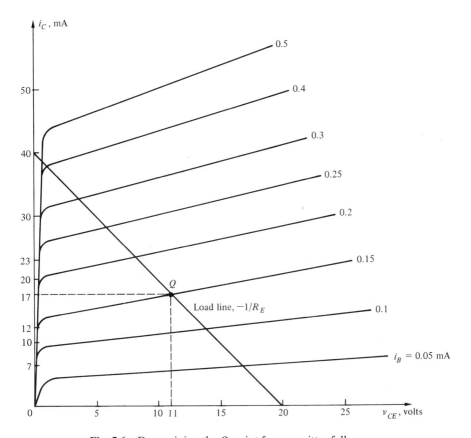

Fig. 5.6 Determining the Q-point for an emitter follower.

5.2   Stabilizing the Q-Point

Now that we have learned how to use a single-bias source for the input and output circuits of a transistor amplifier, even for the common-base connection, our attention is directed to the stabilization of the quiescent-operating point. For example, if the temperature changes or different transistors of the same kind are substituted in a given amplifier circuit, what happens to the Q-point? Let us consider first the substitution of transistors of the same kind but having different current gains.

Figure 5.7 shows a load line superimposed on the collector characteristics of a particular transistor. The intersection of the load line with the collector characteristic curve for $i_B = I_{B1}$ yields the quiescent operating point Q_1.

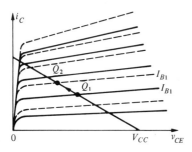

Fig. 5.7   Shifting of Q-point owing to a higher gain transistor or increasing I_{CO}.

Assume the transistor is replaced with another of the same type number but having a higher current gain; the new characteristics are indicated by the dashed curves of Fig. 5.7. Because the collector-supply source V_{CC}, resistance R_1, and V_{BE} have the same values, base current I_{B1} remains constant regardless of the transistor used. The new quiescent point Q_2, therefore, intersects the dashed curve $i_B = I_{B1}$; the Q-point has moved up along the load line. For the same amplitude input signal the output signal may be clipped during a portion of the positive half input cycle.

If the transistor has a lower gain, the new operating point Q_2 will lie below the initial operating point Q_1. For this case, the output signal may be clipped during the negative-half cycle of the input signal.

Because of intrinsic generation of electron-hole pairs, which increases with rising temperature, the collector characteristics change with temperature in a manner similar to that shown in Fig. 5.7. The reverse saturation current of a transistor I_{CO}, or I_{CBO} (the collector-base current with emitter open), approximately doubles for each 10°C rise in temperature for silicon or germanium. To develop a mathematical picture of the stabilization process, some basic equations relating base current I_B, collector current I_C, and emitter current I_E will be reviewed.

For any transistor configuration, the following relationship must hold:

$$I_E = I_B + I_C. \tag{5.9}$$

For the common-base configuration,

$$I_C = h_{FB}I_E + I_{CO}, \tag{5.10}$$

where h_{FB} is the dc current gain for the transistor in the common-base configuration and I_{CO} the reverse saturation current. Current gain h_{FB} is also referred to as the *dc alpha* (α).

In the common-emitter configuration, I_C is a function of base current and is expressed as

$$I_C = h_{FE}I_B + I_{CEO}, \tag{5.11}$$

where h_{FE} is the dc current gain for the transistor in the common-emitter configuration, also referred to as the *dc beta* (β). Current I_{CEO} is the reverse saturation current for the transistor (with base open) in the common-emitter configuration.

To determine the relationships between h_{FE} and h_{FB}, and I_{CO} and I_{CEO}, we substitute (5.9) for I_E in (5.10) and solve for I_C

$$I_C = \left(\frac{h_{FB}}{1 - h_{FB}}\right)I_B + \frac{I_{CO}}{1 - h_{FB}}. \tag{5.12}$$

Comparison of (5.11) with (5.12) yields

$$h_{FE} = h_{FB}/(1 - h_{FB}) \tag{5.13}$$

and

$$I_{CEO} = I_{CO}/(1 - h_{FB}) = (1 + h_{FE})I_{CO}. \tag{5.14}$$

The final form of (5.14) was obtained with the aid of (5.13).

It is noted that in the common-emitter configuration, I_{CO} is multiplied by the quantity $(1 + h_{FE})$, which is much greater than unity. As the operating temperature rises, $(1 + h_{FE})I_{CO}$ rises and I_C is increased; this results in a shift of the Q-point similar to that owing to an increase in h_{FE}.

Our discussion to this point has concentrated on the stability of the Q-point with respect to changes in current gain h_{FE} and reverse saturation current I_{CO}. One may proceed further and consider the effect on the quiescent point caused by other parameter changes. Additional parameters of significance affecting the quiescent point are the base-emitter voltage V_{BE} and the collector-supply voltage V_{CC}. All we have to consider in evaluating the changes in I_{CO}, h_{FE}, V_{BE}, and V_{CC} is their effect on I_C; the resulting change in the quiescent collector voltage ΔV_{CE} is $\Delta I_C R_C$, where R_C is the dc resistance in the collector circuit.

The functional relationship between I_C and I_{CO}, h_{FE}, V_{BE}, and V_{CC} may be expressed as

$$I_C = f(I_{CO}, h_{FE}, V_{BE}, V_{CC}). \tag{5.15}$$

A change in I_C, dI_C, is obtained from (5.15) as

$$dI_C = \frac{\partial I_C}{\partial I_{CO}} dI_{CO} + \frac{\partial I_C}{\partial h_{FE}} dh_{FE} + \frac{\partial I_C}{\partial V_{BE}} dV_{BE} + \frac{\partial I_C}{\partial V_{CC}} dV_{CC}. \qquad (5.16)$$

Each partial derivative of (5.16) is evaluated with the other variables held fixed. Assuming linear conditions, the partial terms can be replaced by constants: $\partial I_C/\partial I_{CO} = S_i$, $\partial I_C/\partial h_{FE} = S_h$, $\partial I_C/\partial V_{BE} = S_v$, and $\partial I_C/\partial V_{CC} = S_e$. Also, a differential such as dI_{CO} can be written as ΔI_{CO}. Making these substitutions in (5.16), one obtains

$$\Delta I_C = S_i \Delta I_{CO} + S_h \Delta h_{FE} + S_v \Delta V_{BE} + S_e \Delta V_{CC}. \qquad (5.17)$$

The S terms of (5.17) are referred to as *sensitivity* or *stability* factors, similar to those encountered in the analysis of regulated power supplies. The lower the value of a stability factor, the smaller is the change in collector current.

better

Voltage Feedback Stabilization

There are two basic methods for stabilizing the operating point of an amplifier: one uses *linear* elements such as resistances and the other employs *nonlinear* elements such as diodes. In this section we shall examine methods of stabilizing the Q-point with linear elements. Two techniques used are *voltage feedback* and *current feedback* stabilization. Both methods attempt to change automatically the base current such that the quiescent operating point remains essentially fixed, regardless of changes in I_{CO}, h_{FE}, V_{BE}, or V_{CC}.

Figure 5.8 shows a common-emitter amplifier with voltage feedback stabilization. Resistance R_F is called the feedback element. Because the value of R_F depends on the degree of stabilization required, its value may be such that excessive base current flows. Resistance R_2 serves to drain off this excess current permitting the correct amount of base current to be supplied

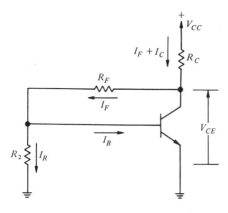

Fig. 5.8 Voltage-feedback stabilization for a *CE* amplifier.

to the transistor. The feedback current I_F is

$$I_F = I_B + I_R$$

or
$$I_B = I_F - I_R. \tag{5.18}$$

Current I_R is essentially constant because the base-emitter voltage V_{BE} does not vary appreciably; consequently, as I_F increases or decreases, I_B will change in a similar manner.

Voltage V_{CE} is the quiescent-collector voltage; current I_F is directly proportional to V_{CE}:

$$I_F = (V_{CE} - V_{BE})/R_F. \tag{5.19}$$

If the Q-point tends to move up the load line, V_{CE} and, therefore, I_F decrease. From (5.18) I_B drops, and the Q-point is pulled back to its approximate initial position. If the Q-point tends to move down the load line (owing to a fall in temperature or a lower h_{FE} transistor), V_{CE} and I_F tend to increase. The base current rises, and the Q-point is pulled up close to its initial position. We thus have a self-regulating mechanism that attempts to keep the Q-point fixed regardless of the direction in which the Q-point may tend to move.

Writing a loop equation for the circuit of Fig. 5.8 that includes V_{CC}, R_C, R_F, and V_{BE}, one obtains

$$V_{CC} = (I_C + I_F)R_C + R_F I_F + V_{BE}$$
$$= (I_C + I_B + I_R)R_C + R_F(I_B + I_R) + V_{BE}. \tag{5.20}$$

Also, from Fig. 5.8,

$$I_R = V_{BE}/R_2. \tag{5.21}$$

From (5.11) and (5.14),

$$I_B = [I_C - (1 + h_{FE})I_{CO}]/h_{FE}. \tag{5.22}$$

Substituting (5.21) for I_R and (5.22) for I_B in (5.20) and solving for I_C yields

$$I_C = \frac{h_{FE}\{V_{CC} - V_{BE}[1 + (R_C + R_F)/R_2] + I_{CO}R_F\}}{R_F + R_C(1 + h_{FE})} + I_{CO}. \tag{5.23}$$

Equation (5.23) will be used to derive the various stability factors. The current stability factor S_i is

$$S_i = \frac{\partial I_C}{\partial I_{CO}} = \frac{h_{FE}R_F}{R_F + R_C(1 + h_{FE})} + 1$$
$$= \frac{1 + h_{FE}}{1 + h_{FE}R_C/(R_C + R_F)}. \tag{5.24}$$

If R_F is infinite—that is, if there is no connection between collector and base—then $S_i = 1 + h_{FE}$ and there is no stabilization. For example, if a change in I_{CO} is 10 μA and $1 + h_{FE} = 100$, the corresponding change in collector current is 1 mA. Also, if $R_C = 0$, $S_i = 1 + h_{FE}$. This result should not be too surprising. If $R_C = 0$, the feedback resistance R_F is returned to the fixed-voltage source V_{CC}; the base current is therefore always constant and the self-regulation mechanism referred to earlier is inoperative.

Assuming $h_{FE} \gg 1$ and $h_{FE}R_C/(R_C + R_F) \gg 1$, (5.24) reduces to

$$S_i = 1 + R_F/R_C. \tag{5.25}$$

Example 5.2

The amplifier of Fig. 5.8 is to be stabilized against variations in I_{CO}; $S_i = 5$ and $h_{FE} = 40$. Assume the quiescent collector voltage and current are $V_{CE} = 10$ V and with $I_C \gg I_F$, $I_C = 4$ mA; $I_B = 0.1$ mA. Collector resistance $R_C = 5$ K, $V_{BE} = 0.7$ V, and $V_{CC} = 30$ V. Find the values of R_F and R_2 by using (a) the exact expression (5.24) and (b) the approximate expression (5.25) for S_i.

Solution

(a) Substituting the given values in (5.24), one obtains

$$5 = \frac{41}{1 + 40 \times 5/(5 + R_F)}.$$

The solution is $R_F = 22.7$ K.

Feedback current $I_F = (10 - 0.7)/(22.7 \times 10^3) = 0.41$ mA. The value of 0.41 mA is very small compared with $I_C = 4$ mA. If I_F turns out to be comparable with I_C, a trial-and-error procedure may be used such that $V_{CC} = R_C(I_F + I_C) + V_{CE}$ is always satisfied.

The current I_R flowing through R_2 is

$$I_R = 0.41 - 0.1 = 0.31 \text{ mA}$$

$$R_2 = 0.7/(0.31 \times 10^{-3}) = 2.25 \text{ K}.$$

(b) From (5.25), $5 = 1 + R_F/5$; therefore $R_F = 20$ K. The value for $R_2 = 1.91$ K. The approximate solution yields an answer for R_F which is less than that obtained from (5.24). If $R_F = 20$ K is substituted back into (5.24), the value of S_i will be less than 5. The approximate solution may therefore be viewed as a conservative one.

Whether the exact or approximate expression for R_F is used, the value of R_2 generally turns out to be low; a low value for R_2 reduces signal gain. To overcome this, a reverse-bias source V_R may be introduced, as shown in Fig. 5.9, to minimize I_R and thereby permit the use of a larger value for R_2.

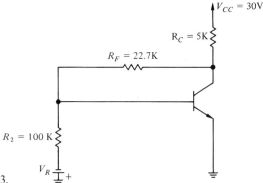

Fig. 5.9 Circuit for Example 5.3.

Example 5.3

Consider Fig. 5.9 in which a value of $R_2 = 100$ K is desired. If the net current flowing through R_2 is limited to 0.1 mA, what is the value of V_R?

Solution

A voltage equation for the base-emitter circuit is

$$V_R - 0.1 \times 100 + 0.7 = 0$$

$$V_R = 9.3 \text{ V.}$$

Besides providing dc stabilization, feedback resistance R_F results in *negative feedback* for the input signal and reduces the signal gain of the amplifier. If the source resistance is low compared with R_F, signal feedback is minimized. For a high source resistance, a *decoupling* capacitor C is used as shown in Fig. 5.10. If the value of C is properly chosen to approximate

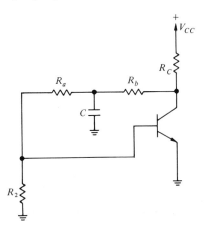

Fig. 5.10 Decoupling the feedback resistance; $R_a + R_b = R_F$.

a short circuit at the lowest operating frequency of the amplifier, R_a is reflected across the input and R_b across the output. As far as the signal is concerned, no feedback exists; however, dc feedback is present for stabilization. The sum of $R_a + R_b$ must be made equal to the value of R_F.

Differentiating (5.23) with respect to V_{BE} yields

$$S_v = \frac{\partial I_C}{\partial V_{BE}} = \frac{-h_{FE}[1 + (R_C + R_F)/R_2]}{R_F + R_C(1 + h_{FE})}$$

$$= \frac{-h_{FE}(R_2 + R_C + R_F)}{R_2[R_F + R_C(1 + h_{FE})]}. \tag{5.26}$$

(The base-emitter voltage for germanium and silicon devices changes by approximately $-2\,\text{mV/°C}$.)

Differentiating (5.23) with respect to V_{CC} gives

$$S_e = \frac{\partial I_C}{\partial V_{CC}} = \frac{h_{FE}}{R_F + R_C(1 + h_{FE})}. \tag{5.27}$$

Finally, differentiation of (5.23) with respect to h_{FE} and neglect of V_{BE} and I_{CO} for simplicity result in

$$S_h = \frac{\partial I_C}{\partial h_{FE}} = \frac{V_{CC}(R_F + R_C)}{[R_F + R_C(1 + h_{FE})]^2}. \tag{5.28}$$

The problem with (5.28) is that S_h is a function of h_{FE}, something not encountered with the other stability expressions. What value of h_{FE} should be used? This is not an easy question to answer. To avoid this difficulty, finite differences will be used, that is, S_h will be defined as $S_h = \Delta I_C/\Delta h_{FE}$, where $\Delta I_C = I_{C2} - I_{C1}$ and $\Delta h_{FE} = h_{FE2} - h_{FE1}$. Neglecting I_{CO} in (5.23) and taking the ratio of I_{C2}/I_{C1} results in

$$\frac{I_{C2}}{I_{C1}} = \frac{h_{FE2}[R_F + (1 + h_{FE1})R_C]}{h_{FE1}[R_F + (1 + h_{FE2})R_C]}. \tag{5.29}$$

Subtracting 1 from each side of (5.29) yields

$$\frac{I_{C2} - I_{C1}}{I_{C1}} = \frac{\Delta I_C}{I_{C1}} = \frac{\Delta h_{FE}(R_F + R_C)}{h_{FE1}[R_F + (1 + h_{FE2})R_C]}$$

or

$$S_h = \frac{\Delta I_C}{\Delta h_{FE}} = \frac{I_{C1}(R_F + R_C)}{h_{FE1}[R_F + (1 + h_{FE2})R_C]}. \tag{5.30}$$

The use of this stability factor is illustrated in the following example.

Example 5.4

For a specified value of $S_i = 5$ in Example 5.2 it was found that $R_F = 22.7$ K and $R_2 = 2.25$ K. The silicon transistor used has the following specifications at 25°C: $I_{CO} = 2 \times 10^{-9}$ A (2 nA), $V_{BE} = 0.7$ V, $h_{FE} = 40$. Assume that I_{CO} doubles for each 10°C rise in temperature, h_{FE} doubles for a 100°C rise in temperature, and V_{BE} decreases 2 mV for a 1°C temperature rise. Find (a) the values for S_v and S_h for constant V_{CC} and (b) the total change in collector current and voltage at 125°C; $I_{C1} = 4$ mA.

Solution

(a) From (5.26)

$$S_v = \frac{-40(2.25 + 5 + 22.7)}{2.25[22.7 + 5(1 + 40)]} = -2.35 \text{ mA/V}.$$

Because h_{FE} doubles for each 100°C rise in temperature, $h_{FE2} = 80$; $h_{FE1} = 40$. Therefore,

$$S_h = \frac{4(22.7 + 5)}{40[22.7 + (1 + 80)5]} = 6.5 \times 10^{-3} \text{ mA/}\Delta h_{FE}.$$

(b) To find the total change in collector current, (5.17) is used with $\Delta V_{CC} = 0$. The change in V_{BE} is $-2 \times 10^{-3} \times 100 = -0.2$ V and $\Delta h_{FE} = 80 - 40 = 40$. A simple method for finding ΔI_{CO} on a slide rule is as follows: because $e^{0.7} = 2$, then $e^{0.7(125 - 25)/10} = e^7 = 1010$; therefore

$$\Delta I_{CO} = 1010 \times 2 \times 10^{-9} - 2 \times 10^{-9} = 2 \times 10^{-3} \text{ mA}.$$

Substituting these values in (5.17), one obtains

$$\Delta I_C = 5 \times 2 \times 10^{-3} + (-2.35)(-0.2) + 40 \times 6.5 \times 10^{-3} = 0.74 \text{ mA}$$

Therefore,

$$\Delta V_{CE} = \Delta I_C R_C = 0.74 \times 5 = 3.7 \text{ V}.$$

For a silicon transistor, the change in V_{BE} is dominant in affecting the quiescent point; for germanium, however, I_{CO} is the critical parameter.

Current Feedback Stabilization

Voltage feedback stabilization is not effective if the collector circuit resistance is low, as borne out by (5.24) or (5.25). For example, if the load is coupled to the collector through a transformer, the dc resistance of the primary transformer winding may be in the order of 30 to 100 ohms for R_C.

Current feedback stabilization, illustrated in Fig. 5.11A, provides a means of stabilizing the Q point regardless of the value of R_C. Resistances R_1 and R_2 comprise the biasing network, and emitter resistance R_E with $R_1//R_2$ serve to stabilize the operating point. In the ensuing analysis, it is convenient to use the Thevenin's equivalent for the biasing network developed earlier, as shown in Fig. 5.11B. The Thevenin's resistance R_B is

$$R_B = R_1 R_2/(R_1 + R_2),\qquad(5.3)$$

and the Thevenin's voltage V_B is

$$V_B = R_2 V_{CC}/(R_1 + R_2).\qquad(5.4)$$

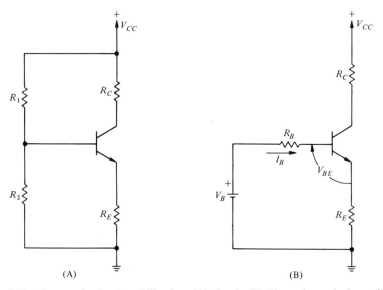

Fig. 5.11   Current feedback stabilization. (A) circuit. (B) Thevenin equivalent of bias network.

   To illustrate the regulating action obtained with current feedback stabilization, assume the collector current is rising because of an increase in I_{CO} or h_{FE}. The voltage drop across R_E also rises, but in a direction to oppose V_B; consequently I_B tends to decrease. As I_B decreases, the collector current tends to return toward its initial operating point.
   From the input circuit of Fig. 5.11B,

$$V_B = I_B R_B + V_{BE} + I_E R_E.\qquad(5.31)$$

But $I_B = I_E(1 - h_{FB}) - I_{CO}$; therefore

$$V_B = I_E(1 - h_{FB})R_B + V_{BE} + I_E R_E - I_{CO}R_B,$$

or

$$I_E = \frac{V_B - V_{BE} + I_{CO}R_B}{R_E + (1 - h_{FB})R_B}. \tag{5.32}$$

Multiplying (5.32) by h_{FB} and adding I_{CO} yields, as seen from (5.10),

$$I_C = \frac{h_{FB}(V_B - V_{BE} + I_{CO}R_B)}{R_E + (1 - h_{FE})R_B} + I_{CO}, \tag{5.33}$$

or

$$I_C = \frac{h_{FE}(V_B - V_{BE} + I_{CO}R_B)}{R_B + (1 + h_{FE})R_E} + I_{CO}. \tag{5.34}$$

To obtain S_i, (5.34) is differentiated with respect to I_{CO}:

$$S_i = \frac{\partial I_C}{\partial I_{CO}} = \frac{h_{FE}R_B}{R_B + (1 + h_{FE})R_E} + 1$$

$$= \frac{1 + h_{FE}}{1 + R_E h_{FE}/(R_E + R_B)}. \tag{5.35}$$

With $R_E h_{FE}/(R_E + R_B) \gg 1$, (5.35) reduces to

$$S_i \approx 1 + R_B/R_E. \tag{5.36}$$

By analogous methods used for voltage feedback stabilization, differentiation of (5.34) with respect to V_{BE} or V_{CC} yields S_v or S_e, respectively:

$$S_v = \frac{-h_{FE}}{R_B + R_E(1 + h_{FE})}, \tag{5.37}$$

$$S_e = \frac{h_{FE}R_2/(R_1 + R_2)}{R_B + R_E(1 + h_{FE})}. \tag{5.38}$$

By finite differences,

$$S_h = \frac{I_{C1}(R_B + R_E)}{h_{FE1}[R_B + R_E(1 + h_{FE2})]}. \tag{5.39}$$

Example 5.5

For the amplifier with current feedback stabilization of Fig. 5.11A, the transistor parameters are the same as those used in Example 5.4. For an $S_i = 5$, find the values of R_E, R_C, R_1, and R_2. The Q-point is $V_{CE} = 10$ V, $I_C = 4$ mA, and $I_B = 0.1$ mA; $V_{CC} = 30$ V.

Solution

A reasonable assumption to make for small-signal transistors is that $I_C \approx I_E$; therefore the equation for the output circuit is

$$V_{CC} = I_C(R_E + R_C) + V_{CE},$$

or

$$R_E + R_C = (V_{CC} - V_{CE})/I_C = (30 - 10)/(4 \times 10^{-3}) = 5 \text{ K}.$$

Equation (5.35) has two unknowns for this problem, R_B and R_E. The simplest procedure is to let $R_B = R_1//R_2 = 10$ K. This value ensures that the biasing network will have small effect on the ac gain of the amplifier (if the emitter resistance is bypassed, as discussed later) and generally yields reasonable values for R_E. Using $R_B = 10$ K and substituting in (5.35), one obtains

$$5 = \frac{41}{1 + 40R_E/(10 + R_E)}$$

$$R_E = 2.2 \text{ K}.$$

Therefore, $R_C = 5 - 2.2 = 2.8$ K,

$$V_B = 10 \times 0.1 + 0.7 + 2.2 \times 4 = 10.5 \text{ V},$$

$$10.5 = 30R_2/(R_1 + R_2) \text{ and } 10 = \frac{R_1 R_2}{R_1 + R_2};$$

Solving for R_1

$$R_1 = 28.5 \text{ K}$$

$$10 = 28.5R_2/(28.5 + R_2); R_2 = 15.4 \text{ K}.$$

5.3 Nonlinear Compensation

Because the base-emitter junction of a transistor has characteristics similar to those of a junction diode, a junction diode may be used to compensate against changes in I_{CO} and V_{BE}. If the diode is of the same material as the transistor and is maintained at the same temperature, nearly perfect compensation is obtained. In some cases the base-emitter junction of the same transistor type that is being stabilized is used instead of a diode. This, in fact, is common practice for integrated circuit amplifiers. As mentioned earlier, I_{CO} is the predominant factor that causes a shifting of the Q-point in germanium devices; for silicon, V_{BE} is the dominant cause.

A circuit for compensating against changes in I_{CO} is shown in Fig. 5.12. Diode D across the base and emitter is reverse biased, that is, the n-side is

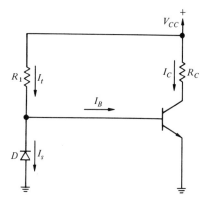

Fig. 5.12 Nonlinear compensation for I_{CO}.

positive with respect to the p-side. It is assumed that the diode has the same
characteristics as the base-emitter junction of the transistor being stabilized.
The base current I_B is equal to

$$I_B = I_t - I_s, \tag{5.40}$$

where $I_t = (V_{CC} - V_{BE})/R_1$ and I_s is the reverse-saturation current of the
diode. Collector current I_C is

$$I_C = h_{FE}I_B + (1 + h_{FE})I_{CO}. \tag{5.41}$$

Substituting (5.40) for I_B in (5.41) yields

$$I_C = h_{FE}I_t - h_{FE}I_s + (1 + h_{FE})I_{CO}.$$

If $I_s = I_{CO}$, $I_C = h_{FE}I_t + I_{CO}$; the stability factor is therefore $S_i = 1$.

An example of using a diode to compensate against changes in V_{BE} is
shown in Fig. 5.13A. Diode D, having the same characteristics as the base-
emitter junction, is placed in the emitter leg and forward biased by source
V_D; resistance R_D limits the current through the diode to a safe value.
Representing the bias network by its Thevenin's equivalent results in
Fig. 5.13B; the model of the diode with its forward resistance neglected is
shown as voltage V_o.

The voltage equation around the input circuit of Fig. 5.13B is

$$V_B = I_B R_B + V_{BE} - V_o.$$

If $V_{BE} = V_o$ at all temperatures, $I_B = V_B/R_B$ and the collector current is
independent of changes in V_{BE}. The reverse-biased diode in the base circuit
of Fig. 5.12 can be also used in Fig. 5.13 to compensate for changes in I_{CO}.

It should be noted that neither the reverse-biased diode of Fig. 5.12 nor the
forward-biased diode of Fig. 5.13 has any effect on the ac signal gain of the
amplifier. A reverse-biased diode has a very high resistance, of the order of
megohms for silicon; the forward resistance of a diode is low and can be

generally neglected. Any capacitance associated with the reverse-biased diode, however, will affect the frequency response of the amplifier.

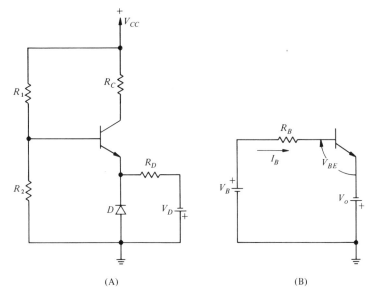

Fig. 5.13   Nonlinear compensation for V_{BE}. (A) Circuit. (B) D.C. model.

5.4   The Field-Effect Transistor

Both the junction field-effect transistor (JFET) and the depletion-mode operated IGFET (or MOSFET) are operated with the gate-source junction reverse biased. This permits *self-biasing* to be used, as illustrated in Fig. 5.14.

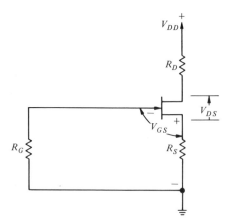

Fig. 5.14   Self biasing a field-effect transistor.

The voltage drop across R_S is $I_D R_S$; thus, the source terminal is positive with respect to ground. The gate is therefore negative with respect to the source and the gate-source junction is reverse biased. Resistance R_G provides a dc return path. Because there is negligible current flow through R_G, the dc voltage drop across it is approximately zero. Values of R_G range from 50 K to a few megohms.

Knowing the desired operating point, I_D and V_{DS}, and the corresponding bias voltage V_{GS}, one can calculate the source resistance R_S from $V_{GS} = -I_D R_S$, or

$$R_S = -V_{GS}/I_D. \tag{5.42}$$

Example 5.6

For the drain characteristics of a JFET shown in Fig. 5.15, the Q-point is located at $V_{DS} = 25$ V and $I_D = 1.5$ mA; $V_{GS} = -1$ V. Find the values of R_D and R_S. Drain voltage $V_{DD} = 50$ V.

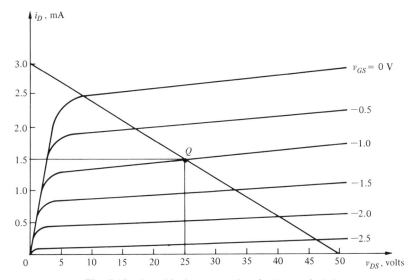

Fig. 5.15   Graphical construction for Example 5.6.

Solution

From (5.42), $R_S = -V_{GS}/I_D = 1/(1.5 \times 10^{-3}) = 670$ ohms. The slope of the total dc load line is $-1/(R_S + R_D)$; therefore, $R_S + R_D = 50,000/3 = 16,670$ ohms and $R_D = 16,670 - 670 = 16$ K.

A situation may arise in which R_S and R_D are known, and the quiescent point is to be determined. To obtain a solution to this problem, a *bias curve* has to be drawn, as illustrated in Example 5.7. The intersection of the bias curve with the dc load line yields the Q-point.

Example 5.7

    Given $R_S = 500$ ohms and $R_D = 19.5$ K, $V_{DD} = 40$ V. The drain characteristics of the device are available. Find the Q-point.

Solution

    From Fig. 5.16, the dc load line has a slope of $-1/(500 + 19,500) = -1/20,000$. The load line intersects the v_{DS}-axis at $v_{DS} = V_{DD} = 40$ V and the i_D-axis at $40/20 = 2$ mA.

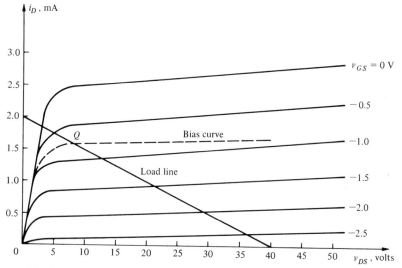

Fig. 5.16   Determining the Q-point in Example 5.7 using a bias curve.

From i_D, values of $V_{GS} = -i_D R_S$ are calculated:

i_D (mA)	V_{GS} (V)
0	0
1	-0.5
1.5	-0.75
1.6	-0.8

The resulting bias curve, plotted in Fig. 5.16, intersects the load line at approximately $I_D = 1.5$ mA and $V_{DS} = 8$ V, the quiescent point.

Using the Transfer Characteristic

Like the junction transistor, the field-effect transistor is sensitive to temperature changes. The gate leakage current I_{GSS}, which doubles for each 10°C rise in temperature, can usually be neglected. In many units, the gate leakage current is only of the order of 50 nA at temperatures as high as 125°C.

Because the mobility of majority carriers in the channel of a field-effect transistor has a negative temperature coefficient, in general, channel conductance, transconductance, and drain current also exhibit a negative coefficient. Further, transistors of the same type display considerable variability in their parameters. Owing to resistance R_S connected between source and ground, the self-biasing scheme provides bias stabilization similar to current feedback stabilization. One can also develop stability or sensitivity factors for the FET as was done for the junction transistor.

Another approach is to use the transfer characteristic curve of the field-effect transistor. The transfer characteristic is a plot of drain current i_D as a function of the gate-to-source voltage v_{GS} for a given drain-source voltage. A set of such curves with maximum and minimum values of drain current I_{DSS}, and pinch-off voltage V_p (see Chapter 3), for a particular field-effect transistor is shown in Fig. 5.17. Assume that the drift of the quiescent drain current I_D is confined between a maximum drain current I_{D2} and a minimum drain current I_{D1}. A line, called the *bias line*, is located through the Q-point, below the maximum drain current I_{D2} and above the minimum current I_{D1} (See Fig. 5.18A.). The intercept of the bias line along the v_{GS}-axis is V_{GG}; the equation of the line is

$$v_{GS} = -i_D R_S + V_{GG}. \tag{5.43}$$

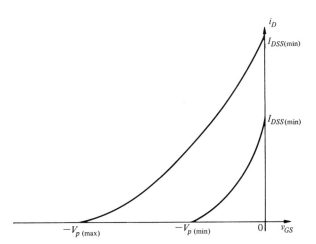

Fig. 5.17 Transfer characteristic curves.

Intercept V_{GG} in some cases may turn out to be zero or negative. If it is zero, source resistance R_S is all that is needed; if negative, an additional power supply is required.

Example 5.8

For a particular junction field-effect transistor the manufacturer specifies that the maximum and minimum values of I_{DSS} and V_p are 6 mA, −6 V and 2 mA, −2 V, respectively. Transfer curves for these extreme values are plotted in Fig. 5.18A. The desired Q-point current is $I_D = 1.5$ mA, ± 0.5 mA. Determine the component values for the biasing network.

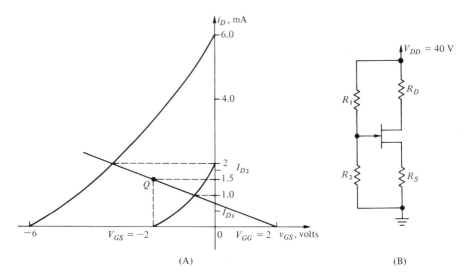

(A)   (B)

Fig. 5.18   Example 5.8. (A) Transfer curves. (B) Circuit.

Solution

In Fig. 5.18A, a bias line is drawn through the Q-point at 1.5 mA, intersecting the maximum transfer curve at $1.5 + 0.5 = 2$ mA and the minimum transfer curve at $1.5 - 0.5 = 1$ mA; $V_{GG} = 2$ V and $V_{GS} = -2$ V. Substituting these values in (5.43) and solving for R_S, one has

$$-2 = -1.5R_S + 2; \quad R_S = 2.65 \text{ K}.$$

Because the v_{GS} intercept is +2 V, a positive bias is necessary. This is obtained in the manner (similar to that for a junction transistor) illustrated in Fig. 5.18B. A reasonable value for $R_1//R_2 = R_G$ is 100 K. By voltage division,

$$V_{GG} = V_{DD}R_2/(R_1 + R_2),$$

$$2 = 40R_2/R_1 + R_2)$$

therefore

$$R_1 + R_2 = 20R_2$$

$$R_G = 100 \text{ K} = R_1R_2/(R_1 + R_2) = R_1R_2/(20R_2)$$

$$R_1 = 2 \text{ Megs}$$

$$2 \text{ Megs} + R_2 = 20R_2$$

$$R_2 = 105 \text{ K}.$$

Enhancement-mode IGFETS or MOSFETS cannot be self-biased because the gate-source junction is forward biased. A reasonable method for obtaining bias and stabilization is illustrated in Fig. 5.19. Feedback resistance R_F provides voltage stabilization. Like the junction transistor, the ac signal gain of the amplifier will be reduced; this can be minimized by using capacitor decoupling as shown in Fig. 5.10. Although the gate-source junction is forward biased, the gate current is zero. From Fig. 5.19, it is seen that

$$V_{GS} = V_{DS}R_2/(R_F + R_2), \tag{5.44}$$

where V_{DS} is the quiescent drain-source voltage.

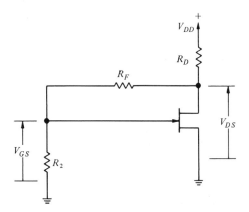

Fig. 5.19 Biasing a enhancement-mode operated IGFET.

5.5 The Vacuum Tube

A method for self-biasing a triode vacuum tube, similar to that of the field-effect transistor, is illustrated in Fig. 5.20. The voltage drop across cathode resistance R_K has the indicated polarity, that is, the cathode is positive with respect to ground. Grid resistance R_G provides a dc return path from grid to ground; the grid-cathode circuit is therefore reverse biased. For a grid-cathode voltage of $-V_c$ volts and a quiescent plate current I_b, the value of R_K is

$$R_K = -V_c/I_b. \tag{5.45}$$

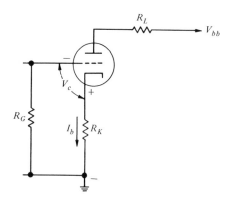

Fig. 5.20 Developing self bias for a triode vacuum tube.

The analytical and graphical techniques used in the analysis of biasing the JFET or the depletion-mode IGFET are applicable, in general, to vacuum tubes.

If a pentode is used, (5.45) is modified to include the screen-grid current I_{c2}; the total cathode current then becomes $I_K = I_b + I_{c2}$ and

$$R_K = -V_c/I_K. \tag{5.46}$$

The screen voltage V_{c2} for a pentode is normally obtained from the plate supply source V_{bb}. From Fig. 5.21, the value of the required screen resistance R_S is

$$R_S = (V_{bb} - V_{c2})/I_{c2}. \tag{5.47}$$

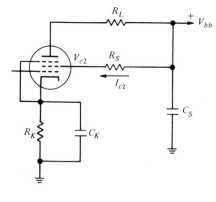

Fig. 5.21 Bypassing the cathode and screen resistances.

The vacuum tube is operated in an intensely hot environment because of the high temperature of the heater (1000°C or higher). Consequently there are no thermal stability problems like those encountered with the transistor. Resistance R_K, however, does provide some stabilization for the quiescent operating point against variations in gain and ageing of the tube.

5.6 Bypassing Resistances

In our discussion of current feedback stabilization and self-biasing of field-effect transistors and vacuum tubes, the resistance connected either to the emitter (R_E), source (R_S), or cathode (R_K) was not bypassed with a capacitor. Just as in voltage feedback stabilization, an unbypassed resistance like R_E, R_S, and R_K will reduce the ac signal gain of the amplifier; this behavior will be examined in greater detail in the following chapters. For voltage feedback, the decoupling network of Fig. 5.10 was used to minimize the reduction of gain; for an emitter, source, or cathode resistance, a capacitor across the resistance is used.

To illustrate this point, consider the pentode amplifier of Fig. 5.21; capacitance C_K is in shunt with cathode resistance R_K. In practice, if the capacitive reactance of C_K is one-tenth the value of resistance R_K at the lowest signal frequency, the effect of R_K can be neglected. As far as the ac signal is concerned, the cathode is shorted to ground (or the capacitor acts as a short circuit).

Also shown in Fig. 5.21 is screen resistance R_S bypassed with capacitor C_S. If the screen resistance is not bypassed, the signal gain of the amplifier will be reduced. The same approximation used for the cathode resistance is valid here; the reactance of C_S should be at least one-tenth the value of R_S at the lowest signal frequency.

There are occasions in which it may be desirable to leave the cathode (or source, or emitter) resistance unbypassed. This is done to achieve greater gain stability, higher input resistance, etc. These topics are considered in detail in the chapter on feedback.

5.7 Summary

Although the biasing and stabilization of three different devices were considered, the most important aspect of our discussion was the similarity of techniques used in their analyses. Whether one uses stability factors or transfer curves, the same methods may be applied to each of the devices. Similarity of other analytical methods will become also apparent in our study of the ac signal performance of amplifiers.

In the future a new three-terminal device, let us call it here the XYZistor, may make its debut. It would be indeed surprising if the methods considered in this, as well as other chapters, were not applicable to the XYZistor.

References

COCHRUN, B. L., *Transistor Circuit Engineering*, Chapters 5 and 11, Macmillan, New York, 1967.

EVANS, A. D., "Field-Effect Transistors," *Electronics World*, July 1967, pp. 49–52.

PIERCE, J. F., *Transistor Circuit Theory and Design*, Chapter 6, Merrill, Columbus, Ohio, 1963.

WALLMARK, J. T., and H. JOHNSON (ed.), *Field-Effect Transistors, Physics, Technology and Applications*, Prentice-Hall, Englewood Cliffs, New Jersey, 1966.

Problems

5.1 In the single-bias circuit of Fig. 5.1B, $R_C = 500$ ohms, $V_{CE} = 10$ V, $V_{BE} = 0.7$ V, $I_C = 30$ mA, and $h_{FE} = 100$. Find the values of V_{CC} and R_1.

5.2 Assume that $R_1 = 10R_2$ in the circuit of Fig. 5.2A. If the base current is 50 μA, $V_{BE} = 0.7$ V, and $V_{CC} = 30$ V, determine the values of R_1 and R_2.

5.3 If $R_2 = 10$ K in Prob. 5.2, what is the value of R_1 for a base current of 80 μA?

5.4 Determine the Q-point for the circuit of Fig. 5.2A. Assume that $V_{CC} = 20$ V, $V_{BE} = 0.7$ V, $R_1 = 200$ K, $R_2 = 10$ K, $R_C = 1.5$ K, and $h_{FE} = 100$.

5.5 Repeat Prob. 5.4 for $V_{CC} = 40$ V. If the Q-point found is poor, what must be done to obtain a better operating point?

5.6 Referring to Fig. P5.6, determine the value of R_1. Assume that $h_{FE} = 50$ and $V_{BE} = 0$.

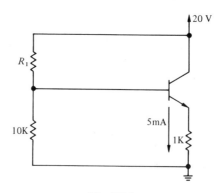

Fig. P5.6.

5.7 Repeat Prob. 5.6 for $V_{BE} = 0.7$ V. Compare results.

5.8 In Example 5.1, assume that $R_E = 1$ K. Determine (a) the Q-point and (b) the value of R_1.

5.9   Referring to Fig. P5.9, assume that $h_{FE} = 50$ and $V_{BE} = 0.7$ V. Calculate the value of R_F if $R_2 = 5$ K. Assume $I_F \ll I_C$.

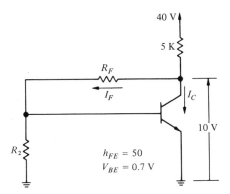

Fig. P5.9.

5.10   Repeat Prob. 5.9 for $V_{CC} = 50$ V. Compare results.
5.11   A current stability factor $S_i = 6$ is required for the circuit of Fig. P5.9. (a) Find the values of R_F and R_2. (b) If I_{CO} doubles for a 10°C rise in temperature, what is the change in V_{CE} at 125°C if, at room temperature, $I_{CO} = 1.5$ nA?
5.12   In the circuit of Fig. P5.12, assume that the change in I_{CO} is negligible; V_{BE} decreases by 2 mV/°C; h_{FE} increases by 50% for a 100°C rise in temperature. At 25°C, $h_{FE} = 40$, $V_{BE} = 0.7$ V, and $V_{CE} = 10$ V. (a) What is the value of R_2? (b) What is the value of V_{CE} at 125°C?

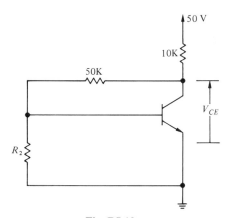

Fig. P5.12.

5.13   Verify equations (a) (5.37); (b) (5.38); and (c) (5.39).

5.14 Referring to Fig. 5.11A, $R_1 = 325$ K, $R_2 = 10$ K, $R_C = 14$ K, $R_E = 1$ K, $V_{CC} = 30$ V, $V_{BE} = 0.7$ V, and $h_{FE} = 50$. Calculate (a) I_B, (b) I_C, and (c) V_{CE}.

5.15 If, in Prob. 5.14, $\Delta V_{BE} = -0.2$ V and $\Delta h_{FE} = +20$, determine the change in collector current and voltage.

5.16 In Fig. 5.11A, $R_1 = 400$ K, $R_E = 1$ K, $V_{CC} = 40$ V, $V_{BE} = 0.3$ V, $V_{CE} = 15$ V, $h_{FE} = 50$, and $I_C = 1$ mA; determine the values of R_2 and R_C.

5.17 An amplifier was tested over a temperature range of 25°C to 125°C. For this range in temperature it was found that V_{CE} decreased by 1.5 V and I_{CO} increased by 0.01 mA. Determine the value of S_i. $R_C = 15$ K.

5.18 For an amplifier using current-feedback stabilization, $S_v = -2$ mA/V and $h_{FE} = 50$. Assume that $I_{CO} = 1$ μA at 25°C and doubles for each 10°C rise in temperature; $V_{BE} = 0.2$ V at 25°C and decreases 2 mV/°C. Neglecting changes in h_{FE} and V_{CC}, the total change in collector current should not exceed 0.36 mA at 75°C. Calculate the values of (a) S_i, (b) R_B, and (c) R_E.

5.19 In the circuit of Fig. 5.12, $V_{CC} = 20$ V, $R_C = 2$ K, $V_{CE} = 10$ V, $V_{BE} = 0.3$ V, and the reverse saturation current of the diode is 0.01 mA. If $h_{FE} = 100$, determine the value of R_1.

5.20 Repeat Prob. 5.19 for $h_{FE} = 80$.

5.21 When diode D in Fig. 5.13A conducts it may be represented by a 0.7 V battery in series with 100 ohms. If $V_{BE} = 0.7$ V, $R_1 = 60$ K, $R_2 = 12$ K, $R_C = 2$ K, $h_{FE} = 100$, and $V_{CC} = 24$ V, find the Q-point if the diode current is 2 mA.

5.22 Repeat Prob. 5.21 for $V_{CC} = 30$ V.

5.23 The FET used in the amplifier of Fig. P5.23 is an E300. The Q-point is located at $V_{DS} = 16$ V and $I_D = 4$ mA. Determine the values of R_D and R_S.

5.24 Repeat Prob. 5.23 for a Q-point at $V_{DS} = 20$ V and $I_D = 8$ mA.

5.25 Maximum and minimum transfer curves for a FET are given in Fig. P5.25A. The desired Q-point is at 1 ± 0.25 mA. Determine the component values for the biasing network of Fig. P5.25B. Assume that $R_1 // R_2 = 100$ K.

5.26 In Fig. 5.20 a 6BZ7 triode is used. For $V_{bb} = 300$ V, $R_L = 10$ K and $R_K = 1$ K, determine the Q-point.

5.27 For a pentode amplifier, the plate current is 2 mA; screen current is 0.5 mA; $V_{bb} = 300$ V; $V_{c2} = 150$ V; and $V_{c1} = -2.5$ V. (a) Calculate the value of R_K and R_S. (b) If the lowest frequency to be amplified is 100 Hz, estimate the values of C_K and C_S to approximate short circuits for the signal.

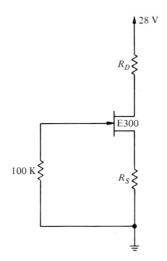

Fig. P5.23.

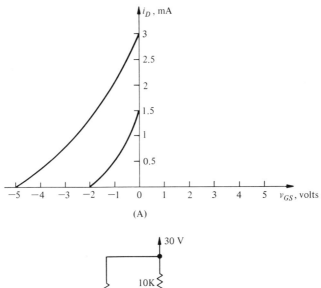

(A)

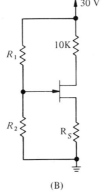

(B)

Fig. P5.25.

Electronic
Network
Theory

Before proceeding further with the study of electronic circuits, it is necessary to develop some basic network concepts that serve as the basis for drawing models of transistors and other active devices. We shall also review a few network theorems that are used often to facilitate the analysis of electronic circuits.

The analysis of an amplifier can be done in two parts. The first part is concerned with the location of the dc quiescent operating, or Q-point; calculations related to the Q-point of the amplifier and its stabilization have been already developed in the preceding chapter. The second part is concerned with signals. Here, an amplifier may be considered either as a large-signal or a small-signal amplifier. Large-signal amplifiers are required if appreciable output power is to be obtained; because of large current and voltage swings, the relationships between output and input are nonlinear. For this mode of operation, graphical or piecewise-linear analysis may be used, as indicated earlier in the text.

In many cases, such as the input stage of an amplifier, the signals are of very small amplitude, that is, in the order of microvolts or millivolts. Such magnitudes are too minute to handle graphically. Furthermore, the average values of device parameters cannot be used, as in piecewise-linear analysis, because the errors introduced would be appreciable. A model, called an *incremental model*, that was discussed in Chapter 1, is used for small-signal amplifiers. The incremental model uses the parameters of the device, like a transistor, for small variations of voltage and current about the quiescent operating point. The incremental model of a transistor or vacuum tube may be represented as a three- or four-terminal linear network. Because these networks have been completely studied, we may borrow the results and apply them to develop the incremental models of electronic devices.

6.1 Four-Terminal Networks

A four-terminal (or two-port) network may be defined as a "black box" with two input terminals and two output terminals, as shown in Fig. 6.1.

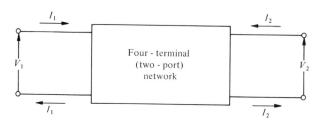

Fig. 6.1 Four-terminal (two-port) network.

The current flowing into one input terminal is always equal to the current flowing out of the other input terminal. Positive current and voltage directions are also indicated in the figure. The behavior of such a network is completely described by the relationship between the input and output voltages and currents. For instance, if currents I_1 and I_2 are chosen as independent variables, one may write

$$V_1 = f_1(I_1, I_2) \tag{6.1a}$$

$$V_2 = f_2(I_1, I_2). \tag{6.1b}$$

For linear networks, two linear equations relating the terminal voltages and currents are sufficient to completely describe the properties of a four-terminal network. There are a number of possibilities for writing the two equations. Three useful relationships will be discussed that lead to the important concepts of open-circuit impedance (z), short-circuit admittance (y), and hybrid (h) parameters. It is also possible to develop these linear relationships for circuits or devices that are inherently nonlinear. For this situation, linear operation can usually be assumed for the region where small-signal operation occurs.

Open-Circuit Impedance Parameters and Corresponding Model

Because the circuits of interest will be operating with ac, or changing signals, the increments of voltage, dV_1 and dV_2, may be obtained with the aid of (6.1):

$$dV_1 = \frac{\partial V_1}{\partial I_1} dI_1 + \frac{\partial V_1}{\partial I_2} dI_2 \tag{6.2a}$$

$$dV_2 = \frac{\partial V_2}{\partial I_1} dI_1 + \frac{\partial V_2}{\partial I_2} dI_2. \tag{6.2b}$$

The increments may be considered as being the ac components of voltages and currents. For linear operation, the relationships of (6.2) can be simplified. The partial derivatives become constants, called *z parameters*, with the dimensions of impedance (ohms). Therefore, for small-signal ac operation, letting $v_1 = dV_1$, $v_2 = dV_2$, etc., one may write

$$v_1 = z_{11}i_1 + z_{12}i_2 \tag{6.3a}$$
$$v_2 = z_{21}i_1 + z_{22}i_2. \tag{6.3b}$$

From (6.3), the z parameters are defined as follows:

$$z_{11} = \left.\frac{v_1}{i_1}\right|_{i_2=0} = \text{open-circuit input impedance (ohms),} \tag{6.4a}$$

$$z_{12} = \left.\frac{v_1}{i_2}\right|_{i_1=0} = \text{open-circuit reverse transfer impedance (ohms),} \tag{6.4b}$$

$$z_{21} = \left.\frac{v_2}{i_1}\right|_{i_2=0} = \text{open-circuit forward transfer impedance (ohms),} \tag{6.4c}$$

$$z_{22} = \left.\frac{v_2}{i_2}\right|_{i_1=0} = \text{open-circuit output impedance (ohms).} \tag{6.4d}$$

It must be emphasized that the notations $i_1 = 0$ and $i_2 = 0$ at the lower right of the vertical bar in (6.4) refer to ac signal quantities. Electronic circuits are normally powered from dc sources that establish a quiescent operating or Q-point. In practice, the setting of an ac quantity to zero is done in such a manner as not to disturb the dc operating point of the circuit.

The definitions of the z parameters given by (6.4) are not merely academic ones. For example, to measure z_{11}, the output terminals are unconnected and therefore output current i_2 is zero. Measurements are made of v_1 and i_1; their ratio v_1/i_1 is taken as prescribed by (6.4a), to determine z_{11}. Of course, the dc operating point is not affected. A similar procedure is employed for measuring the remaining z parameters. In all these measurements, the amplitude of the signal is kept small to ensure small-signal and therefore linear operation.

Example 6.1

The circuit of Fig. 6.2 is called a tee network. Find its z parameters.

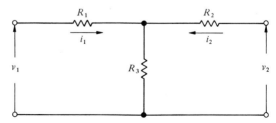

Fig. 6.2 Finding the z parameters of an *r*-tee network (Example 6.1).

Solution

Application of Kirchhoff's voltage law results in the following equations:

$$v_1 = i_1(R_1 + R_3) + i_2 R_3$$
$$v_2 = i_1 R_3 + (R_2 + R_3)i_2.$$

By the definitions of (6.4), $z_{11} = R_1 + R_3$; $z_{12} = z_{21} = R_3$; and $z_{22} = R_2 + R_3$.

The relationships expressed by (6.3a) and (b) suggest a model shown in Fig. 6.3A. This model, however, has two controlled, or dependent, sources and is not very practical. A modification of (6.3) provides a more useful network, called the tee model, of Fig. 6.3B. This may be obtained by adding and subtracting $z_{12}(i_1 + i_2)$ from (6.3b) and $z_{12}(i_1)$ from (6.3a). Upon simplification, the following expressions are obtained:

$$v_1 = (z_{11} - z_{12})i_1 + z_{12}(i_1 + i_2) \tag{6.5a}$$

$$v_2 = (z_{22} - z_{12})i_2 + (z_{21} - z_{12})i_1 + z_{12}(i_1 + i_2). \tag{6.5b}$$

With the aid of Fig. 6.3b, the reader should verify (6.5a) and (6.5b).

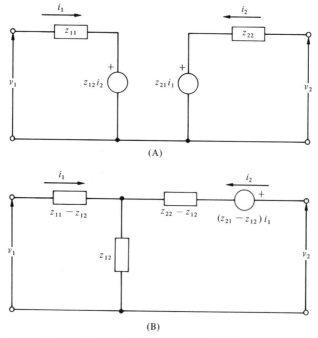

(A)

(B)

Fig. 6.3 Two possible models based on z parameters. (A) Two-source model. (B) One-source (tee) model.

Short-Circuit Admittance Parameters and Corresponding Model

If V_1 and V_2 are taken as independent variables, the four-terminal network may be described by the following equations:

$$I_1 = f_1(V_1, V_2) \tag{6.6a}$$

$$I_2 = f_2(V_1, V_2). \tag{6.6b}$$

With small signals, the increments of current, dI_1 and dI_2, may be expressed as

$$dI_1 = \frac{\partial I_1}{\partial V_1} dV_1 + \frac{\partial I_1}{\partial V_2} dV_2, \tag{6.7a}$$

$$dI_2 = \frac{\partial I_2}{\partial V_1} dV_1 + \frac{\partial I_2}{\partial V_2} dV_2. \tag{6.7b}$$

For ac incremental operation, (6.7) reduces to

$$i_1 = y_{11}v_1 + y_{12}v_2, \tag{6.8a}$$

$$i_2 = y_{21}v_1 + y_{22}v_2, \tag{6.8b}$$

where y_{11}, y_{12}, y_{21}, and y_{22} are the y parameters. These parameters are defined as

$$y_{11} = \frac{i_1}{v_1}\bigg|_{v_2=0} = \text{short-circuit input admittance (mhos),} \tag{6.9a}$$

$$y_{12} = \frac{i_1}{v_2}\bigg|_{v_1=0} = \text{short-circuit reverse transfer admittance (mhos),} \tag{6.9b}$$

$$y_{21} = \frac{i_2}{v_1}\bigg|_{v_2=0} = \text{short-circuit forward transfer admittance (mhos),} \tag{6.9c}$$

$$y_{22} = \frac{i_2}{v_2}\bigg|_{v_1=0} = \text{short-circuit output admittance (mhos).} \tag{6.9d}$$

As an example, to determine y_{11}, the output is short circuited ($v_2 = 0$). Measurements of i_1 and v_1 are then made and the ratio i_1/v_1 yields y_{11} (6.9a). The dc operating point is not disturbed in the process of making the ac measurements.

Equations (6.8a) and (b) suggest the model illustrated in Fig. 6.4. It is noted that the model has two current sources, $y_{12}v_2$ and $y_{21}v_1$; conversion to a model having a single current source is left as a homework problem.

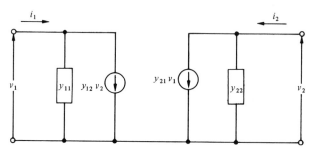

Fig. 6.4 Model based on y parameters.

Example 6.2

Find the y parameters for the pi network of Fig. 6.5.

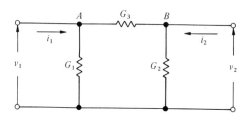

Fig. 6.5 Finding the y parameters of a pi network (Example 6.2).

Solution

The application of Kirchhoff's current law to nodes A and B yields

$$i_1 = (G_1 + G_3)v_1 - G_3 v_2,$$

$$i_2 = -G_3 v_1 + (G_2 + G_3)v_2.$$

The y parameters are therefore $y_{11} = G_1 + G_3$; $y_{12} = y_{21} = -G_3$; and $y_{22} = G_2 + G_3$.

Hybrid Parameters and the Hybrid Model

A third useful selection of independent variables is I_1 and V_2 (input current and output voltage, respectively). Based on this choice, the following expressions may be written:

$$V_1 = f_1(I_1, V_2) \tag{6.10a}$$

$$I_2 = f_2(I_1, V_2). \tag{6.10b}$$

The corresponding increments of voltage and current are

$$dV_1 = \frac{\partial V_1}{\partial I_1} dI_1 + \frac{\partial V_1}{\partial V_2} dV_2, \tag{6.11a}$$

$$dI_2 = \frac{\partial I_2}{\partial I_1} dI_1 + \frac{\partial I_2}{\partial V_2} dV_2. \tag{6.11b}$$

For ac signal quantities, one obtains

$$v_1 = h_{11} i_1 + h_{12} v_2, \tag{6.12a}$$

$$i_2 = h_{21} i_1 + h_{22} v_2. \tag{6.12b}$$

The hybrid, or h, parameters are most useful for characterizing the junction, or bipolar, transistor (BJT). A model based on (6.12) is illustrated in Fig. 6.6. The h parameters are defined as follows:

$$h_{11} = \left.\frac{v_1}{i_1}\right|_{v_2 = 0} = \text{short-circuit input impedance (ohms)}, \tag{6.13a}$$

$$h_{12} = \left.\frac{v_1}{v_2}\right|_{i_1 = 0} = \text{open-circuit reverse voltage ratio (numeric)} \tag{6.13b}$$

$$h_{21} = \left.\frac{i_2}{i_1}\right|_{v_2 = 0} = \text{short-circuit forward current ratio (numeric)}, \tag{6.13c}$$

$$h_{22} = \left.\frac{i_2}{v_2}\right|_{i_1 = 0} = \text{open-circuit output admittance (mhos).} \tag{6.13d}$$

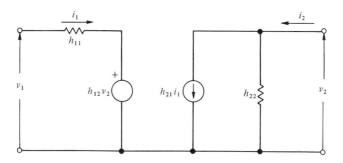

Fig. 6.6 The hybrid model.

To determine h_{11}, the output is shorted ($v_2 = 0$) and quantities v_1 and i_1 are measured; the ratio v_1/i_1, as defined by (6.13a), yields h_{11}. Similar procedures would be used for determining the other h parameters.

Input and Output Impedances of a Four-Terminal Network

The input impedance Z_i of a four-terminal network with a load Z_L (see Fig. 6.7A) is defined as the ratio of input voltage v_1 to input current i_1.

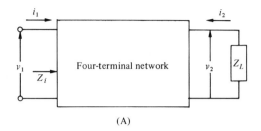

(A)

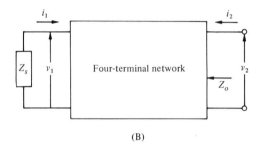

(B)

Fig. 6.7 The calculation of (A) Input impedance Z_i and (B) Output impedance Z_o.

Assuming the network is characterized by z parameters, one has, from (6.3a),

$$Z_i = v_1/i_1 = z_{11} + z_{12}(i_2/i_1). \tag{6.14a}$$

From (6.3b) and Fig. 6.7A, one may write

$$v_2/i_2 = -Z_L = z_{21}(i_1/i_2) + z_{22}. \tag{6.14b}$$

Solution of (6.14b) for i_2/i_1 yields

$$i_2/i_1 = -z_{21}/(z_{22} + Z_L). \tag{6.15}$$

Substituting (6.15) for i_2/i_1 in (6.14a) gives the input impedance, Z_i:

$$Z_i = z_{11} - z_{12}z_{21}/(z_{22} + Z_L). \tag{6.16}$$

The output impedance of a four-terminal network Z_o is defined as v_2/i_2 with the input source set to zero. With the source impedance at Z_s, from Fig. 6.7B and (6.3b) one obtains

$$Z_o = v_2/i_2 = z_{22} + z_{21}(i_1/i_2) \tag{6.17a}$$

$$v_1/i_1 = -Z_s = z_{11} + z_{12}(i_2/i_1). \tag{6.17b}$$

Solution of (6.17b) for i_1/i_2 yields

$$i_1/i_2 = -z_{12}/(z_{11} + Z_s). \tag{6.18}$$

Substituting (6.18) in (6.17a) gives the output impedance Z_o:

$$Z_o = z_{22} - z_{21}z_{12}/(z_{11} + Z_s). \tag{6.19}$$

Relations Between Different Sets of Parameters

It is helpful to be able to convert one set of parameters to another; for example, one set of parameters might be measured easily and a second set might be more practical for computation purposes. Suppose one sets out to find the z parameters in terms of the y parameters. From (6.4a),

$$z_{11} = \frac{v_1}{i_1}\bigg|_{i_2 = 0}$$

Hence, to find z_{11} in terms of y parameters, one should determine

$$\frac{v_1}{i_1}\bigg|_{i_2 = 0}$$

from (6.8). If $i_2 = 0$, then (6.8b) yields

$$\frac{v_1}{v_2}\bigg|_{i_2 = 0} = -\frac{y_{22}}{y_{21}}. \tag{6.20}$$

Substitution of (6.20) in (6.8a) yields

$$i_1|_{i_2 = 0} = y_{11}v_1 - y_{12}(y_{21}/y_{22})v_1$$

or

$$\frac{v_1}{i_1}\bigg|_{i_2 = 0} = \frac{y_{22}}{y_{11}y_{22} - y_{12}y_{21}}.$$

Therefore,

$$z_{11} = \frac{y_{22}}{y_{11}y_{22} - y_{12}y_{21}}. \tag{6.21}$$

To calculate z_{12} from (6.4b),

$$z_{12} = \frac{v_1}{i_2}\bigg|_{i_1 = 0}.$$

From (6.8a),

$$\frac{v_1}{v_2}\bigg|_{i_1 = 0} = -\frac{y_{12}}{y_{11}}. \tag{6.22}$$

Replacement of (6.22) in (6.8b) yields

$$i_2|_{i_1 = 0} = y_{21}v_1 - y_{11}y_{22}v_1/y_{12}$$

or

$$z_{12} = y_{12}/(y_{12}y_{21} - y_{11}y_{22}). \tag{6.23}$$

If the preceding method is used to find z_{21} and z_{22}, the following results are obtained:

$$z_{21} = -y_{21}/(y_{11}y_{22} - y_{12}y_{21}) \tag{6.24}$$

$$z_{21} = y_{11}/(y_{11}y_{22} - y_{12}y_{21}). \tag{6.25}$$

The h parameters may also be calculated in terms of y or z parameters. For example, in terms of y parameters, referring to (6.8a) and (6.13a), one has

$$i_1|_{v_2=0} = y_{11}v_1.$$

Therefore,

$$\left.\frac{v_1}{i_1}\right|_{v_2=0} = \frac{1}{y_{11}}.$$

Consequently,

$$h_{11} = 1/y_{11}. \tag{6.26}$$

From (6.8a) and (6.13b), one obtains

$$\left.\frac{v_1}{v_2}\right|_{i_1=0} = -\frac{y_{12}}{y_{11}}.$$

Therefore,

$$h_{12} = -y_{12}/y_{22}. \tag{6.27}$$

Table 6.1 summarizes the relationships between the y, z, and h parameters.

Table 6.1   Parameter relationships

z_{11}	$y_{22}/\Delta y$	$\Delta h/h_{22}$
z_{12}	$-y_{12}/\Delta y$	h_{12}/h_{22}
z_{21}	$-y_{21}/\Delta y$	$-h_{21}/h_{22}$
z_{22}	$y_{11}/\Delta y$	$1/h_{22}$
y_{11}	$z_{22}/\Delta z$	$1/h_{11}$
y_{12}	$-z_{12}/\Delta z$	$-h_{12}/h_{11}$
y_{21}	$-z_{21}/\Delta z$	h_{21}/h_{11}
y_{22}	$z_{11}/\Delta z$	$\Delta h/h_{11}$
h_{11}	$\Delta z/z_{22}$	$1/y_{11}$
h_{12}	z_{12}/z_{22}	$-y_{12}/y_{11}$
h_{21}	$-z_{21}/z_{22}$	y_{21}/y_{11}
h_{22}	$1/z_{22}$	$\Delta y/y_{11}$

where

$$\Delta y = y_{11}y_{22} - y_{12}y_{21}$$
$$\Delta z = z_{11}z_{22} - z_{12}z_{21}$$
$$\Delta h = h_{11}h_{22} - h_{12}h_{21}$$

6.2   Generalized Equations for Three-Terminal Networks

Active devices, such as transistors and vacuum tubes, are characterized by three rather than four terminals. One of the three terminals is usually common to both input and output as shown in Fig. 6.8A. Because the three-terminal network may be considered a simplified case of the four-terminal

network, all relations and equations presented for four-terminal networks
are therefore valid for three-terminal networks. There are, however, additional simplifications possible in using a three-terminal network.

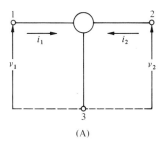 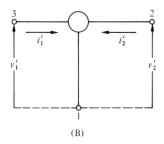

(A)   (B)

Fig. 6.8 Symbolic representation of a three-terminal network. (A) Terminal 3 is
common to the input and output sides. (B) Terminal 1 is now common.

In practice an active device, symbolically represented by a circle in Fig.
6.8A, is not used always with terminals 1 and 3 as input and 2 and 3 as output.
Theoretically, any pair of terminals could be chosen as an input or output
pair; for practical reasons, however, the choice of terminal pairs is limited.
In this section we shall develop a general method of calculating one set of
parameters in terms of the given parameters for a three-terminal network,
with the assumption that any one of the terminals is common to the remaining
two terminals.

The y equations obtained for Fig. 6.8A are the same as (6.8) and are
repeated here:

$$i_1 = y_{11}v_1 + y_{12}v_2, \tag{6.8a}$$

$$i_2 = y_{21}v_1 + y_{22}v_2. \tag{6.8b}$$

If terminal 1 is common, as shown in Fig. 6.8B, a new set of equations may
be written:

$$i_1' = y_{11}'v_1' + y_{12}'v_2', \tag{6.28a}$$

$$i_2' = y_{21}'v_1' + y_{22}'v_2'. \tag{6.28b}$$

How can the new y' parameters be calculated in terms of y_{11}, y_{12}, and
y_{21}, and y_{22}? Referring again to Figs. 6.8A and B, one can see that $i_2 = i_2'$,
$v_1 = -v_1'$, $v_2 = v_2' - v_1'$, and $i_1 = -(i_1' + i_2')$. Substituting these expressions in (6.8), one obtains

$$-(i_1' + i_2') = -y_{11}v_1' + y_{12}(v_2' - v_1')$$

and

$$i_2' = -y_{21}v_1' + y_{22}(v_2' - v_1').$$

Solving for i_1' and i_2', one has

$$i_1' = (y_{11} + y_{12} + y_{21} + y_{22})v_1' - (y_{12} + y_{22})v_2' \tag{6.29a}$$

$$i_2' = -(y_{21} + y_{22})v_1' + y_{22}v_2'. \tag{6.29b}$$

Comparison of (6.29) with (6.28) yields

$$y_{11}' = y_{11} + y_{12} + y_{21} + y_{22} \tag{6.30a}$$

$$y_{12}' = -(y_{12} + y_{22}) \tag{6.30b}$$

$$y_{21}' = -(y_{21} + y_{22}) \tag{6.30c}$$

$$y_{22}' = y_{22}. \tag{6.30d}$$

If we were to use the previously described derivation each time terminals are changed, we must repeat our calculations. We are, however, seeking a general solution to the problem that can handle every possible combination of terminals. To arrive at this expression, we add an arbitrary voltage reference v_3 to our three-terminal network, as shown in Fig. 6.9. Because the network is assumed linear, the following relations may be written:

$$i_1 = y_{11}v_1 + y_{12}v_2 + y_{13}v_3 \tag{6.31a}$$

$$i_2 = y_{21}v_1 + y_{22}v_2 + y_{23}v_3 \tag{6.31b}$$

$$i_3 = y_{31}v_1 + y_{32}v_2 + y_{33}v_3. \tag{6.31c}$$

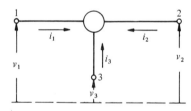

Fig. 6.9 Adding an arbitrary reference voltage, v_3.

But according to Kirchhoff's current law, $i_3 = -(i_1 + i_2)$. Adding (6.31a) to (6.31b), changing the sign, and equating to i_3, one obtains

$$-(y_{11} + y_{21})v_1 - (y_{12} + y_{22})v_2 - (y_{13} + y_{23})v_3$$
$$= y_{31}v_1 + y_{32}v_2 + y_{33}v_3. \tag{6.32}$$

Equation (6.32) must be independent of voltages v_1, v_2, and v_3. Equating coefficients on each side of the equation gives

$$y_{31} = -(y_{11} + y_{21}) \tag{6.33a}$$

$$y_{22} = -(y_{12} + y_{32}) \tag{6.33b}$$

$$y_{33} = -(y_{13} + y_{23}). \tag{6.33c}$$

Because the voltage reference level chosen is arbitrary, the currents will not change if all the voltages are referred to a new level Δv volts lower or higher with respect to their initial values; that is,

$$i_1 = y_{11}(v_1 + \Delta v) + y_{12}(v_2 + \Delta v) + y_{13}(v_3 + \Delta v) \tag{6.34a}$$

$$i_2 = y_{21}(v_1 + \Delta v) + y_{22}(v_2 + \Delta v) + y_{23}(v_3 + \Delta v) \tag{6.34b}$$

$$i_3 = y_{31}(v_1 + \Delta v) + y_{32}(v_2 + \Delta v) + y_{33}(v_3 + \Delta v). \tag{6.34c}$$

Comparing (6.31) with (6.34) and simplifying, one obtains

$$(y_{11} + y_{12} + y_{13})\Delta v = 0$$

$$(y_{21} + y_{22} + y_{23})\Delta v = 0$$

$$(y_{31} + y_{32} + y_{33})\Delta v = 0.$$

Because $\Delta v \neq 0$, it may be cancelled and

$$y_{13} = -(y_{11} + y_{12}) \tag{6.35a}$$

$$y_{23} = -(y_{21} + y_{22}) \tag{6.35b}$$

$$y_{33} = -(y_{31} + y_{32}). \tag{6.35c}$$

The preceding results for three-terminal networks can be summarized in an elegant and useful form called the *generalized y matrix*, $[y]_i$.

$$[y]_i = \begin{matrix} & 1 & 2 & 3 \\ & \begin{bmatrix} y_{11} & y_{12} & y_{13} \\ y_{21} & y_{22} & y_{23} \\ y_{31} & y_{32} & y_{33} \end{bmatrix} & \begin{matrix} 1 \\ 2. \\ 3 \end{matrix} \end{matrix} \tag{6.36}$$

We have already found the relationship between the elements in the same row or column of the matrix as summarized by (6.33) and (6.35); the sum of any row or column must be equal to zero. For example, for row one, $y_{11} + y_{12} + y_{13} = 0$ or $y_{13} = -(y_{11} + y_{12})$. From the matrix we can obtain the y parameters of any terminal combination of the three-terminal network.

Assume terminal 1 is the input and terminal 2 the output; therefore terminal 3 is common to terminals 1 and 2. By striking out the third row and the third column of (6.36) the y parameters for terminal 3 as common are obtained. If we strike out row 2 and column 2 we get the y parameters for terminal 2 as common. Finally, by striking out row 1 and column 1 the parameters for terminal 1 as common are obtained. In each of these cases, the result will be a two-by-two matrix. For example, if terminal 1 is common to input terminal 2 and output terminal 3, the y parameters are

$$[y]_1 = \begin{bmatrix} y_{22} & y_{23} \\ y_{32} & y_{33} \end{bmatrix}. \tag{6.37}$$

and the equations are written as

$$i_1'' = y_{22}v_1'' + y_{23}v_2''$$ (6.38a)

$$i_2'' = y_{32}v_1'' + y_{33}v_2''.$$ (6.38b)

If terminal 3 is the input but 1 the output, we strike out the row and column corresponding to the common terminal and *interchange* the y elements of the resulting matrix along the diagonal. As an illustration, the corresponding matrix for Fig. 6.8B is

$$[y]_{1'} = \begin{bmatrix} y_{33} & y_{32} \\ y_{23} & y_{22} \end{bmatrix}.$$ (6.39)

Compare (6.39) with (6.37). The resulting equations for Fig. 6.8B are

$$i_1' = y_{33}v_1' + y_{32}v_2'$$ (6.40a)

$$i_2' = y_{23}v_1' + y_{22}v_2'.$$ (6.40b)

The y parameters of (6.40) must be the same as that defined by (6.30).

Example 6.3

The three-terminal network of Fig. 6.8A has the following y parameters:

$$y_{11} = 5 \qquad y_{12} = j$$
$$y_{21} = 1 + j \qquad y_{22} = 5 + j$$

Calculate the corresponding y parameters if the network is rotated such that terminal 1 is common, 2 the input, and 3 the output.

Solution

Before we construct the generalized **y** matrix, we use (6.33) and (6.35) to determine the following values:

$$y_{13} = -(y_{11} + y_{12}) = -5 - j$$
$$y_{23} = -(y_{21} + y_{22}) = -6 - j2$$
$$y_{33} = -(y_{13} + y_{23}) = 11 + j3$$
$$y_{32} = -(y_{12} + y_{22}) = -5 - j2$$
$$y_{31} = -(y_{11} + y_{21}) = -6 - j.$$

The generalized **y** matrix then becomes

$$[y]_i = \begin{bmatrix} 5 & j & -5 - j \\ 1 + j & 5 + j & -6 - j2 \\ -6 - j & -5 - j2 & 11 + j3 \end{bmatrix}.$$

By striking out the first row and column, we obtain

$$y''_{11} = j + 5 \qquad y''_{12} = -6 - j2$$
$$y''_{21} = -5 - j2 \qquad y''_{22} = 11 + j3.$$

The analysis in this section, which resulted in the generalized **y** matrix, was based on y parameters. Consequently, if a network is described initially in z or h parameters, the parameters must be converted first to y parameters (with the aid of Table 6.1) and a generalized **y** matrix formed. After striking out the appropriate row and column, the y parameters for the new configuration can be converted back in terms of the z or h parameters, again with the aid of Table 6.1.

6.3 Controlled Sources

To better understand the meaning of a controlled source, let us recall the definition of an independent source. An independent source, voltage or current, is one that is not dependent on currents or voltages at any point in the network. Referring to Figs. 6.3, 6.4, and 6.6, we can see that each of the sources in these diagrams is dependent on currents or voltages of one of the branches in the network. These are called *controlled*, or *dependent*, sources. The following are the definitions of different kinds of controlled sources encountered in the analysis of active networks.

Current-controlled voltage source: A voltage source dependent on a current in a branch of the network.

Voltage-controlled voltage source: A voltage source dependent on a voltage across a branch of the network.

Current-controlled current source: A current source dependent on the current in one of the branches of the network.

Voltage-controlled current source: A current source dependent on the voltage across a branch of the network.

A general definition of a controlled source may be given as follows: A controlled-voltage source is a network element whose behavior is described by a voltage which is not independent, but is a function of a voltage or current somewhere in the network in which the source is connected. Similarly, a controlled-current source may be defined as a network element which is a function of a voltage or a current somewhere in the network in which the source is connected. From these definitions, any impedance may be replaced by a current-controlled voltage source and any admittance may be replaced by a voltage-controlled current source.

Thevenin's and Norton's Theorems

In the application of Thevenin's or Norton's theorems to circuits containing controlled sources, one must be careful not to set controlled sources to zero, that is, short circuit voltage sources or open circuit current sources. The following example illustrates the method to be used.

Example 6.4

For the network of Fig. 6.10A, calculate the Thevenin equivalent circuit with respect to terminals a–b. Note the controlled source present.

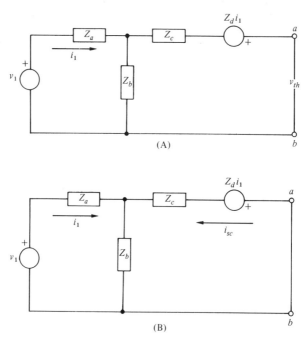

Fig. 6.10 Applying Thevenin's theorem to a network containing a controlled source, $Z_d i_1$ (Example 6.4). (A) Finding v_{th}. (B) Determining the short-circuit current, i_{sc}.

Solution

From Fig. 6.10A, the open-circuit voltage v_o is

$$v_o = v_1 Z_b/(Z_a + Z_b) + Z_d i_1 \qquad (6.41a)$$

$$i_1 = v_1/(Z_a + Z_b). \qquad (6.41b)$$

Substitution of (6.41b) in (6.41a) yields the open-circuit voltage v_o; but the open-circuit voltage is the Thevenin voltage v_{th}; therefore

$$v_{th} = v_1(Z_b + Z_d)/(Z_a + Z_b). \qquad (6.42)$$

A method for finding the Thevenin impedance Z_{th}, which is required when controlled sources are present, is to calculate the ratio of the Thevenin voltage to the short-circuit current i_{sc}. Loop equations for Fig. 6.10B yield

$$v_1 = (Z_a + Z_b)i_1 + Z_b i_{sc} \tag{6.43a}$$

$$0 = (Z_b + Z_d)i_1 + (Z_b + Z_c)i_{sc}. \tag{6.43b}$$

Solution of (6.43) for i_{sc} gives

$$i_{sc} = \frac{v_1(Z_b + Z_d)}{(Z_b + Z_d)Z_b - (Z_a + Z_b)(Z_b + Z_c)}. \tag{6.44}$$

Hence,

$$Z_{th} = \frac{v_{th}}{i_{sc}} = \frac{(Z_b + Z_d)Z_b - (Z_a + Z_b)(Z_b + Z_c)}{Z_a + Z_b}. \tag{6.45}$$

Finding Z_{th} by setting the voltage source to zero yields

$$Z_{th} = Z_c + Z_a Z_b/(Z_a + Z_b),$$

which is incorrect because a controlled source $Z_d i_1$ was set to zero.

If a Norton equivalent circuit is desired, the Norton current source i_{sc} is found as in Example 6.4. The equivalent impedance is equal to Z_{th}.

6.4 The Substitution Theorem

The application of this theorem (also known as the compensation or alteration theorem) to controlled sources often simplifies circuit analysis. The theorem states that, under certain conditions, a current-controlled voltage source or a voltage-controlled current source may be replaced by a resistance or an admittance, respectively.

From Fig. 6.11, the terminal current of network N is i. If ki represents a current-controlled voltage source (where k is a real number), ki may be replaced by a resistance of k ohms. The currents and voltages within network N remain unchanged.

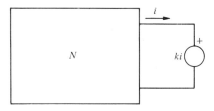

Fig. 6.11 Application of the substitution theorem to a circuit containing a current-controlled voltage source. Source ki is replaced by a resistance of k ohms.

For the voltage-controlled current source kv of Fig. 6.12, the controlled source may be replaced by an admittance of k mhos. The voltages and currents in network N are not affected.

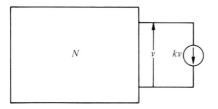

Fig. 6.12 Application of the substitution theorem to a circuit with a voltage-controlled current source. Souce kv is replaced by an admittance of k mhos.

Example 6.5

In the circuit of Fig. 6.13A, find voltage v_2 as a function of voltage v_1 and the circuit parameters.

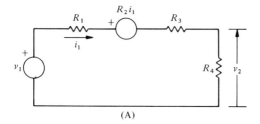

(A)

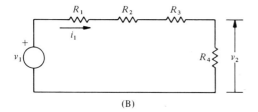

(B)

Fig. 6.13 Example 6.5: Replacing a current-controlled voltage source using the substitution theorem. (A) Given network. (B) Reduced network.

Solution

By the substitution theorem, controlled source $R_2 i_1$ is replaced by resistance R_2. The resulting network is given in Fig. 6.13B. By inspection,

$$v_2 = v_1 R_4/(R_1 + R_2 + R_3 + R_4).$$

6.5 The Reduction Theorem

This theorem may be considered an extension of the substitution theorem. By the reduction theorem, a controlled source may be eliminated by multiplication or division of the impedances located on one side of the controlled source. The statement of the reduction theorem is as follows:

(I) If two networks and a voltage-controlled voltage source are connected in series (Fig. 6.14A), so that v_1 and kv_1 are additive with respect to the loop that they form, all currents in networks N_1 and N_2 remain the same if kv_1 is replaced by a short circuit *and*

(a) Each resistance, inductance, the reciprocal of capacitance (elastance), and voltage source in N_1 is multiplied by $1 + k$,
or
(b) Each resistance, inductance, elastance, and voltage source in N_2 is divided by $1 + k$.

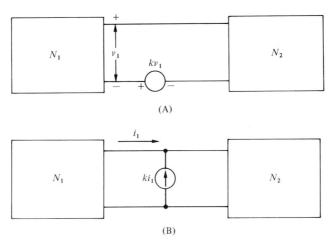

(A)

(B)

Fig. 6.14 Development of the reduction theorem for a network containing (A) Voltage-controlled voltage source. (B) Current-controlled current source.

The dual form of (I) is also applicable:
(II) If two networks N_1 and N_2 and a current source are connected as in Fig. 6.14B, all voltages in the networks remain the same if ki is replaced with an open circuit *and*

(a) Each conductance, capacitance, reciprocal inductance, and current source in N_1 is multiplied by $1 + k$,
or
(b) Each conductance, capacitance, reciprocal inductance, and current source in N_2 is divided by $1 + k$.

To show, for example, that parts (a) and (b) of reduction theorem statement (I) are equivalent, consider the voltage source kv_1 of Fig. 6.14A. The input voltage to N_2 is $(1 + k)v_1$ and the output voltage of N_1 is v_1. In part (a) network N_2 is untouched; for currents to remain the same in N_2 the voltage at its input must equal $(1 + k)v_1$. When kv_1 is removed, the voltage at the input to N_2 is maintained as $(1 + k)v_1$ by multiplying each resistance, inductance, and elastance, as well as the voltage sources in N_1, by $1 + k$.

This ensures that currents in N_1 remain the same with an output voltage of $(1 + k)v_1$ volts.

In (b), N_1 is not touched; therefore the currents in the branches of N_1 remain the same. At the input to N_2, however, the input voltage is reduced by a factor of $1 + k$. The only way to maintain the same current in the branches of N_2 is to divide all voltage sources, resistances, inductances, and elastances in N_2 by $1 + k$.

As an example of the use of the reduction theorem, the circuit of Fig. 6.15A has been reduced to either Fig. 6.15B or to Fig. 6.15C. In (B), ki_o has been eliminated; to the left of ki_o, i_1 and C have been multiplied by $1 + k$ and R_1 and R_2 have been divided by $1 + k$. Dividing a resistance by $1 + k$ is equivalent to multiplying a conductance by $1 + k$. Source ki_o in Fig. 6.15A can also be removed by applying II(b). Figure 6.15C results.

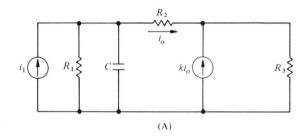

(A)

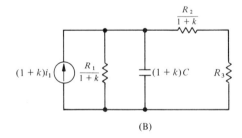

(B)

Fig. 6.15 Application of the reduction theorem. (A) Given network. (B) The removal of current source ki_o and (C) ki_1.

(C)

6.6 Current and Voltage Source Transformation

In the analysis of networks, like the high-frequency model of the common-base amplifier, a situation illustrated in Fig. 6.16A can arise. Here, a current source i is connected across two resistances R_a and R_b in series. It is often convenient to transform the single current source to two equal current sources across each resistance, as shown in Fig. 6.16B. The inverse, of course, is equally valid; the configuration of Fig. 6.16B can be transformed to that of Fig. 6.16A.

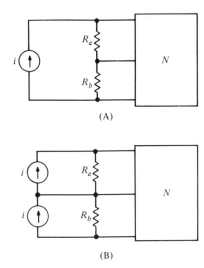

(A)

(B)

Fig. 6.16 Transforming a current source.

In Fig. 6.17A, a voltage source v is connected to two resistances, R_a and R_b. The circuit may be transformed to that of Fig. 6.17B, where voltage source v is placed in series with each of the resistances. The inverse is also true; the circuit of Fig. 6.17B can be transformed back to the circuit of Fig. 6.17A.

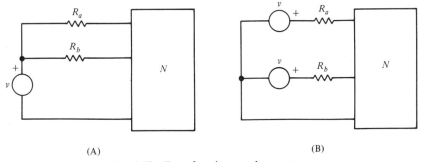

(A)

(B)

Fig. 6.17 Transforming a voltage source.

6.7 Summary

The four-terminal network is a basic configuration that can be used to represent active devices, such as transistors and vacuum tubes. If currents i_1 and i_2 are chosen as independent variables, z parameters are obtained. The y parameters result when v_1 and v_2 are made independent. Finally, when i_1 and v_2 are independent variables, the h parameters are realized. Based on the choice of parameters, one can obtain the impedance, admittance, or hybrid models of devices. The generalized y matrix is useful for finding the parameters of a new configuration in terms of the parameters of another configuration. The Thevenin, Norton, substitution, reduction, and source transformation theorems can be used in simplifying the analysis of many electronic networks.

References

ANGELO, E. J., JR., *Electronic Circuits*, 2nd ed., McGraw-Hill, New York, 1964.

BALABANIAN, N., *Fundamentals of Circuit Theory*, Allyn and Bacon, Boston, 1961.

CLOSE, C. M., *The Analysis of Linear Circuits*, Harcourt Brace and Jovanovich, New York, 1966.

DE PIAN, L., *Linear Active Network Theory*, Prentice-Hall, Englewood Cliffs, New Jersey, 1962.

KUO, B. C., *Linear Networks and Systems*, McGraw-Hill, New York, 1967.

Problems

6.1 Draw a model that satisfies each of the following sets of equations:
  (a) $i_1 = 10v_1 - 5v_2$; $i_2 = (2 - 5)v_1 + 15v_2$.
  (b) $v_1 = 0i_1 + 20i_2$; $v_2 = -50i_1 + 12i_2$.
  (c) $v_1 = 1000i_1 + 10^{-3}v_2$; $i_2 = 40i_1 + 10^{-6}v_2$.
6.2 Determine the appropriate parameters, such as h, y, and z, for each set of equations given in Prob. 6.1.
6.3 Calculate the z parameters for the network of Fig. P6.3 and draw a model containing two controlled sources.

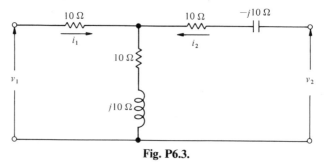

Fig. P6.3.

6.4   Calculate the y parameters for the network of Fig. P6.4 and draw a
model containing two controlled sources.

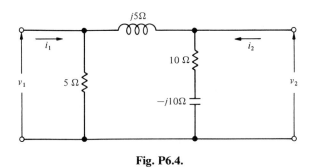

Fig. P6.4.

6.5   Determine the h parameters for the network of Fig. P6.5.

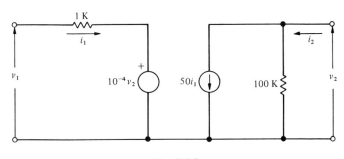

Fig. P6.5.

6.6   Reduce the model of Fig. 6.4 to one containing a single controlled
current source.

6.7   Find the (a) input impedance Z_i and (b) output impedance Z_o for the
network of Fig. P6.7.

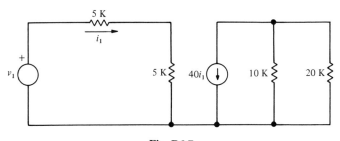

Fig. P6.7.

6.8   Derive expressions for h_{21} in terms of (a) z parameters and (b) y parameters.

6.9   Repeat Prob. 6.8 for h_{12}.

6.10   For the 3-terminal network represented by Fig. 6.8A, the y parameters are $y_{11} = 5$; $y_{12} = 1 + j$; $y_{21} = 3$; and $y_{22} = j10$. The network is rotated such that the terminal 2 is common, 1 the input, and 3 the output. (a) Develop the generalized y matrix. (b) Find the y parameters for the rotated network.

6.11   Repeat Prob. 6.10 for $y_{11} = j5$; $y_{12} = 5 - j3$; $y_{21} = 8$; and $y_{22} = 1$.

6.12   For the network of Fig. P6.12, (a) write the y equations and define the y parameters. (b) Develop the generalized y matrix. (c) Assume that the network is rotated such that terminal 1 is common, 3 the input, and 2 the output. What are the y parameters for the rotated network?

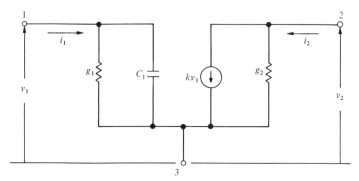

Fig. P6.12.

6.13   Repeat Prob. 6.12 for the network of Fig. P6.13.

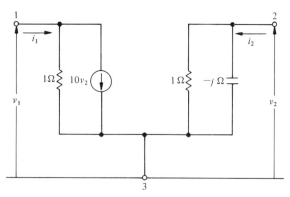

Fig. P6.13.

6.14   Find the Thevenin equivalent circuit with respect to terminals a–b for the network of Fig. P6.14.

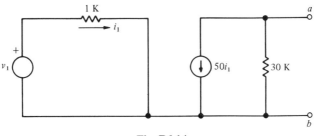

Fig. P6.14.

6.15 Find the Norton equivalent circuit with respect to terminals a–b for the network of Fig. P6.14.

6.16 Using the substitution theorem, replace the controlled sources of Fig. P6.16 with appropriate resistances and calculate the value of V_2.

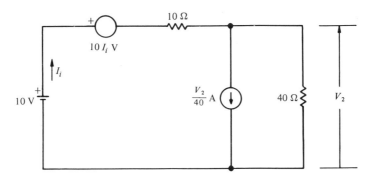

Fig. P6.16.

6.17 Applying the reduction theorem, remove the controlled sources in Fig. P6.17 and determine the value of v_3.

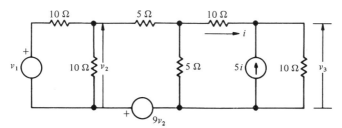

Fig. P6.17.

6.18 Figure P6.18 shows a 3-terminal device which is dc biased to yield a specific Q-point. Explain how the z, y, and h parameters may be determined at a frequency of 1 kHz without affecting the Q-point.

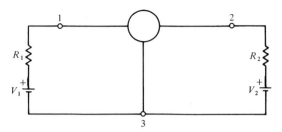

Fig. P6.18.

6.19 Given the **h**-matrix of an active device in the configuration of Fig.
6.8A:

$$[h] = \begin{bmatrix} 1\,\text{K} & 10^{-5} \\ 100 & 10^{-6} \end{bmatrix}$$

(a) Draw the model of the active device for which the matrix applies.
(b) What are the *h* parameters if the network is rotated as shown in
Fig. 6.8B?

6.20 Calculate the ratio v_2/v_1 for the network of Fig. P6.5.
6.21 Using source transformation, find the output voltage V_o for the networks of Fig. P6.21.

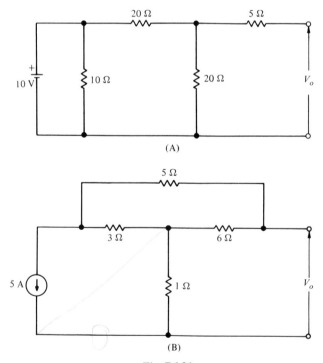

Fig. P6.21.

Incremental Operation of Electronic Amplifiers

Electronic amplifiers are used to amplify signals coming from a variety of transducers, such as a microphone, a phonograph pickup, or a radio antenna. The signal entering the amplifier may be extremely weak, of the order of microvolts, microamperes, or microwatts. For example, an amplifier, containing a number of stages, is required to raise the signal emanating from a dynamic microphone from the level of a few microvolts to the several watts of power required to drive a loudspeaker.

An amplifier stage is composed of an active device, such as a BJT or field-effect transistor (FET), and associated passive components. The stages are usually in cascade where the output of one stage is connected to the input of the following stage. The final stage, required to drive a loudspeaker, motor, or some other transducer, is the power amplifier. The object of this chapter is to examine the methods of analysis of the stages preceding the power amplifier. These are low-level stages and lend themselves to small-signal analysis. Only individual stages will be considered and high-frequency effects will be neglected. The effects of cascading stages and the determination of low- and high-frequency response of amplifiers will be left for later chapters.

It was shown in Chapter 1 that incremental operation of nonlinear devices could *not* be studied graphically or with the aid of piecewise-linear models. For this purpose, an incremental model based on four-terminal network theory is developed for transistors and vacuum tubes.

7.1 Incremental Model of a Vacuum Tube

To initiate our analysis, let us solve the y equations (developed in Chapter 6 and repeated here) for a triode with the cathode common to the input (grid) and output (plate):

$$i_1 = y_{11}v_1 + y_{12}v_2 \tag{7.1a}$$

$$i_2 = y_{21}v_1 + y_{22}v_2. \tag{7.1b}$$

Assuming the grid–cathode circuit is reverse biased so that there is zero grid current, one has

$$0 = y_{11}v_1 + y_{12}v_2 \qquad (7.2a)$$

$$i_2 = y_{21}v_1 + y_{22}v_2. \qquad (7.2b)$$

Because v_1 and v_2 have the same polarity and are not zero, then y_{11} and y_{12} must be zero. For this condition, (7.2b) is normally written as

$$i_p = g_m v_g + g_p v_p \qquad (7.3)$$

where $i_p = i_2$ is the plate current; $v_g = v_1$, the *grid–cathode* voltage; $g_m = y_{21}$ is the mutual transconductance of the tube; $g_p = y_{22}$, the plate conductance ($g_p = 1/r_p$, where r_p is the tube plate resistance); $v_p = v_2$ is the plate–cathode voltage. Equation (7.3) suggests the vacuum tube model shown in Fig. 7.1.

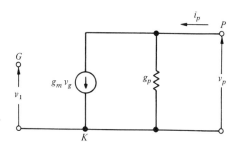

Fig. 7.1 Incremental model of a triode containing a voltage-controlled current source.

Parameters g_m and g_p may be defined from (7.3) as

$$g_m = \left.\frac{i_p}{v_g}\right|_{v_p=0} \text{ (mhos)} \qquad (7.4a)$$

and

$$g_p = \left.\frac{i_p}{v_p}\right|_{v_g=0} \text{ (mhos)} \qquad (7.4b)$$

Figure 7.2 demonstrates how g_m and g_p can be found from the tube characteristics at the quiescent point of operation. To calculate g_m, for example, use

$$g_m = \left.\frac{\Delta i_b}{\Delta v_c}\right|_{v_b \text{ constant}} = \left.\left|\frac{i_{b1} - i_{b2}}{v_{c1} - v_{c2}}\right|\right|_{v_b \text{ constant}} \qquad (7.5)$$

The value of g_p is obtained by drawing a tangent to the Q-point; the slope of the tangent $\Delta i_b/\Delta v_b$ is equal to g_p.

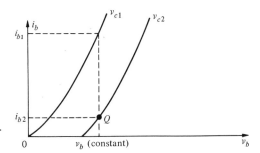

Fig. 7.2 Finding the transconductance g_m graphically.

The model of Fig. 7.1 is a current-source model. The current source can be
replaced by an equivalent voltage source. This results in Fig. 7.3, where

$$\mu = g_m r_p \qquad \qquad (7.6)$$

is the *incremental voltage amplification factor* and is dimensionless. From the
voltage-source model of Fig. 7.3 one may write

$$v_p = r_p i_p - \mu v_g \qquad \qquad (7.7)$$

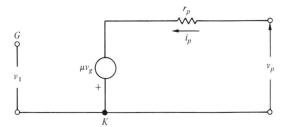

Fig. 7.3 Voltage-source
model of a triode.

The current-source and voltage-source incremental models developed for
the triode apply to the tetrode and pentode if the screen is bypassed with a
suitable capacitance.

Let us evaluate the performance of the amplifier shown in Fig. 7.4; Fig.

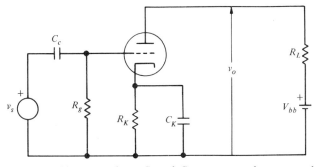

Fig. 7.4 Triode amplifier; capacitors C_c and C_K are assumed to act as short circuits
to signal frequencies.

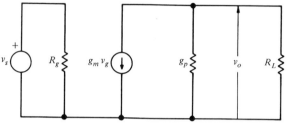

Fig. 7.5 Current-source model of amplifier of Fig. 7.4.

7.5 gives the corresponding current-source model. Capacitors C_c and C_K are assumed to act as short circuits. Since we are interested in signal, or ac performance, all dc sources are set to zero. For calculating voltage gain $A_v = v_o/v_s$, the voltage-source model of Fig. 7.6 is more practical to use.

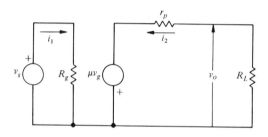

Fig. 7.6 Voltage-source model of amplifier of Fig. 7.4.

From the figure,

$$v_g = v_s$$

$$v_o = \frac{-\mu v_s R_L}{r_p + R_L}.$$

Therefore,

$$A_v = -\mu R_L/(r_p + R_L). \qquad (7.8)$$

The negative sign indicates a phase reversal, that is, the output voltage is 180 degrees out of phase with respect to the input voltage. From (7.8) it is seen that maximum voltage gain is $-\mu$, occurring when R_L approaches infinity or r_p approaches zero.

The input impedance of the amplifier at low frequencies is resistive and from Fig. 7.6 is equal to R_g. The output impedance may be calculated, for example, in terms of the z parameters. From Chapter 6,

$$Z_o = z_{22} - z_{12}z_{21}/(z_{11} + Z_s). \qquad (6.19)$$

Referring again to Fig. 7.6, one can write the following equations:

$$v_s = R_g i_1 + 0$$

$$v_o = -\mu R_g i_1 + r_p i_2.$$

Since $z_{12} = 0$ and $z_{22} = r_p$, from (6.19)

$$Z_o = r_p.$$

7.2   Incremental Model of the Field-Effect Transistor (FET)

It was seen in Chapter 3 that the vacuum tube and FET characteristics are very similar. A FET connected in the common-source configuration, where the input and output terminals share the source terminal, is similar to the common-cathode connected triode. For a field-effect transistor $i_1 = 0$; therefore

$$0 = y_{11}v_1 + y_{12}v_2 \tag{7.9a}$$

$$i_2 = y_{21}v_1 + y_{22}v_2. \tag{7.9b}$$

Equations (7.9a) and (7.9b) are the same as (7.2a) and (7.2b); it appears then that the incremental model for the FET is identical to that of the vacuum tube at low frequencies. We can therefore use the same parameters as for the vacuum tube; $y_{21} = g_m$, $y_{22} = g_p$, and $y_{11} = y_{12} = 0$. In the literature, $g_d(=1/r_d)$ is also used instead of $g_p(=1/r_p)$.

Field-effect transistors have been made with input resistances exceeding a megohm and with transconductance values in the range of 1 to 5 millimhos. The same methods used for vacuum tubes in finding g_p and g_m are applicable in analyzing the field-effect transistor.

If a FET replaces the triode in Fig. 7.4, a common-source FET amplifier is obtained. Let R_S replace R_K and C_S replace C_K. If capacitor C_S acts as a short circuit to ac signals, the incremental model becomes identical to that of Fig. 7.6; the expression for voltage gain is therefore (7.8). If source resistance R_S is left unbypassed, the incremental model appears as shown in Fig. 7.7.

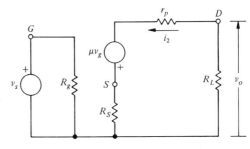

Fig. 7.7 Incremental model of common-source FET amplifier with source resistance R_S unbypassed.

The voltage gain is determined as follows:

$$v_g = v_s - R_S i_2$$

$$i_2 = -v_0/R_L$$

$$\mu v_s = [R_S(1 + \mu) + r_p + R_L]i_2.$$

Solving for $A_v = v_0/v_s$, one obtains

$$A_v = -\mu R_L/[r_p + R_L + (1 + \mu)R_S]. \tag{7.10}$$

Comparison of (7.10) with (7.8) shows that the gain falls when a source resistance (or cathode resistance for the vacuum tube) is left unbypassed. For this reason the resistance will be normally bypassed.

Rotation of the FET and Vacuum Tube

The FET or vacuum tube can be connected in other ways. As pointed out in Chapter 6, a three-terminal network may be considered a device with any of its two terminals as input and its other two terminals as output. Besides the common-source (common-cathode), other practical configurations for the FET or vacuum tube are the common-drain (common-plate) and the common-gate (common-grid) amplifiers.

In finding the corresponding model for these connections, we should bear in mind that changing the common terminal of a device does not alter its nature. Consider the common-cathode amplifier of Fig. 7.1; if P is replaced by D (drain) and K replaced by S (source), the model is that for a common-source amplifier. By rotating the terminals of Fig. 7.1 we obtain the configurations of Fig. 7.8A and B. If we elect, we can proceed now to solve for voltage gain, input impedance, etc., for these circuits. Another approach is to define a new set of y parameters for each of these configurations in terms of the original parameters y_{11}, y_{12}, y_{21}, and y_{22}. The resulting model will have the same form as described by (7.1). This procedure permits the use of the same basic y-model for any configuration.

To illustrate the method, we shall find the y parameters for the common-gate and common-drain circuits in terms of the y parameters for the common-source configuration. The y parameters for the common-source connection were found to be

$$y_{11} = y_{12} = 0$$

$$y_{21} = g_m$$

$$y_{22} = g_p$$

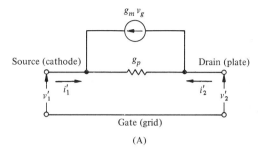

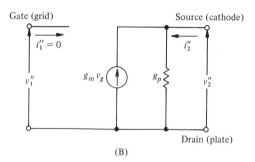

Fig. 7.8 Rotating the terminals of the common-source (cathode) amplifier yields models of (A) Common-gate (grid) and (B) Common-drain (plate) amplifiers.

The generalized **y** matrix is therefore given by

$$[y]_i = \begin{bmatrix} & G & D & S & \\ 0 & 0 & y_{13} & \\ g_m & g_p & y_{23} & \\ y_{31} & y_{32} & y_{33} & \end{bmatrix} \begin{matrix} G \\ D. \\ S \end{matrix} \qquad (7.11a)$$

The values of the remaining y parameters in (7.11a) are calculated by the methods developed in Chapter 6; the results are given in (7.11b).

$$[y]_i = \begin{bmatrix} & G & D & S & \\ 0 & 0 & 0 & \\ g_m & g_p & -(g_m + g_p) & \\ -g_m & -g_p & g_m + g_p & \end{bmatrix} \begin{matrix} G \\ D. \\ S \end{matrix} \qquad (7.11b)$$

For example, to find the common-gate parameters, we strike out row G and column G of (7.11b). Because source S is the input and drain D the output, the matrix for the common-gate configuration therefore becomes

$$[y]_{(CG)} = \begin{bmatrix} g_m + g_p & -g_p \\ -(g_p + g_m) & g_p \end{bmatrix}. \qquad (7.12)$$

The resulting y equations are

$$i_1 = (g_m + g_p)v_1 - g_p v_2 \tag{7.13a}$$

$$i_2 = -(g_p + g_m)v_1 + g_p v_2. \tag{7.13b}$$

The corresponding model appears in Fig. 7.9; this model has the same form as the y model based on (7.1).

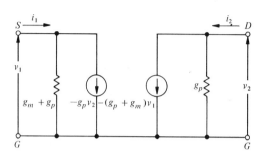

Fig. 7.9 Common-gate incremental model obtained from the generalized y matrix.

Example 7.1

A common-gate amplifier (biasing sources not shown) is given in Fig. 7.10A. Using the model of Fig. 7.9, derive an expression for the voltage gain A_v.

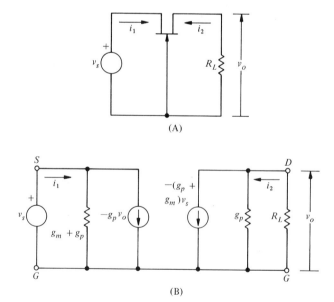

Fig. 7.10 Common-gate amplifier of Example 7.1. (A) Circuit. (B) Model.

Solution

Reference to the model of Fig. 7.10B shows that $i_2 = -v_0/R_L$, $v_1 = v_s$, and $v_2 = v_0$. At node D

$$-v_0/R_L = -(g_m + g_p)v_s + g_pv_0.$$

Solving for $A_v = v_0/v_s$, one obtains

$$A_v = \frac{g_m + g_p}{1/R_L + g_p} = \frac{(1 + \mu)R_L}{r_p + R_L}, \tag{7.14}$$

where $r_p = 1/g_p$ and $\mu = g_m/g_p$. Note that the voltage gain is somewhat greater for the common-gate amplifier than for the common-source amplifier. Furthermore, there is no phase reversal between input and output signal voltages.

To find the y parameters for the common-drain, or source follower, amplifier, row D and column D are struck out of (7.11b) to yield

$$[y]_{(CD)} = \begin{bmatrix} 0 & 0 \\ -g_m & g_m + g_p \end{bmatrix}. \tag{7.15}$$

The y equations become

$$i_1 = 0v_1 + 0v_2 \tag{7.16a}$$

$$i_2 = -g_mv_1 + (g_m + g_p)v_2. \tag{7.16b}$$

The resulting model is shown in Fig. 7.11.

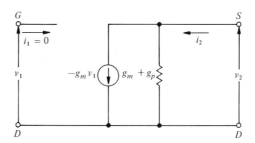

Fig. 7.11 Common-drain (source follower) model obtained from the generalized y matrix.

Assuming the output is terminated in resistance R_S, the voltage gain is found to be

$$A_v = \frac{g_mR_S}{1 + R_S(g_m + g_p)} \approx \frac{g_mR_S}{1 + g_mR_S}, \tag{7.17}$$

if $g_p \ll g_m$. There is no phase reversal and the voltage gain can never exceed unity. The output resistance R_o is

$$R_o = r_p/(1 + \mu). \tag{7.18}$$

The input resistance is in the order of megohms. Because of its high input resistance and low output resistance, the source follower is useful for driving low-impedance loads.

Assume that a voltage source v_s having a series resistance of 100 K is driving a 1-K load. The voltage across the load, v_o, is

$$v_0 = v_s/101.$$

If a source follower is placed between the voltage source and the 1-K load, as shown in Fig. 7.12, the voltage across the load will be much greater. Capacitor C_c prevents the dc present in the source follower from affecting the 1-K load. Assume that $\mu = 200$, $g_m = 10^{-2}$ mho, and $r_p = 20$ K; then from (7.17) $A_v \approx 1$ and from (7.18) $R_0 = 100$ ohms. Because of the low output resistance, $v_0 \approx v_s$.

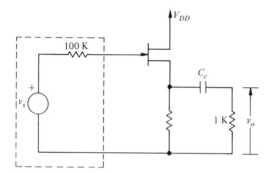

Fig. 7.12 Application of the source follower.

7.3 Incremental Models of Junction Transistor Amplifiers

The junction transistor, like the field-effect transistor and vacuum tube, has three terminals. Two incremental models used to characterize the junction transistor at low frequencies are the hybrid and occasionally the tee models. To develop the hybrid model we begin by writing the hybrid equations that were developed in Chapter 6 for a four-terminal network:

$$v_1 = h_{11}i_1 + h_{12}v_2 \tag{7.19a}$$

$$i_2 = h_{21}i_1 + h_{22}v_2. \tag{7.19b}$$

Expressions (7.19) will be applied now to the transistor in the common-emitter configuration; the hybrid model is shown in Fig. 7.13. For junction transistors it is customary to designate the h parameters in a manner such that they indicate the connection (common emitter, common base, or common collector) as well as the input and output of a given configuration. For example, the common-emitter h parameters are written as

$$h_{11} = h_{ie}, \qquad h_{12} = h_{re},$$
$$h_{21} = h_{fe}, \qquad h_{22} = h_{oe}.$$

The second subscript e indicates the common-emitter parameters; the first subscripts i, r, f, and o stand for input, reverse, forward, and output, respectively.

The hybrid model shown in Fig. 7.13 can also represent the incremental model for the common base and common collector (emitter follower) connections; the only difference is that the values of the parameters are different. For the common base, the parameters are designated as

$$h_{11} = h_{ib}, \qquad h_{12} = h_{rb},$$
$$h_{21} = h_{fb}, \qquad h_{22} = h_{ob}.$$

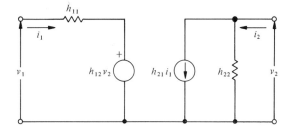

Fig. 7.13 Hybrid model suitable for low frequencies.

For the common collector,

$$h_{11} = h_{ic}, \qquad h_{12} = h_{rc},$$
$$h_{21} = h_{fc}, \qquad h_{22} = h_{oc}.$$

We will derive the basic equations used to characterize transistor amplifiers; these involve current gain A_i; voltage gain A_{vs}, where the second subscript s indicates the presence of a source resistance which is included in the calculation; power gain A_p; input resistance R_i; and output resistance R_o. Since we are interested in the response of the amplifier to ac signals, the dc biasing sources are not shown in the model. The source resistance is R_s and the load resistance is R_L.

Referring to the generalized model of Fig. 7.14, one finds

$$i_2 = h_{21}i_s + h_{22}v_o \qquad (7.20)$$

$$v_0 = -R_L i_2. \qquad (7.21)$$

Therefore,

$$i_2(1 + h_{22}R_L) = h_{21}i_s$$

and

$$A_i = \frac{i_2}{i_s} = \frac{h_{21}}{1 + h_{22}R_L}. \tag{7.22}$$

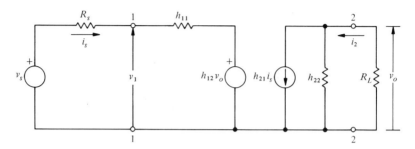

Fig. 7.14 Generalized transistor amplifier model.

Writing an equation for the input side, one obtains

$$v_s = (R_s + h_{11})i_s + h_{12}v_o.$$

Substituting $i_s = i_2/A_i$, one finds

$$v_s = (R_s + h_{11})i_2/A_i + h_{12}v_o.$$

But $i_2 = -v_0/R_L$ and $A_i = h_{21}/(1 + h_{22}R_L)$. Simplifying and solving for $A_{vs} = v_o/v_s$, one obtains the result

$$A_{vs} = \frac{h_{21}R_L}{h_{12}h_{21}R_L - (1 + h_{22}R_L)(h_{11} + R_s)}. \tag{7.23}$$

To obtain the input resistance R_i across terminals 1-1 of Fig. 7.14, one writes

$$v_1 = h_{11}i_s + h_{12}v_o$$

$$R_i = v_1/i_s = h_{11} + h_{12}v_o/i_s. \tag{7.24}$$

From (7.20) and (7.21),

$$v_o/i_s = -h_{21}/(h_{22} + 1/R_L). \tag{7.25}$$

Substituting (7.25) in (7.24), one has

$$R_i = h_{11} - h_{12}h_{21}/(h_{22} + 1/R_L). \tag{7.26}$$

In finding the output resistance R_o, the load resistance is removed and a source v is applied to output terminals 2-2; signal source v_s is set to zero and i_s becomes i_1. By definition, the output resistance is defined as $R_o = v/i$, where i is the current flowing into the output terminal. Referring to Fig. 7.15, one can write

$$i = h_{22}v + h_{21}i_1 \tag{7.27}$$

$$i_1 = -h_{12}v/(h_{11} + R_s). \tag{7.28}$$

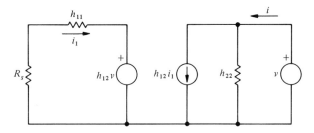

Fig. 7.15 Incremental model used for finding output resistance, R_o.

Substituting (7.28) in (7.22) and solving for $v/i = R_o$, one finds

$$R_o = \frac{1}{h_{22} - h_{12}h_{21}/(h_{11} + R_s)}. \tag{7.29}$$

The power gain A_p for resistive loads is the product of voltage and current gains:

$$A_p = A_{vs}A_i. \tag{7.30}$$

For many applications, the preceding equations can be simplified. If

$$h_{22}R_L \ll 1$$

and

$$h_{12} \approx 0,$$

equations (7.22), (7.23), (7.26), and (7.29) reduce to

$$A_i \approx h_{21}, \tag{7.31}$$

$$A_{vs} \approx -h_{21}R_L/(h_{11} + R_s), \tag{7.32}$$

$$R_i \approx h_{11}, \tag{7.33}$$

$$R_o = 1/h_{22}. \tag{7.34}$$

These results point out the utility of the hybrid parameters. They can provide information pertaining to amplifier performance very rapidly. For example, from (7.33) the input resistance of the amplifier is equal to the short-circuit input resistance of the transistor (if the approximation $h_{12} \approx 0$ is valid—as it is for many small-signal transistors). From (7.32), the voltage gain can be interpreted as the product of the short-circuit current gain of the transistor h_{21} and the ratio of the load to input resistances. Again, it should be emphasized that the approximate or the exact expressions can be used for any configuration with the appropriate h parameters.

If the parameters of one configuration can be measured or are known to the user, the parameters of another configuration may be calculated from the first with the aid of the generalized **y** matrix. We first transform the given h parameters to y parameters and then construct the generalized **y** matrix. Let us assume that the common-emitter h parameters are given. If we refer to Table 6.1 we may construct the generalized matrix as

$$[y]_h = \begin{matrix} B \quad\quad\quad C \quad\quad\quad E \\ \begin{bmatrix} 1/h_{ie} & -h_{re}/h_{ie} & y_{13} \\ h_{fe}/h_{ie} & \Delta h_e/h_{ie} & y_{23} \\ y_{31} & y_{32} & y_{33} \end{bmatrix} \begin{matrix} B \\ C \\ E \end{matrix} \end{matrix} \tag{7.35}$$

where $\Delta h_e = h_{ie}h_{oe} - h_{fe}h_{re}$.

The y elements in (7.35) are defined as

$$y_{13} = (h_{re} - 1)/h_{ie},$$

$$y_{23} = -(h_{fe} + \Delta h_e)/h_{ie},$$

$$y_{31} = -(1 + h_{fe})/h_{ie},$$

$$y_{32} = (h_{re} - \Delta h_e)/h_{ie},$$

$$y_{33} = (1 + h_{fe} + \Delta h_e - h_{re})/h_{ie}.$$

The **y** matrix for the common-base configuration therefore becomes

$$[y]_{(CB)} = \begin{bmatrix} (1 + h_{fe} + \Delta h_e - h_{re})/h_{ie} & (h_{re} - \Delta h_e)/h_{ie} \\ -(h_{fe} + \Delta h_e)/h_{ie} & \Delta h_e/h_{ie} \end{bmatrix}. \tag{7.36}$$

Using Table 6.1 again, we transform the y parameters of (7.36) into the h parameters for the common-base configuration:

$$h_{ib} = h_{ie}/(1 + h_{fe} + \Delta h_e - h_{re}),$$

$$h_{rb} = (\Delta h_e - h_{re})/(1 + h_{fe} + \Delta h_e - h_{re}),$$

$$h_{fb} = -(h_{fe} + \Delta h_e)/(1 + h_{fe} + \Delta h_e - h_{re}),$$

$$h_{ob} = \frac{\Delta h_e + h_{fe}h_{re}}{h_{ie}(1 + h_{fe} + \Delta h_e - h_{re})}.$$

The derivation of the common-collector h parameters is performed in a similar manner.

The Tee Model

The tee model for the transistor in the common-base configuration is given in Fig. 7.16. Comparing this figure with Fig. 6.3B, we see that

$$r_e = z_{11} - z_{12}, \tag{7.37a}$$

$$r_b = z_{12}, \tag{7.37b}$$

$$r_c = z_{22} - z_{12}, \tag{7.37c}$$

$$r_m = z_{21} - z_{12}. \tag{7.37d}$$

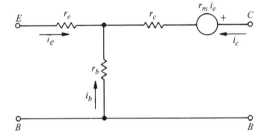

Fig. 7.16 Tee model of transistor in the common-base configuration.

To develop the appropriate model for the two other configurations, we may rotate the model of Fig. 7.16 to fit the connection. For example, the common-emitter model appears in Fig. 7.17. The current-controlled voltage source is, however, a function of emitter current i_e. Because the base is the input terminal, it is appropriate to make the controlled source a function of base current i_b. From Fig. 7.17 we see that $i_e = -(i_b + i_c)$. Substituting this in

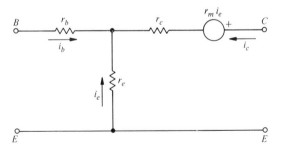

Fig. 7.17 Common-emitter tee model of transistor.

$r_m i_e$ yields $-r_m(i_b + i_c)$. Using the substitution theorem, we can represent $-r_m i_c$ by a resistance $-r_m$ in the collector circuit. Combining this with r_c, we obtain $r_c - r_m = r_d$. The resultant model finally appears as shown in Fig. 7.18. The tee model for the common-collector amplifier (emitter follower), obtained from rotating Fig. 7.18, is shown in Fig. 7.19.

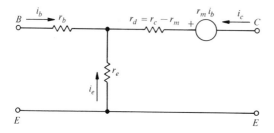

Fig. 7.18 Common-emitter model with the controlled source a function of base current, i_b.

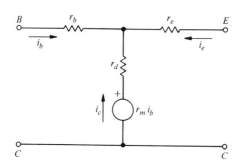

Fig. 7.19 Common-collector (emitter follower) tee model.

The tee parameters may be expressed in terms of h parameters with the use of Table 6.1. Using expressions (7.37), we obtain

$$r_e = h_{11} - h_{12}(1 + h_{21})/h_{22}, \qquad (7.38a)$$

$$r_b = h_{12}/h_{22}, \qquad (7.38b)$$

$$r_c = (1 - h_{12})/h_{22}, \qquad (7.38c)$$

$$r_m = -(h_{12} + h_{21})/h_{22}. \qquad (7.38d)$$

The values of the h parameters used in (7.38) are for the CB configuration. The tee parameters are the same for all configurations.

Example 7.2

A transistor with the following h parameters is used in the amplifier of Fig. 7.20: $h_{fe} = 40$, $h_{ie} = 2$ K, and $h_{re} = h_{oe} \approx 0$. The circuit values are $R_L = 2$ K, $R_E = 100$ ohms, $R_1 = 100$ K, $R_2 = 5$ K, $R_s = 50$ K, and $V_{CC} = 40$ V. Assume capacitor C_E acts as a short circuit to ac signals and at the quiescent point $I_C/I_B = 50$. (a) Draw an incremental model for the amplifier. (b) Calculate the quiescent point assuming that $V_{BE} \approx 0$. (c) Compute the voltage gain $A_{vs} = v_o/v_s$.

Solution

(a) The model is given in Fig. 7.21.

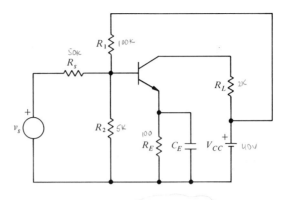

Fig. 7.20 Common-emitter amplifier; assume capacitor C_E acts as a short circuit to signal frequencies.

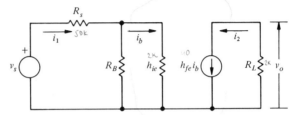

Fig. 7.21 Hybrid model of common-emitter amplifier of Fig. 7.20; $R_B = R_1//R_2$.

(b) To determine I_B, we calculate the Thevenin's equivalent dc voltage and resistance at the base. From Fig. 7.20;

$$R_B = R_1 R_2/(R_1 + R_2) = (100 \times 5)/(100 + 5) = 4.75 \text{ K},$$

$$V_B = V_{CC} R_2/(R_1 + R_2) = 40 \times 5/105 = 1.9 \text{ V},$$

$$I_B = \frac{V_B}{R_B + (1 + h_{FE})R_E} = \frac{1.9}{4.75 + 51 \times 0.1} = 0.193 \text{ mA},$$

$$I_C = h_{FE}I_B = 50 \times 0.193 = 9.65 \text{ mA},$$

$$V_{CE} = V_{CC} - I_C(R_L + R_E) - R_E I_B$$

$$= 40 - 9.65 \times 2.1 - 0.1 \times 0.193 = 19.7 \text{ V}.$$

(c) Because of source resistance R_s and equivalent base resistance R_B, the signal is attenuated when it appears across the base-emitter junction of the transistor. Taking the Thevenin equivalent at B, we obtain

$$v_{th} = 4.75 v_s/54.75$$

$$R_{th} = R_s' = 4.75//50 = 4.34 \text{ K}.$$

Replacing R_s with R_s' in (7.32) and taking into account the signal attenuation owing to R_s and R_B, we obtain

$$A_{vs} = -(4.75/54.75)(40 \times 2)/(2 + 4.34) = -1.1.$$

Example 7.3

Assume the amplifier of Fig. 7.20 is excited by a current source i_s in parallel with source resistance R_s; the model is shown in Fig. 7.22. Find the current gain i_2/i_s.

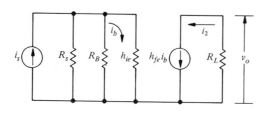

Fig. 7.22 The signal represented by a current source.

Solution

$$R_s//R_B = 50\text{K}//4.75\text{K} = 4.34 \text{ K}.$$

Therefore,

$$i_b/i_s = 4.34/(4.34 + 2) = 0.685$$

From (7.31), $A_i = 0.685 \times 40 = 27.5$.

To become familiar with the use of tee parameters, let us derive expressions for the input and output resistances, as well as the current and voltage gains, of the common-base amplifier of Fig. 7.23; the tee model is given in Fig. 7.24. From Chapter 6 we may write

$$Z_i = z_{11} - z_{12}z_{21}/(z_{22} + Z_L) \tag{6.16}$$

and
$$Z_o = z_{22} - z_{12}z_{21}/(Z_s + z_{11}). \tag{6.19}$$

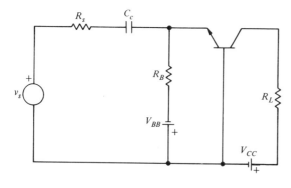

Fig. 7.23 Common-base amplifier. Assume resistance R_B is very large and may be neglected; capacitor C_c acts as a short circuit to signals.

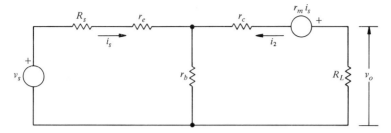

Fig. 7.24   Tee model for circuit of Fig. 7.23.

From Fig. 7.24,

$$z_{11} = r_e + r_b,$$

$$z_{12} = r_b,$$

$$z_{21} = r_m + r_b,$$

$$z_{22} = r_b + r_c,$$

then

$$Z_i = r_e + r_b - (r_b + r_m)r_b/(r_c + r_b + R_L) \tag{7.39}$$

and

$$Z_o = r_c + r_b - r_b(r_b + r_m)/(r_e + r_b + R_s). \tag{7.40}$$

With $i_e = i_s$, the following loop equations are obtained from Fig. 7.24:

$$v_s = (R_s + r_e + r_b)i_s + r_b i_2 \tag{7.41a}$$

$$0 = (r_b + r_m)i_s + (r_b + r_c + R_L)i_2. \tag{7.41b}$$

From (7.41b),

$$A_i = \frac{i_2}{i_s} = \frac{-(r_b + r_m)}{r_b + r_c + R_L}. \tag{7.42}$$

Note that the current gain will be always less than unity and the output and input currents are 180 degrees out of phase.

If we now solve (7.42) for i_s and substitute in (7.41a), we get

$$v_s = -\left[\frac{(R_s + r_e + r_b)(r_b + r_c + R_L)}{r_b + r_m} - r_b\right]i_2. \tag{7.43}$$

But $v_o = -i_2 R_L$; hence, solving (7.43) for i_2, multiplying by R_L to obtain v_o, and simplifying, we arrive at an expression for voltage gain:

$$A_{vs} = \frac{(r_b + r_m)R_L}{(R_s + r_e + r_b)(r_b + r_c + R_L) - r_b(r_b + r_m)}. \tag{7.44}$$

Note that for the common-base amplifier, the output and input voltages are in phase.

In practice, generally

$$r_b \ll r_m$$

and
$$r_b + R_L \ll r_c.$$

Furthermore, $r_m = \alpha r_c$ where α is the short-circuit current gain of the transistor in the common-base configuration and is equal to h_{fb}. Therefore, (7.39), (7.40), (7.42), and (7.44) become

$$Z_i = r_e + r_b(1 - \alpha), \tag{7.45}$$

$$Z_o = r_c\left(1 - \frac{\alpha r_b}{r_e + r_b + R_s}\right), \tag{7.46}$$

$$A_i = -\alpha, \tag{7.47}$$

$$A_{vs} = \frac{\alpha R_L}{R_s + r_e + r_b(1 - \alpha)}. \tag{7.48}$$

In analyzing small-signal transistor amplifiers at low frequencies, either the tee or hybrid model may be used; both models will yield the same results. There are, however, two good reasons for using the hybrid model. First, most manufacturers provide hybrid parameters—not tee parameters—on their data sheets. Second, as indicated by equations (7.31) through (7.34), current and voltage gains and input and output impedances can be ascertained quickly in terms of the hybrid parameters for many applications.

7.4 Summary

Although active devices are basically nonlinear, for small-signal operation we can develop small-signal, or incremental, models. Several models were developed for vacuum tubes, field-effect, and junction transistors. Parameter conversion using the generalized **y** matrix and relations for voltage gain, current gain, etc., were derived assuming low-frequency operation where reactances can be ignored. The effect of these reactances on amplifier operation will be the subject of the following chapter.

References

COCHRUN, B. L., *Transistor Circuit Engineering*, Macmillan, New York, 1967.

COMER, D. J., *Introduction to Semiconductor Circuit Design*, Addison-Wesley, Reading, Mass., 1968.

DE PIAN, L. *Linear Active Network Theory*, Prentice-Hall, Englewood Cliffs, New Jersey, 1962.

SEIDMAN, A. H., and S. L. MARSHALL, *Semiconductor Fundamentals: Devices and Circuits*, Wiley, New York, 1963.

Problems

×   7.1   For a 6BZ7 triode operating at a Q-point of 200 V and 15 mA, determine the values of μ, r_p, and g_m.

✓   7.2   Repeat Prob. 7.1 for an E300 FET biased at 16 V and 7 mA.

×   7.3   Assume that a 2N3440 BJT is biased at 70 V and 50 mA. Find the values of h_{fe}, h_{oe}, and h_{ie}.

     7.4   For the FET amplifier of Fig. P7.4, $R_1//R_2 = 100$ K, $r_p = 100$ K, $g_m = 10^{-3}$ mho, and the coupling and bypass capacitors act as shorts. Draw an incremental model of the amplifier. Calculate the voltage gain v_o/v_s if (a) $R_s = 0$; (b) $R_s = 1$ K; and (c) $R_s = 100$ K. Compare results.

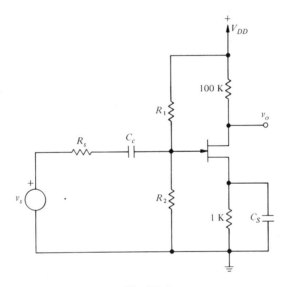

Fig. P7.4.

×   7.5   Repeat Prob. 7.4 if capacitor C_S is omitted.

✓   7.6   Repeat Prob. 7.4. for $R_1//R_2 = 10$ K. Discuss your results.

×   7.7   Referring to Fig. P7.7, (a) draw its incremental model; assume that capacitor C_c acts as a short to the signal. (b) Derive an expression for the voltage gain v_o/v_s.

     7.8   Derive expressions for v_d/v_i and v_s/v_i for the *split-load phase inverter* of Fig. P7.8. What values should R_S and R_D have for equal voltage gains?

✓   7.9   Referring to Fig. P7.9, (a) draw an incremental model of the circuit. (b) Derive expressions for v_o/v_1 with v_2 set to zero, and v_o/v_2 with v_1 set to zero. (c) Why can this circuit be useful?

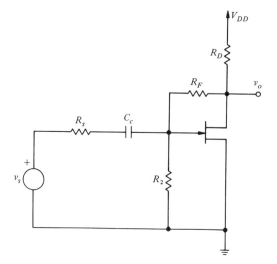

Fig. P7.7.

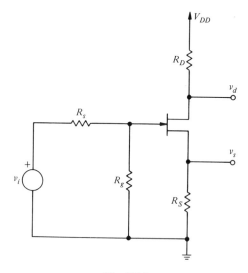

Fig. P7.8.

7.10 The following common-base h parameters are supplied by a manufacturer: $h_{ib} = 20$ ohms, $h_{rb} = 0$, $h_{fb} = -0.98$, and $h_{ob} = 10^{-6}$ mho.
(a) Using Table 6.1, convert the above parameters to y parameters.
(b) Form the generalized y matrix. (c) Find the common-emitter h
parameters.

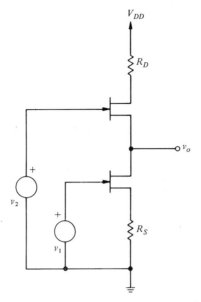

Fig. P7.9.

7.11 For the transistor amplifier of Fig. P7.11, $h_{ie} = 1$ K, $h_{re} = 0$, $h_{fe} = 50$, and $1/h_{oe} = 20$ K. Assuming that the capacitors act as shorts to the signals, calculate the current gain i_L/i_s.

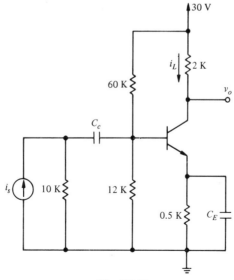

Fig. P7.11.

7.12 In Fig. P7.11 the current source and parallel 10-K resistance are replaced by a voltage source v_s in series with a 10-K resistance. Calculate (a) voltage gain v_o/v_s; (b) power gain; (c) input resistance; and (d) output resistance.

7.13 Repeat Prob. 7.12 assuming that the emitter resistance is unbypassed. Compare results.

7.14 Repeat Prob. 7.12 for $h_{re} = 10^{-4}$. Compare results.

7.15 Using the common-emitter h parameters of Prob. 7.11, find the common-collector h parameters.

7.16 Using the values $h_{ic} = 2\,K$, $h_{fc} = -90$, $n_{oc} = 10^{-6}$ mho, and $h_{rc} = 1$, calculate (a) voltage gain; (b) current gain; (c) input resistance; and (d) output resistance for the emitter follower of Fig. P7.16. For simplicity, the biasing is not shown.

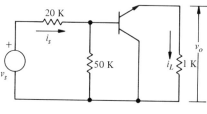

Fig. P7.16.

7.17 Based on the tee model of a transistor in the common-emitter configuration of Fig. 7.18, derive expressions for A_{vs}, A_i, R_i and R_o. The load resistance is R_L, and the source resistance is R_s. Simplify your

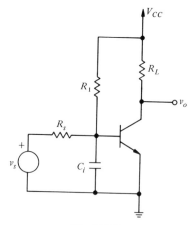

Fig. P7.18.

expressions by making use of the following approximations: $r_e \ll r_b$ and $r_b \ll r_m, r_c, r_d$.

7.18 Referring to Fig. P7.18, (a) draw an equivalent circuit, using the hybrid model of the transistor. (b) Derive an expression for the voltage gain, v_o/v_s, as a function of frequency. Neglect h_{re} and the transistor capacitances. (c) If $h_{ie} = 1$ K, $h_{re} = 0$, $h_{fe} = 60$, $1/h_{oe} = 20$ K, $R_s = R_L = 1$ K, and $C_i = 100$ pF, what is the expression for voltage gain?

7.19 For the circuit of Fig. P7.19, draw the hybrid incremental model and determine the voltage gain v_o/v_s. What is the configuration called? Assume that all capacitances act as shorts to the signals and $h_{ib} = 40$ ohms, $h_{fb} = -0.98$. Neglect h_{rb} and h_{ob}.

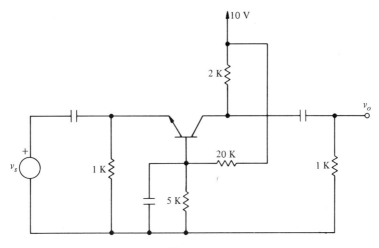

Fig. P7.19.

High-
Frequency
Models

In our analysis of small-signal amplifiers thus far, the range of signal frequencies handled by the amplifier was limited. We generally assumed mid- or low-frequency operation, which implied frequencies approximately less than 5 kilohertz (kHz). This imposed limitation enabled us to analyze the various amplifier configurations of Chapter 7 with relatively simple models for the active device, composed of controlled sources and resistive networks; in this manner, we were able to concentrate on the essentials of model development. Furthermore, some practical circuits operate at frequencies below 5 kHz, so our analysis is indeed useful.

There are, however, innumerable applications where the operating frequency range extends to tens of kilohertz, megahertz (MHz), or gigahertz (GHz). For example, a hi-fi system operates at frequencies up to 20 kHz; an fm receiver tunes from 88 to 108 MHz. Many more examples can be cited to show that we must refine our analytical techniques and models to take into account the effects of higher frequencies on active device operation.

In this chapter we shall examine the inherent qualities of active devices that make them frequency sensitive. For transistors, the diffusion and space-charge capacitances limit high-frequency operation; for vacuum tubes, the interelectrode capacitances are the limiting parameters. Appropriate models that take frequency effects into account, called *high-frequency* models, will be developed for the junction transistor, the field-effect transistor (FET), and the vacuum tube. To pave the way, a review of the frequency response of passive networks will precede the development of high-frequency models.

8.1 Frequency-Dependent Networks

Consider the lowpass network (referred to also as an integrator) of Fig. 8.1. The transfer function of any network may be defined in terms of the complex variable s as the ratio of an output quantity to an input quantity, such as voltage to voltage, voltage to current, current to voltage, or current to current. Therefore, voltage gain $V_o(s)/V_i(s)$ for Fig. 8.1 is

$$\frac{V_o(s)}{V_i(s)} = \frac{1}{1 + sRC_o}. \tag{8.1}$$

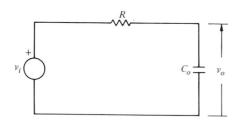

Fig. 8.1   A lowpass (integrator) network.

A pole exists at $-1/RC_o$ rad/s in the s-plane. A pole is a root of the denominator; if $s = -1/RC_o$ is substituted in (8.1), the denominator equals zero and the expression goes to infinity. A zero is a root of the numerator; in (8.1) no zeros are present. We shall, however, meet functions that contain both zeros and poles.

If $s = j\omega$ is substituted in (8.1), we obtain

$$\frac{V_o(j\omega)}{V_i(j\omega)} = \frac{1}{1 + j\omega RC_o}. \tag{8.2}$$

Frequency response plots of (8.2), obtained by point-to-point plotting, are shown in Fig. 8.2; it is seen that the gain of the network decreases with increasing frequency because of the presence of capacitance across the output of the lowpass network. The *bandwidth* is defined as the frequency at which the normalized gain is 0.707. In terms of decibels (dB), this becomes

$$20 \log|V_0(j\omega_H)/V_i(j\omega_H)| = -20 \log(1/0.707) = -3 \text{ dB}.$$

The frequency at which the normalized gain is 0.707 is referred to as the upper break frequency, upper -3 dB frequency, upper corner frequency, or the upper half-power frequency.

The upper break frequency f_H is defined as

$$f_H = 1/2\pi RC_o \text{ (Hz).} \tag{8.3a}$$

In terms of angular frequency,

$$\omega_H = 1/RC_o \text{ (rad/s).} \tag{8.3b}$$

Substitution of (8.3b) in (8.2) yields

$$G(j\omega) = \frac{V_o(j\omega)}{V_i(j\omega)} = \frac{1}{1 + j\omega/\omega_H}. \tag{8.4}$$

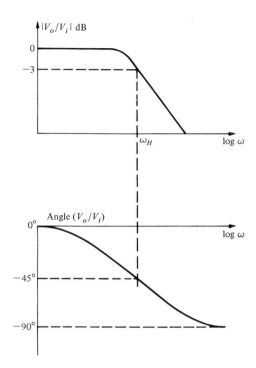

Fig. 8.2 Response of a lowpass network.

When $\omega = \omega_H$, (8.4) reduces to

$$G(j\omega) = 1/(1 + j) = 0.707\underline{/-45°}.$$

At the upper break frequency the gain is 0.707, and the phase shift is $-45°$ (see Fig. 8.2). From (8.3) it is seen that to increase bandwidth, that is, to increase the upper break frequency, either R or C_o has to be reduced.

In analyzing the high-frequency behavior of active devices, it will be seen the frequency response of the device is ultimately determined by an equivalent lowpass network similar to that of Fig. 8.1. Capacitance C_o will represent a shunting capacity, either at the input or the output side of the device, that influences the upper break frequency of the amplifier.

It is worth considering the relationship that exists between the time and frequency domains for the lowpass network. Let v_i in Fig. 8.1 be a unit step input; multiplying its transform by the network transfer function, one obtains

$$V_o(s) = \frac{1/RC_o}{s(s + 1/RC_o)} \tag{8.5}$$

for the transform of the output voltage. The inverse transform of (8.5) is

$$v_o(t) = 1 - \exp(-t/RC_o), \tag{8.6}$$

where RC_o is the *time constant* of the network, with the unit of time.

The rise time of the output waveform t_r is defined as the time required for the output to rise from 0.1 to 0.9 (or from 10 to 90%) of its maximum value. Solution of (8.6) for t_r yields

$$t_r = 2.2\,RC_o. \tag{8.7}$$

From (8.3), $RC_o = 1/(2\pi f_H)$. Substitution of this value in (8.7) gives

$$t_r f_H = 0.35. \tag{8.8}$$

Equation (8.8) states that the product of the rise time and the upper break frequency for a network containing a single pole is always equal to a constant. Based on this result, the upper break frequency f_H of a network, like an amplifier, can be found by taking measurements in the time domain. Instead of a step input, a square wave is used; the rise time is measured on a cathode-ray oscilloscope, and the upper break frequency is calculated from (8.8). In applying this method to a network containing more than one pole, the poles must be widely separated for reasonably accurate results. The frequency response of an amplifier, however, is generally determined by making measurements in the frequency domain.

Example 8.1

A square-wave generator is impressed across the input terminals of an audio amplifier. The rise time measured on a scope is 10 μs. What is the upper break frequency f_H?

Solution

From (8.8), $f_H = 0.35/t_r = 0.35/(10 \times 10^{-6}) = 35\,\text{kHz}.$

8.2 Asymptotic (Bode) Plots

Instead of plotting amplitude-frequency response curves point by point, a method is available that permits an approximation to the actual curve by straight line segments, or *asymptotes*. Referred to as the *Bode* plot, the resulting curve provides essentially the same information obtained from point-to-point plots, with much less effort. Curves of phase angle as a function of frequency are also easily approximated.

Equation (8.4) may be expressed as a magnitude and phase angle:

$$G(j\omega) = |G(j\omega)|/\underline{\theta} = \frac{1}{[1 + (\omega/\omega_H)^2]^{1/2}}/\underline{-\tan^{-1}(\omega/\omega_H)}. \tag{8.9}$$

Concentrating for the moment on the magnitude expression of (8.9), for frequencies $\omega \ll \omega_H$, one has $|G(j\omega)| \approx 1/1 = 1$; therefore,

$$20 \log_{10}|(G(j\omega)| = 20 \log_{10}(1) = 0 \text{ dB}.$$

If ω assumes values such that $\omega \gg \omega_H$, term $(\omega/\omega_H)^2$ in (8.9) is much greater than unity; for this range of frequencies, therefore,

$$20 \log_{10}|G(j\omega)| = -20 \log_{10}(\omega/\omega_H). \tag{8.10}$$

For values $\omega \gg \omega_H$, $|G(j\omega)|$ decreases at the rate of 20 dB per decade; for example, if $\omega/\omega_H = 10$, $-20 \log_{10}(10) = -20$ dB. If $\omega/\omega_H = 2$, $-20 \log_{10}(2) = -6$ dB. The frequency ratio $\omega/\omega_H = 2$ is called an *octave*; therefore, instead of speaking of -20 dB/decade, one can also refer to the decrease in amplitude with frequency as -6 dB/octave.

The preceding results lead to a simple method for plotting the amplitude response curve of a transfer function. As shown in Fig. 8.3A, for values of $\omega \ll \omega_H$ a straight line is plotted along the ω/ω_H-axis at a value of 0 dB to $\omega/\omega_H = 1$. (Note that the frequency scale is logarithmic to permit the compression of a large frequency range to a reasonable length of frequency axis and linear plots.) For $\omega \gg \omega_H$, $|G(j\omega)|$ decreases at a rate of -20 dB/decade (or -6 dB/octave). A line from $\omega/\omega_H = 1$ is therefore drawn with a slope of -20 dB/decade. The point at which $\omega = \omega_H$ ($\omega/\omega_H = 1$) is the upper break frequency and $20 \log_{10}|G(j\omega)| = -3$ dB, as may be verified from (8.9).

In Fig. 8.3A, the actual amplitude response is shown as a dashed curve.

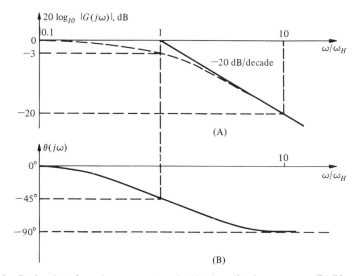

Fig. 8.3 Bode plots for a lowpass network. (A) Amplitude response. (B) Phase angle response.

The curve approaches the line segments asymptotically for $\omega \ll \omega_H$ and $\omega \gg \omega_H$; compare this result with that shown in Fig. 8.2.

The variation of phase angle with frequency, from (8.9), is

$$\theta(j\omega) = -\tan^{-1}(\omega/\omega_H).$$

For $\omega \ll \omega_H$, $\theta \approx 0°$; for $\omega \gg \omega_H$, $\theta \approx -90°$. At the upper break frequency, $\omega = \omega_H$; therefore $-\tan^{-1}(1) = -45°$. The resultant plot of $\theta(j\omega)$ is given in Fig. 8.3B. The curve approaches $0°$ asymptotically at low frequencies and $-90°$ asymptotically at high frequencies.

Example 8.2

Consider the highpass network (referred to also as a differentiator), which is obtained from Fig. 8.1 by interchanging R and C_o. (a) Determine its transfer function $G(j\omega)$. (b) Draw Bode plots of its amplitude and phase characteristics.

Solution

(a) $G(j\omega) = \dfrac{V_o(j\omega)}{V_i(j\omega)} = \dfrac{1}{1 + 1/j\omega RC_o}.$

Let $\omega_L = 1/RC_o$; therefore

$$G(j\omega) = \frac{1}{1 - j(\omega_L/\omega)} = \frac{1}{\sqrt{1 + (\omega_L/\omega)^2}} \Big/ \tan^{-1}(\omega_L/\omega) \tag{8.11}$$

(b) For $\omega \gg \omega_L$, $|G(j\omega)| \approx 1$ and $20\log_{10}(1) = 0\,\mathrm{dB}$. For $\omega \ll \omega_L$, $|G(j\omega)| = 1/\sqrt{(\omega_L/\omega)^2} = \omega/\omega_L$ and $20\log_{10}|G(j\omega)| \approx 20\log_{10} \times (\omega/\omega_L)$.

Phase angle $\theta(j\omega) = \tan^{-1}(\omega_L/\omega)$; for $\omega \gg \omega_L$, θ approaches $0°$; for $\omega \ll \omega_L$, θ approaches $90°$. At the break frequency, $\theta = 45°$.

The asymptotic amplitude and the phase angle plots are given in Fig. 8.4.

Example 8.3

Plot the Bode diagrams for the transfer function

$$G(s) = 100(s + 0.5)/s(s + 5).$$

Solution

Upon substitution of $j\omega$ for s, the ac steady-state transfer function becomes

$$G(j\omega) = \frac{100(j\omega + 0.5)}{j\omega(j\omega + 5)} = \frac{10(1 + j2\omega)}{j\omega(1 + j\omega/5)}. \tag{8.12}$$

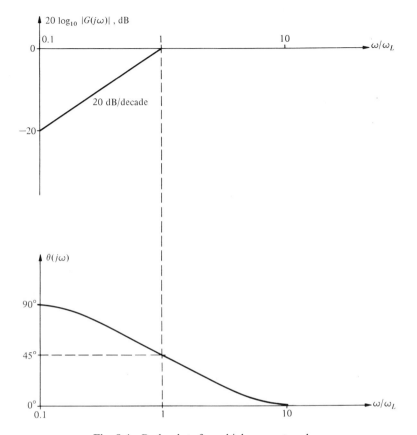

Fig. 8.4 Bode plots for a highpass network.

We consider each term of (8.12) separately and add their individual contributions logarithmically to obtain the overall response.

The constant term 10 in the numerator yields $20 \log_{10}(10) = 20$ dB. For frequencies greater than $\omega = \frac{1}{2}$ rad/s, the other factor in the numerator contributes approximately $20 \log_{10}(2\omega)$ with a breakpoint at $\frac{1}{2}$ rad/s, and a positive slope of 20 dB/decade. In the denominator, the $j\omega$-term contributes $-20 \log_{10} \omega$ and results in a line that has a slope of -20 dB/decade and crosses the ω-axis at $\omega = 1$. If the other factor in the denominator is considered, for frequencies $\omega \gg 5$, the logarithmic expression for the factor is approximately $-20 \log_{10}(\omega/5)$; The breakpoint is at 5 rad/s and the slope is -20 dB/decade. The four curves are drawn as dashed lines in Fig. 8.5A, with their total effect illustrated by the solid curve. The resultant curve intersects the ω-axis at 94 rad/s.

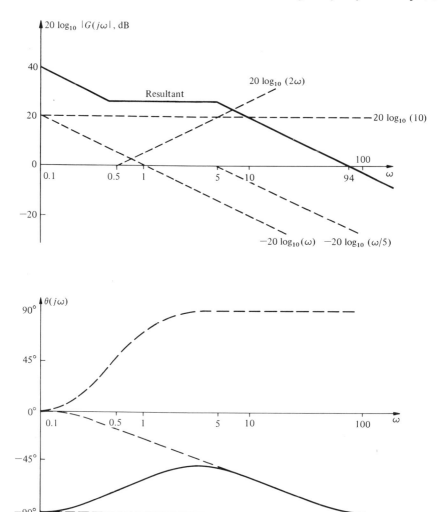

Fig. 8.5 Bode plots for Example 8.3.

In regard to the variation of phase angle with frequency, the total phase angle is determined in a manner similar to that for finding the amplitude response as the sum of the individual contributions for each term in (8.12). The constant term 10 produces 0°, that is, no phase shift. Factor $(1 + j2\omega)$ yields $+45°$ at $\omega = 0.5$; $(1 + j\omega/5)$ gives $-45°$ at $\omega = 5$; the angle for $1/j\omega$ is $-90°$ for all frequencies. These values and the resultant are plotted in Fig. 8.5B.

Quadratic Factors

Consider a transfer function having the following basic form:

$$G(s) = \omega_o^2/(s^2 + 2\zeta\omega_o s + \omega_o^2). \tag{8.13}$$

Equation (8.13) arises for a network containing two energy storage elements, L and C, like a series RLC circuit. Term ω_o is the natural frequency of the network and is equal to $1/\sqrt{LC}$; ζ is the damping factor equal to $(R/2)\sqrt{C/L}$. If $\zeta = 1$, the network is said to be *critically* damped; for $\zeta > 1$, it is *over-damped*; if $\zeta < 1$, the network is *underdamped:* For $\zeta > 1$, the roots of (8.13) are real; for $\zeta = 1$, they are equal. A more interesting case arises for $\zeta < 1$; here, the roots are complex and the resulting amplitude response curve exhibits a peak at the breakpoint. Universal curves for the amplitude and phase angle responses have been developed for various values of $\zeta \leqslant 1$; they are given in Figs. 8.6 and 8.7. The term $\zeta\omega_o$ is sometimes defined by the Greek letter alpha (α).

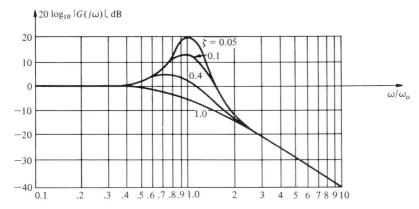

Fig. 8.6 Amplitude responses for sample values of $\zeta \leqslant 1$.

Returning to (8.13), let us substitute $j\omega$ for s:

$$G(j\omega) = \frac{\omega_o^2}{-\omega^2 + j2\zeta\omega_o\omega + \omega_o^2}. \tag{8.14}$$

For $\omega \ll \omega_o$,

$$20\log_{10}|G(j\omega)| \approx 20\log_{10}(\omega_o^2/\omega_o^2) = 0 \text{ dB}.$$

For $\omega \gg \omega_o$,

$$20\log_{10}|G(j\omega)| \approx -20\log_{10}(\omega/\omega_o)^2 = -40\log_{10}(\omega/\omega_o).$$

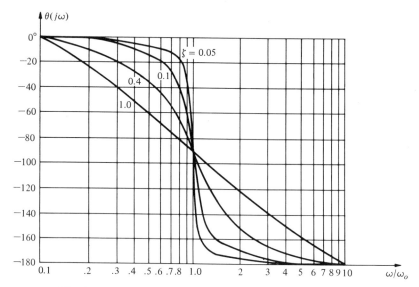

Fig. 8.7 Phase angle responses for sample values of $\zeta \leqslant 1$.

The breakpoint occurs at $\omega = \omega_o$ and the slope is -40 dB/decade (-12 dB/octave) for $\omega > \omega_o$ (see Fig. 8.8A) if $\zeta = 1$. For other values of ζ, the actual shape of the curve and its peak value are determined from the universal curves of Fig. 8.6; this is also indicated in Fig. 8.8A by the dashed curve.

The phase angle $\theta(j\omega)$ of (8.14) is given by

$$\theta(j\omega) = -\tan^{-1}[2\zeta\omega_o\omega/(\omega_o^2 - \omega^2)]. \tag{8.15}$$

For $\omega \ll \omega_o$, $\theta(j\omega) \approx 0°$; for $\omega \gg \omega_o$,

$$\theta(j\omega) \approx -\tan^{-1}(-2\zeta\omega_o/\omega)$$

and approaches $-180°$. At $\omega = \omega_o$, $\theta(j\omega) = -90°$. The resultant curve for $\theta(j\omega)$ is plotted in Fig. 8.8B.

8.3 The Vacuum Tube

Although vacuum tubes are finding fewer applications in new designs than solid-state components, the tube will be analyzed first. The analysis is relatively simple and the techniques used are, in general, applicable to the junction and field-effect transistors.

In our previous discussion of passive circuits, it was seen that capacitance (and at times inductance) affects the frequency and phase responses of a network. This is also true for active circuits. Capacitance exists wherever there are two conductors separated by an insulating medium. The value of

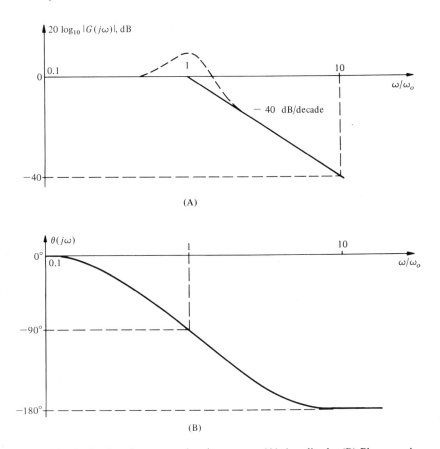

Fig. 8.8 Bode plots for a second-order system. (A) Amplitude. (B) Phase angle.

capacitance C is a function of the area of the conductors A, the separation of the conductors d, and the dielectric constant of the insulating medium k:

$$C = kA/d. \tag{8.16}$$

Because a vacuum tube contains electrodes separated from each other in the vacuum (insulating medium) of the tube, *interelectrode capacitances* exist. A vacuum tube model including interelectrode capacities is shown in Fig. 8.9. It is observed that:

1. The input impedance between the grid G and cathode K is not infinite owing to the presence of capacity C_{gk}.

2. A path between the input and output exists because of interelectrode capacity C_{gp}.

3. Capacity C_{pk} shunts the output side.

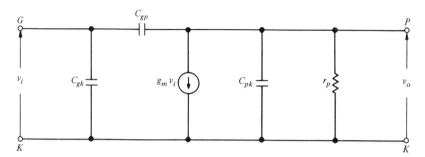

Fig. 8.9 Model of a vacuum tube including interelectrode capacitances.

Assume the vacuum tube is terminated by a resistive load R_L, and the signal is an ideal current source i_s. Because we are concerned with the high-frequency response, if present in the circuit, coupling capacitor C_c and bypass capacitor C_K will be assumed to act as short circuits to the ac signal. The effects of these components on circuit performance are considered in Chapter 9. Applying nodal analysis at node P to the model of Fig. 8.10, one obtains

$$0 = V_i(g_m - sC_{gp}) + V_o[s(C_{gp} + C_{pk}) + G_L + g_p], \qquad (8.17)$$

where $G_L = 1/R_L$ and $g_p = 1/r_p$. Solution of (8.17) for the voltage gain $V_o(s)/V_i(s) = A_v(s)$ yields

$$A_v(s) = \left(\frac{C_{gp}}{C_{gp} + C_{pk}}\right)\left(\frac{s - g_m/C_{gp}}{s + (G_L + g_p)/(C_{gp} + C_{pk})}\right). \qquad (8.18)$$

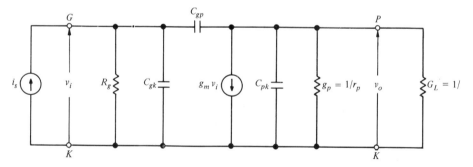

Fig. 8.10 Incremental model of vacuum tube amplifier excited by a current source i_s.

There is a zero at g_m/C_{gp} rad/s and a pole at $-(G_L + g_p)/(C_{pk} + C_{gp})$ rad/s. The relative magnitudes of the zero and pole of (8.18) and their significance will be explored in the following example.

Example 8.4

Assume a 6AU6 pentode vacuum tube properly biased has the following electrical characteristics: $C_{gp} = 3.5 \times 10^{-3}\,\text{pF}$ (maximum), $C_{pk} = 5\,\text{pF}$, $C_{gk} = 5.5\,\text{pF}$, $g_m = 4.5 \times 10^{-3}\,\text{mho}$, $g_p = 10^{-6}\,\text{mho}$. Let $R_L = 10\,\text{K}$ $(G_L = 10^{-4}\,\text{mho})$. Determine the values of the zero z and pole p. Can (8.18) be simplified?

Solution

The zero (z) of (8.18) is $g_m/C_{gp} = (4.5 \times 10^{-3})/(3.5 \times 10^{-15}) \approx 1.3 \times 10^{12}\,\text{rad/s}$. Pole p is located at $-(G_L + g_p)/(C_{gp} + C_{pk}) = -(10^{-4} + 10^{-6})/(5 \times 10^{-12}) = -20 \times 10^6\,\text{rad/s}$. Note that $|p| \ll z$. that is $20 \times 10^6\,\text{rad/s}$ is the *dominant*, or effective upper break, frequency; therefore, s in the numerator may be neglected. With this taken into account, (8.18) can be simplified; in terms of frequency it is

$$A_v(j\omega) = \frac{-g_m/(C_{gp} + C_{pk})}{j\omega + (G_L + g_p)/(C_{gp} + C_{pk})} = \frac{-g_m/(G_L + g_p)}{1 + j\omega/\omega_H}, \qquad (8.19)$$

where

$$\omega_H = (G_L + g_p)/(C_{gp} + C_{pk})$$
$$= 20 \times 10^6\,\text{rad/s}. \qquad (8.20)$$

Substituting numerical values in (8.19) yields

$$A_v(j\omega) = \frac{-45}{1 + j\omega/(20 \times 10^6)}. \qquad (8.21)$$

Equation (8.21) has the same form as (8.4), the transfer function for a low-pass passive network. This verifies, at least in this example, the statement previously made that the high-frequency model of an active device behaves ultimately as a lowpass network. The value of $-g_m/(G_L + g_p) = -45$ is the mid-frequency gain for the amplifier. This also can be seen from (8.21): For $\omega \ll 20 \times 10^6$, $A_v(j\omega) = -45$. The value of $20 \log_{10}(45)$ is $25.6\,\text{dB}$; for $\omega \gg \omega_H$, $|A_v(j\omega)|$ decreases with a slope of $-20\,\text{dB/decade}$, the breakpoint being at $\omega_H\,\text{rad/s}$. The Bode plot* has the same form as the Bode plot for the lowpass network of Fig. 8.3.

Another Approach

If a non-ideal voltage signal source v_s with an internal resistance R_s is substituted for the current source used in Fig. 8.10, the new model appears

---

* Note that for the phase plot, the effect of the minus sign (due to the 180° phase shift at low frequencies) will not be included. For simplicity, this practice is followed in the remainder of this, and other chapters, where applicable.

as shown in Fig. 8.11. Applying nodal analysis at node G, one finds

$$I_i = V_i s(C_{gk} + C_{gp}) - V_o s C_{gp}. \tag{8.22}$$

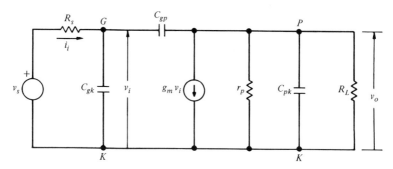

Fig. 8.11 Model of a vacuum tube amplifier excited by a nonideal voltage source.

At node P one has, as before,

$$0 = V_i(g_m - sC_{gp}) + V_o[g_p + G_L + s(C_{gp} + C_{pk})]. \tag{8.23}$$

Equation (8.23) is identical to (8.17). From Example 8.4, the voltage gain $A_v(j\omega)$ can be approximated by (8.19)

$$A_v(j\omega) = \frac{-g_m/(G_L + g_p)}{1 + j\omega/\omega_H}$$

or

$$A_v(j\omega) = \frac{-A_{MF}}{1 + j\omega/\omega_H}, \tag{8.24}$$

where $A_{MF} = g_m/(G_L + g_p)$ is the mid-frequency gain ($\omega \ll \omega_H$).
    Substitution of $A_v V_i$ for V_o in (8.22) yields

$$I_i = V_i s[C_{gk} + (1 - A_v)C_{gp}]. \tag{8.25}$$

Replacing (8.24) in (8.25) and solving for I_i/V_i yields the input admittance in the form

$$Y_i(j\omega) = j\omega\left[C_{gk} + \left(1 + \frac{A_{MF}}{1 + j\omega/\omega_H}\right)C_{gp}\right]. \tag{8.26}$$

If term $j\omega A_{MF}C_{gp}/(1 + j\omega/\omega_H)$ in (8.26) is evaluated, it is equivalent to an impedance $Z(j\omega)$:

$$Z(j\omega) = \frac{1}{\omega_H C_{gp} A_{MF}} + \frac{1}{j\omega C_{gp} A_{MF}}. \tag{8.27}$$

Equation (8.27) states that, *in effect*, a series RC network is reflected across the input. If the real part of (8.27) is neglected, and this is generally possible,

(8.27) reduces to $Y(j\omega) = 1/Z(j\omega) = j\omega C_{gp} A_{MF}$. Therefore, (8.26) becomes

$$Y_i(j\omega) = j\omega[C_{gk} + (1 + A_{MF})C_{gp}] = j\omega C_i, \qquad (8.28)$$

where

$$C_i = C_{gk} + (1 + A_{MF})C_{gp} \qquad (8.29)$$

is the effective input capacitance. The reflection of feedback capacitance C_{gp} to the input side is referred to as the *Miller effect*; capacitance C_i is sometimes called the Miller capacitance. Because $|A_{MF}| \gg 1$, the effective input capacitance C_i can, in general, be much greater than C_{gk}. This will result in a lower upper break frequency.

If $V_i = V_o/A_v$ is substituted for the V_i factor of sC_{gp} in (8.23), one obtains

$$0 = V_i g_m + V_o[G_L + g_p + s\{C_{pk} + C_{gp}(1 - 1/A_v)\}]. \qquad (8.30)$$

Because $A_v \gg 1$, the effective output capacitance C_o is approximately equal to

$$C_o \approx C_{pk} + C_{gp}. \qquad (8.31)$$

Figure 8.12 shows a simplified high-frequency model for the vacuum tube that can be developed based on (8.29) and (8.31). To gain insight into the use of the model, two numerical examples will be considered.

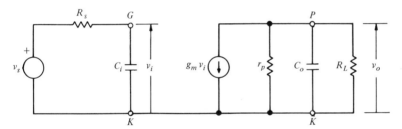

Fig. 8.12   Simplified model of a vacuum tube excited by a nonideal voltage source.

Example 8.5

Using the data of Example 8.4, find the upper break frequency of the model of Fig. 8.12 for (a) $R_s = 1$ K and (b) $R_s = 10$ K.

Solution

(a) From Example 8.4, $A_v = -45$. The input side of Fig. 8.12 appears as a lowpass network; therefore,

$$\omega_{H1} = 1/R_s C_i = 1/(10^3 \times 5.5 \times 10^{-12}) = 190 \times 10^6 \text{ rad/s}.$$

The dominant pole $\omega_{H2} = 20 \times 10^6$ rad/s.

(b) If $R_s = 10\,\text{K}$, $\omega_{H1} = 19 \times 10^6$ rad/s; the break frequency at the output side is the same as in (a), $\omega_{H2} = 20 \times 10^6$ rad/s. To see the effect of these two close break frequencies, the overall voltage gain of the amplifier will be derived.

From Fig. 8.12, an expression for V_i in terms of V_s can be determined:

$$V_i = \frac{V_s(1/sC_i)}{R_s + 1/sC_i} = \frac{V_s}{1 + sR_sC_i}. \tag{8.32}$$

If (8.32) is substituted in (8.30) and simplified, an expression for the overall voltage gain, including the source resistance R_s, $V_o/V_s = A_{vs}$, is obtained:

$$A_{vs} = \frac{V_o}{V_s} = \frac{-g_m/(g_p + G_L)}{(1 + sC_iR_s)[1 + sC_o/(g_p + G_L)]}. \tag{8.33}$$

Term $g_m/(g_p + G_L) = 45$; $\omega_{H1} = 1/C_iR_s = 19 \times 10^6$ rad/s, and $(g_p + G_L)/C_o = \omega_{H2} = 20 \times 10^6$ rad/s. Substituting these numerical values in (8.33) and letting $s = j\omega$, one has

$$A_{vs}(j\omega) = \frac{-45}{[(1 + j\omega/(19 \times 10^6)][(1 - j\omega/(20 \times 10^6)]}. \tag{8.34}$$

The first breakpoint occurs at 19×10^6 rad/s, effectively determining the bandwidth of the amplifier. For frequencies greater than 20×10^6 rad/s, the gain decreases at a rate of -40 dB/decade (-12 dB/octave).

Because of the small internal feedback capacitance C_{gp} of pentodes, its effect on C_i is negligible. For this reason, an amplifier using a pentode has a higher frequency response than a triode.

8.4   The Field-Effect Transistor (FET)

The field-effect transistor can be viewed as a solid-state version of the vacuum tube. A usable high-frequency small-signal model of a FET in the common source (CS) configuration is illustrated in Fig. 8.13; a comparison

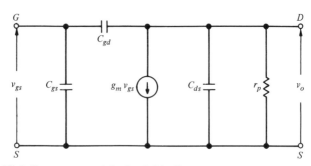

Fig. 8.13 High-frequency model of a field-effect transistor with source common to input and output terminals.

with the high-frequency vacuum tube model of Fig. 8.9 demonstrates that their model structures are identical. Input capacitance C_{gs} and feedback capacitance C_{gd} are the depletion capacitances between gate G and source S, and gate G and drain D, respectively. The channel drain-to-source capacitance is represented by C_{ds}. The short-circuit forward transconductance is g_m; r_p represents the drain-to-source resistance.

Because of the Miller effect, feedback capacitance C_{gd} may be reflected to the input side; the input capacitance C_i is, therefore,

$$C_i = C_{gs} + C_{gd}(1 + A_{MF}), \tag{8.35}$$

which is similar to (8.29). Like in the vacuum tube, C_{ds} is reflected across the output and

$$C_o = C_{gd} + C_{ds}. \tag{8.36}$$

The simplified model of a FET is illustrated in Fig. 8.14.

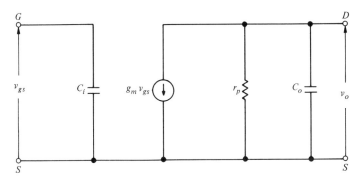

Fig. 8.14 Simplified high-frequency model of common-source FET.

Example 8.6

A high-frequency model of a common-source FET amplifier is given in Fig. 8.15. (a) Derive expressions for $A_{vs}(j\omega)$ and the upper break

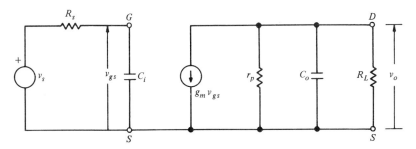

Fig. 8.15 High-frequency model of a common-source FET amplifier excited by a nonideal voltage source.

frequency. (b) For the following values of a JFET, find the mid-frequency gain and the upper break frequency.

$$g_m = 20 \times 10^{-3} \text{ mho}, \quad C_{ds} = 0.5 \text{ pF}, \quad C_{gs} = C_{gd} = 5 \text{ pF}, \quad r_p = 100 \text{ K}$$
$$(g_p = 10^{-5} \text{ mho}), \quad R_s = R_L = 1 \text{ K}; \quad G_L = 1/R_L = 10^{-3} \text{ mho}.$$

Solution

(a) Referring to Fig. 8.15, as a function of s, one has

$$V_{gs} = \frac{V_s}{1 + sR_sC_i}$$

$$V_o = \frac{-g_m V_{gs}}{g_p + G_L + sC_o} = \frac{-g_m V_s}{(1 + sR_sC_i)(g_p + G_L + sC_o)}.$$

Therefore, the voltage gain $A_{vs}(j\omega) = V_o(j\omega)/V_s(j\omega)$ is

$$A_{vs}(j\omega) = \frac{-g_m/(g_p + G_L)}{(1 + j\omega R_sC_i)[1 + j\omega C_o/(g_p + G_L)]}$$

$$= \frac{-g_m/(g_p + G_L)}{(1 + j\omega/\omega_{H1})(1 + j\omega/\omega_{H2})}, \tag{8.37}$$

where $\omega_{H1} = 1/R_sC_i$ and $\omega_{H2} = (g_p + G_L)/C_o$. In general, $\omega_{H2} \gg \omega_{H1}$; hence,

$$A_{vs}(j\omega) \approx \frac{-g_m/(g_p + G_L)}{1 + j\omega/\omega_{H1}}. \tag{8.38}$$

(b) At mid frequencies, (8.38) reduces to

$$A_{vs}(j\omega) = -g_m/(g_p + G_L) \tag{8.39}$$

or $A_{MF} = g_m/(g_p + G_L) = 20 \times 10^{-3}/(10^{-5} + 10^{-3}) \approx 20.$

Therefore, $C_i = 5 + 5(1 + 20) = 110 \text{ pF}$ and $\omega_{H1} = 1/(10^3 \times 110 \times 10^{-12}) = 9.1 \times 10^6 \text{ rad/s}$. Checking the value of ω_{H2}, one obtains

$$\omega_{H2} = (g_p + G_L)/C_o = 11 \times 10^{-4}/(5.5 \times 10^{-12}) = 200 \times 10^6 \text{ rad/s}.$$

Note that $\omega_{H2} \gg \omega_{H1}$, which was assumed in deriving (8.38).

A model of an FET at high frequencies connected as a source follower (common drain amplifier) is shown in Fig. 8.16. At node G,

$$(V_s - V_g)/R_s = sC_{gd}V_g + (V_g - V_o)sC_{gs}. \tag{8.40}$$

Making the approximation that $V_o \approx V_g$ and solving (8.40) for $A_{vs} = V_o/V_s$, one has

$$A_{vs} = 1/(1 + sR_sC_{gd}). \tag{8.41}$$

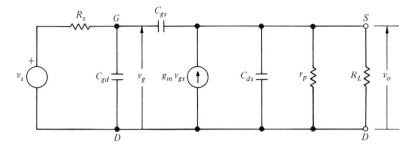

Fig. 8.16   High-frequency model of source follower.

With $s = j\omega$ and the upper cutoff frequency

$$\omega_H = 1/R_s C_{gd},\qquad(8.42)$$

expression (8.41) becomes

$$A_{vs}(j\omega) = \frac{1}{1 + j\omega/\omega_H}.\qquad(8.43)$$

The maximum voltage gain for the source follower is unity.

   With substitution of the parameters of the JFET of Example 8.6 in (8.42), the upper cutoff frequency is

$$\omega_H = 1/(10^3 \times 5 \times 10^{-12}) = 200 \times 10^6 \text{ rad/s}.$$

This value is much greater than $\omega_{H1} = 9.1 \times 10^6$ rad/s found for the common-source amplifier. The source follower, like the cathode and emitter follower circuits, is an example of circuits containing *negative feedback*. As shown in Chapter 11, negative feedback tends to increase the frequency response (bandwidth) of an amplifier.

8.5   The Junction Transistor

   The *hybrid-pi* model for small signals is the most often used model for the BJT operating at high frequencies, to approximately 100 MHz. Its parameters can be defined in terms of h parameters and measured at low frequencies. To derive the model, we shall begin by examining the hybrid model in the common-emitter configuration of Fig. 8.17A. Because small-signal transistors are characterized by a very low value of h_{re}, it is neglected in the figure. At high frequencies, it is useful to represent input resistance h_{ie} by two resistances, $r_{bb'}$ and $r_{b'e}$, where

$$h_{ie} = r_{bb'} + r_{b'e}.\qquad(8.44)$$

Point B' in Fig. 8.17A is an internal point and is not available externally.

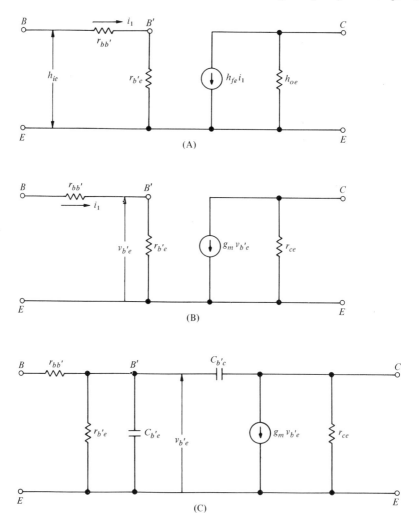

Fig. 8.17 Developing a high-frequency model for the junction transistor (BJT). (A) Hybrid model for low frequencies where h_{re} is neglected. (B) Model containing a voltage-controlled current source. (C) Complete hybrid-pi model.

Resistance $r_{bb'}$, the *base-spreading resistance*, represents the lumped ohmic resistance of the base region. Its value depends on the doping density and geometry of the device and is typically between 20 and 200 ohms. For good frequency performance, the value of $r_{bb'}$ should be small.

Base-emitter resistance $r_{b'e}$ varies inversely with emitter current. As the emitter current rises due to an increase in base current, the base recombination current increases. To accommodate the greater base current, $r_{b'e}$ must decrease. The range of $r_{b'e}$ varies from a few hundred to several thousands of ohms.

For high-frequency calculations, it is more convenient to use the voltage-controlled current source of Fig. 8.17B than the current-controlled source of Fig. 8.17A. The voltage drop $v_{b'e}$ across $r_{b'e}$ is $i_1 r_{b'e}$; therefore, $h_{fe}i_1 = h_{fe}v_{b'e}/r_{b'e} = g_m v_{b'e}$, where

$$g_m = h_{fe}/r_{b'e}. \tag{8.45}$$

In Fig. 8.17B, h_{oe}, the output admittance, has been replaced by r_{ce}; then

$$r_{ce} = 1/h_{oe}. \tag{8.46}$$

Collector resistance r_{ce} has typical values of from 20 to 100 K.

The resulting hybrid-pi model, including internal capacitances, is illustraded in Fig. 8.17C. Capacitance $C_{b'e}$ is the *diffusion* capacity, accounting for the excess minority charge stored in the base. *Space-charge*, or *transition*, capacitance $C_{b'c}$ varies inversely with approximately the square root or the cubic root of the dc collector-base voltage. Typical values for $C_{b'e}$ are from 100 to 1000 pF; $C_{b'c}$ is generally a few picofarads.

One component that is omitted from the hybrid-pi model of Fig. 8.17C is a feedback resistance between points C and B'. Because of the Early effect (base-width modulation), the value of this resistance is typically a few megohms; and because of its large value the feedback resistance generally has no appreciable effect on amplifier performance and will therefore be neglected in our analysis.

Consider a common-emitter amplifier with signal source i_s and load resistance R_L; the small-signal model of the circuit is shown in Fig. 8.18.

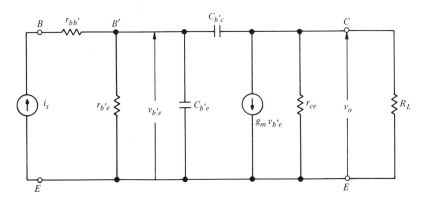

Fig. 8.18 Hybrid-pi model of a common-emitter amplifier excited by a current source.

In nodal equations, as a function of s, at nodes B' and C with respect to emitter E

$$I_s = [g_{b'e} + s(C_{b'e} + C_{b'c})]V_{b'e} - sC_{b'c}V_o \tag{8.47}$$

and $$0 = (g_m - sC_{b'c})V_{b'e} + (g_{ce} + G_L + sC_{b'c})V_o, \tag{8.48}$$

where $g_{b'e} = 1/r_{b'e}$, $g_{ce} = 1/r_{ce}$, and $G_L = 1/R_L$. Generally term $sC_{b'c}$ in (8.48) can be neglected because $sC_{b'c}(V_o - V_{b'e}) \ll$ load current for the useful high-frequency range of transistor amplifiers. Equation (8.48) may then be solved for $A_{vb'} = V_o/V_{b'e}$:

$$A_{vb'} = -g_m/(g_{ce} + G_L). \tag{8.49}$$

Substituting $V_o = V_{b'e}A_{vb'}$ in (8.47) results in

$$Y_i = I_s/V_{b'e} = g_{b'e} + s(C_{b'e} + C_{b'c}) - sC_{b'c}A_{vb'}. \tag{8.50}$$

With $g_{ce} \ll G_L$—a reasonable assumption for most practical applications—(8.49) reduces to $A_{vb'} = -g_mR_L$. Substituting this quantity in (8.50) yields

$$Y_i = g_{b'e} + s[C_{b'e} + C_{b'c}(1 + g_mR_L)] = g_{b'e} + sC_i, \tag{8.51}$$

where $$C_i = C_{b'e} + C_{b'c}(1 + g_mR_L). \tag{8.52}$$

Just as for vacuum tubes and field-effect transistors, the Miller effect arises in transistors due to feedback capacity $C_{b'c}$. From these results, a simple high-frequency model for the transistor is shown in Fig. 8.19. The use of the model is illustrated in the following example.

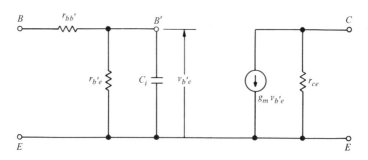

Fig. 8.19 Simplified hybrid-pi model. The reflected capacitance across output terminals C–E is neglected.

Example 8.7

A junction transistor having the following parameters is used in the common-emitter amplifier of Fig. 8.20A:

$$g_m = 0.2 \text{ mho}, \qquad r_{bb'} = 100 \text{ ohms},$$
$$C_{b'e} = 200 \text{ pF}, \qquad r_{b'e} = 1000 \text{ ohms},$$
$$C_{b'c} = 5 \text{ pF}, \qquad r_{ce} = 20 \text{ K}.$$

The values of the external components are $R_s = 900 \text{ ohms}$ and $R_L = 1000 \text{ ohms}$. Assume $R_B \gg R_s$. Stray output capacity of the amplifier is represented by capacitance $C_{os} = 10 \text{ pF}$. Neglecting R_E (assuming C_E acts as a short to all frequencies), (a) draw an equivalent circuit for the amplifier using the hybrid-pi model, (b) find the mid-frequency gain, and (c) determine the upper break frequency.

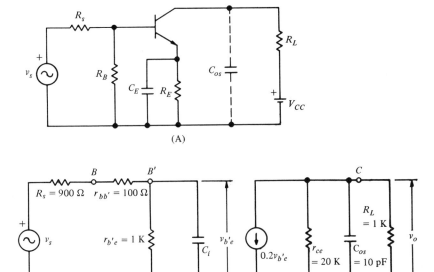

(A)

(B)

Fig. 8.20 Example 8.7. (A) Circuit. (B) Incremental model

Solution

(a) The equivalent circuit (incremental model) is given in Fig. 8.20B.
(b) At mid frequencies, capacitances C_i and C_{os} in Fig. 8.20B may be neglected. From the resulting model:

$$v_{b'e} = 1000 v_s / (900 + 100 + 1000) = 0.5 v_s.$$

At the output side, $1 \text{ K} // 20 \text{ K} \approx 1 \text{ K}$; then,

$$v_o = -g_m v_{b'e} R_L = -0.2 \times 0.5 v_s (1000) = -100 v_s.$$

Therefore,

$$A_{vs} = v_o/v_s = -100.$$

(c) From (8.52), with the effect of C_{os} neglected, $C_i = C_{b'e} + C_{b'c} \times (1 + g_m R_L) \approx 1200$ pF. The effective resistance R' at the input side of Fig. 8.20B is

$$R' = [r_{b'e}(r_{bb'} + R_s)]/(r_{bb'} + r_{b'e} + R_s) \qquad (8.53)$$

and

$$\omega_{H1} = 1/(R'C_i). \qquad (8.54)$$

The value of $R' = 500$ ohms; hence

$$\omega_{H1} = 1/(500 \times 1.2 \times 10^{-9}) = 1.67 \times 10^6 \text{ rad/s}.$$

The upper break frequency ω_{H2} due to the output circuit is

$$\omega_{H2} = 1/(R_L C_{os})$$
$$= 1/(10^3 \times 10 \times 10^{-12}) = 100 \times 10^6 \text{ rad/s}. \qquad (8.55)$$

The value of $\omega_{H2} \gg \omega_{H1}$; therefore ω_{H1} is the dominant upper break frequency.

Hybrid-Pi and Low-Frequency Parameter Relations

In this section additional expressions for the hybrid-pi parameters in terms of the low-frequency parameters will be derived. In addition to being useful in the analysis and in the design of circuits, the derivation of these relationships will point the way to the measurement of the hybrid-pi parameters at low frequencies, usually at one kilohertz.

Transconductance g_m is, by definition,

$$g_m = \left.\frac{\partial i_C}{\partial v_{B'E}}\right|_{v_{ce}=0}$$
$$= \left.\frac{\alpha_o \partial i_E}{\partial v_{B'E}}\right|_{v_{ce}=0}. \qquad (8.56a)$$

Term $\partial i_E/\partial v_{B'E} \approx 1/r_e$, where r_e is the emitter resistance. For a forward-biased base-emitter junction at room temperature, $1/r_e = |I_E|(\text{mA})/26$, where I_E is the dc emitter current. Substituting this value of $1/r_e$ for $\partial i_E/\partial v_{B'E}$ in (8.56a) and noting that the dc collector current I_C is $I_C \approx \alpha_0 I_E$ (α_0 is the value of h_{fb} at low frequencies), one obtains

$$g_m = |I_C| \text{ (mA)}/26 \text{ mhos}. \qquad (8.56b)$$

For values of temperature other than room temperature (300°K), g_m is expressed by

$$g_m = \frac{|I_C|(A)}{T(°K)/11,600} \text{ mhos.} \tag{8.56c}$$

Expressions for figures of merit that characterize transistor operation at high frequency will be now derived. Setting $R_L = 0$, that is, shorting the collector to the emitter (see Fig. 8.20B), one obtains $C_i = C_{b'e} + C_{b'c}$. Therefore,

$$V_{b'e} = \frac{I_s}{1/r_{b'e} + j\omega(C_{b'e} + C_{b'c})}$$

and

$$I_c = g_m V_{b'e} = \frac{g_m I_s}{1/r_{b'e} + j\omega(C_{b'e} + C_{b'c})}.$$

Defining the short-circuit current gain as $A_{is}(j\omega)$, one obtains

$$A_{is}(j\omega) = \frac{I_c}{I_s} = \frac{g_m r_{b'e}}{1 + j\omega(C_{b'e} + C_{b'c})r_{b'e}}. \tag{8.57}$$

The frequency f_β, where the magnitude of the short-circuit current gain is 0.707 of its mid-frequency value, that is $0.707|A_{is}(j\omega)|$, is from (8.57)

$$f_\beta = \frac{1}{2\pi r_{b'e}(C_{b'e} + C_{b'c})}. \tag{8.58}$$

Frequency f_β, called the *short-circuit beta cutoff frequency*, is a function of the transistor capacitances and $r_{b'e}$. It therefore serves as a figure of merit for characterizing a transistor at high frequencies. Substitution of (8.45) for $r_{b'e}$ and (8.58) for f_β in (8.57) yields

$$A_{is}(j\omega) = \frac{h_{fe}}{1 + jf/f_\beta} = \frac{h_{fe}}{1 + j\omega/\omega_\beta}, \tag{8.59}$$

where

$$\omega_\beta = \frac{1}{r_{b'e}(C_{b'e} + C_{b'c})} \text{ (rad/s).}$$

Another figure of merit used to characterize the transistor at high frequencies is f_T, the frequency at which the magnitude of the short-circuit current gain $|A_{is}(j\omega)|$ is unity. Letting $A_{is}(j\omega) = 1$ and $f = f_T$ in (8.59) results in

$$(f_T/f)^2 = h_{fe}^2 - 1.$$

The value of $h_{fe} \gg 1$; hence,

$$f_T \approx h_{fe} f_\beta. \tag{8.60}$$

Because f_T is a product of the short-circuit current gain h_{fe} and cutoff frequency f_β, f_T is referred to as the *short-circuit gain-bandwidth product.* Substituting (8.58) in (8.60), one obtains

$$f_T = \frac{g_m}{2\pi(C_{b'e} + C_{b'c})}. \qquad (8.61)$$

If f_T is known, the value of $C_{b'e}$ may be determined from (8.61) as

$$C_{b'e} \approx g_m/(2\pi f_T), \qquad (8.62)$$

since $C_{b'c} \ll C_{b'e}$. The value of $C_{b'c}$ can be obtained from a measurement of the output capacity C_{ob} of the transistor in the common-base configuration:

$$C_{b'c} \approx C_{ob}. \qquad (8.63)$$

The CB Configuration at High Frequencies

The generalized-y matrix can be used to derive new hybrid parameters, or the basic hybrid-pi model of Fig. 8.17C can be reoriented to produce either the common-base or common-collector (emitter follower) configuration. We shall adopt the latter approach. The hybrid-pi model for a transistor in the common-base configuration is given in Fig. 8.21. (The common-collector circuit is considered in Chapter 9.) The collector-base output circuit is normally terminated in a resistance value of a few kilohms; therefore, $C_{b'c}$ is in parallel with $(R_L + r_{bb'})$, and $r_{b'e}$ is shunted by $C_{b'e}$. At high frequencies, the effective impedance of the two parallel resistance-capacitance combinations will be considerably less than r_{ce}. For this reason, r_{ce} is neglected in our analysis.

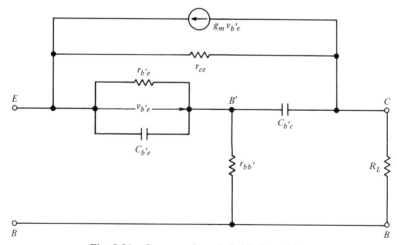

Fig. 8.21   Common-base hybrid-pi model.

If current source $g_m v_{b'e}$ is replaced by two current sources of the same value in series (the current-source transformation theorem), Fig. 8.21 reduces to that of Fig. 8.22. By applying the substitution theorem, $g_m v_{b'e}$ across points E and B' may be replaced by a conductance g_m to yield $g_m + g_{b'e} \approx g_m$ (see Fig. 8.23). Analysis of the model of Fig. 8.23 for the short-circuit current gain $A_{is}(j\omega)$ yields

$$A_{is}(j\omega) \simeq -1(1 + j\omega f/f_\alpha), \tag{8.64}$$

where

$$f_\alpha = g_m/(2\pi C_{b'e}) \tag{8.65}$$

is the *short-circuit alpha-cutoff* frequency of the transistor in the common-base configuration. Because $C_{b'e} + C_{b'c} \approx C_{b'e}$, $f_\alpha \approx f_T$ and therefore $f_\alpha \approx h_{fe} f_\beta$.

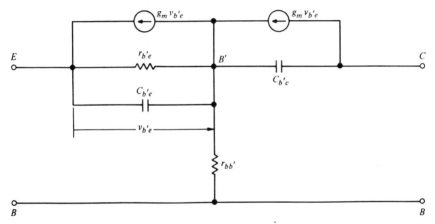

Fig. 8.22 Using the current-source transformation theorem and neglecting r_{ce} in simplifying the common-base model at high frequencies.

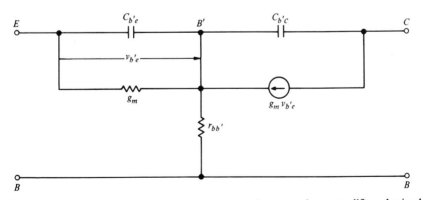

Fig. 8.23 Final simplified model of the common-base transistor amplifier obtained by applying the substitution theorem.

8.6 Scattering (S) Parameters*

Transistors are available that operate at frequencies in the gigahertz region. At these frequencies it is not possible to characterize transistors, with good accuracy, by either hybrid, impedance, or admittance parameters. For example, the short-circuit parameter, h_{21}, is defined as

$$h_{21} = \frac{i_2}{i_1}\bigg|_{v_2=0}.$$

Operating at frequencies greater than 100 MHz, it is not possible to obtain a short circuit, that is to set $v_2 = 0$ for the transistor; the "short" behaves like an inductance.

There is also a problem in making open-circuit measurements. Consider h_{22}, defined as

$$h_{22} = \frac{i_2}{v_2}\bigg|_{i_1=0}.$$

An "open circuit" obtained by setting $i_1 = 0$ acts as a capacitance at the higher frequencies.

To overcome these difficulties, *scattering (S) parameters* are used to characterize transistors at frequencies greater than 100 MHz. A transistor represented as a four-terminal network is shown in Fig. 8.24. Quantities a_1 and a_2 are *incident* voltage waves; b_1 and b_2 are *reflected* voltage waves.

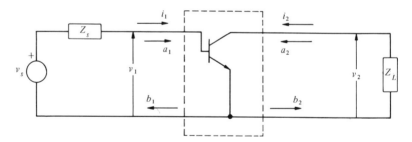

Fig. 8.24 Incident and reflected waves in a four-terminal network.

Equations relating the incident and reflected waves can be written. Letting a_1 and a_2 be the independent variables, one obtains

$$b_1 = s_{11}a_1 + s_{12}a_2 \tag{8.66a}$$

$$b_2 = s_{21}a_1 + s_{22}a_2, \tag{8.66b}$$

* This section assumes that the student has been exposed to basic transmission line theory.

where s_{11}, s_{12}, s_{21}, and s_{22} are the scattering parameters. In matrix form,

$$[S] = \begin{bmatrix} s_{11} & s_{12} \\ s_{21} & s_{22} \end{bmatrix}. \tag{8.67}$$

The a and b variables are related to the terminal voltages and currents by equations having a form similar to that found for equations describing transmission lines. These are

$$a_1 = \frac{1}{2\sqrt{R_0}}(v_1 + R_0 i_1), \tag{8.68a}$$

$$a_2 = \frac{1}{2\sqrt{R_0}}(v_2 + R_0 i_2), \tag{8.68b}$$

$$b_1 = \frac{1}{2\sqrt{R_0}}(v_1 - R_0 i_1), \tag{8.68c}$$

$$b_2 = \frac{1}{2\sqrt{R_0}}(v_2 - R_0 i_2), \tag{8.68d}$$

where R_0 is the *characteristic*, or *reference*, impedance.

From (8.66a, b) the scattering parameters may be defined in terms of the incident and reflected waves:

$$s_{11} = \frac{b_1}{a_1}\bigg|_{a_2=0} = \text{input reflection coefficient}, \tag{8.69a}$$

$$s_{12} = \frac{b_1}{a_2}\bigg|_{a_1=0} = \text{reverse transmission gain}, \tag{8.69b}$$

$$s_{21} = \frac{b_2}{a_1}\bigg|_{a_2=0} = \text{forward transmission gain}, \tag{8.69c}$$

$$s_{22} = \frac{b_2}{a_2}\bigg|_{a_1=0} = \text{output reflection coefficient}. \tag{8.69d}$$

To set $a_2 = 0$, the load impedance Z_L is made equal to the reference impedance R_0; for $a_1 = 0$, $Z_S = R_0$.

Representative s-parameter values for a Texas Instrument 2N3571 transistor in the common-emitter configuration, measured at 100 MHz and 1000 MHz, are given in Table 8.1. The scattering parameters are in general complex quantities. Note that the forward gain s_{21} dropped from $9.0\underline{/130°}$ at 100 MHz to $1.36\underline{/35°}$ at 1000 MHz. Measuring techniques, conversion of *s* to *y*, *h*, and *z* parameters, and design procedures using *s* parameters are described in the literature.*

Table 8.1   Scattering Parameters for a TI-2N2571 Transistor in the CE Configuration (25°C)

Test frequency	100 MHz	1000 MHz
s_{11}	$0.62\underline{/-44°}$	$0.196\underline{/175°}$
s_{12}	$0.0115\underline{/75°}$	$0.165\underline{/103°}$
s_{21}	$9.0\underline{/130°}$	$1.36\underline{/35°}$
s_{22}	$0.955\underline{/-6°}$	$0.850\underline{/-53°}$

8.7   Summary

After reviewing the frequency response of simple passive networks and Bode diagrams, methods of analysis for determining the high-frequency performance of currently used active devices in small-signal operation were considered. High-frequency models for the vacuum tube, the field-effect transistor, and the junction transistor were analyzed; for each device the most useful configurations were examined. The models and methods of analysis were similar for all devices; for the vacuum tube and field-effect transistor they were identical. It is expected that future three-terminal active devices will be amenable to the same kinds of analyses. Scattering parameters, used to characterize transistors generally operating at frequencies greater than 100 MHz, were introduced.

References

CLOSE, C. M., *The Analysis of Linear Circuits*, Harcourt Brace Jovanovich, New York, 1966.

Application Note 95, "S-Parameters...Circuit analysis and design," published by Hewlett-Packard Co., Palo Alto, California, 1968.

SEARLE, C. L., et al., *Elementary Circuit Properties of Transistors*, Vol. 3 of the SEEC series, Wiley, New York, 1964.

* An excellent collection of papers is contained in Application Note 95, "S-Parameters...Circuit analysis and design," by Hewlett-Packard Co., Palo Alto, California, 1968.

Problems

8.1 Derive the transfer functions for the networks of Fig. P8.1.

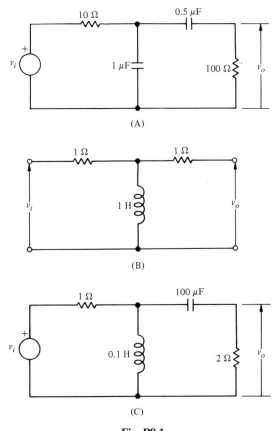

Fig. P8.1

8.2 Plot the Bode (amplitude and phase) response curves for the networks of Fig. P8.1.

8.3 In the small-signal model of Fig. 8.10, assume that $C_{gk} = 4\,\text{pF}$, $C_{pk} = 5\,\text{pF}, C_{gp} = 0, g_p = 10^{-6}\,\text{mho}, R_L = 50\,\text{K, and } g_m = 5\,\text{mmhos}$. If the current source is replaced by a voltage source v_s in series with a 1-K resistance, calculate (a) the voltage gain $A_{vs}(j\omega)$ at mid and high frequencies and (b) the dominant upper break frequency.

8.4 Writing nodal equations, repeat Prob. 8.3 for $C_{gp} = 0.5 \times 10^{-3}\,\text{pF}$. Compare results.

8.5 Repeat Prob. 8.4 by making direct use of the Miller effect in the calculations. Are there any difference in the results?

8.6 For the FET amplifier of Fig. P8.6, determine (a) $A_{vs}(j\omega)$ and (b) the upper break frequency assuming that R_S is negligible. The parameters of the FET are $g_m = 20$ mmhos, $r_p = 100$ K, $C_{ds} = 1$ pF, and $C_{gs} = C_{dg} = 4$ pF.

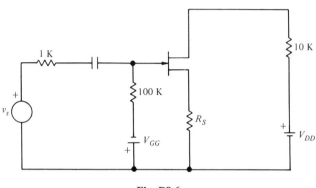

Fig. P8.6

8.7 Repeat Prob. 8.6 for a load resistance of 1 K. Compare results.

8.8 A technique for increasing the bandwidth of an amplifier is to place an inductance L in series with the load resistance R_L, as shown in Fig. P8.8. This method is referred to as *shunt compensation.* (a) Derive an expression for voltage gain as a function of frequency. (b) Using the values given in Prob. 8.6, examine the amplitude response for $L = 1$ μH, 10 μH, and 100 μH. Compare results.

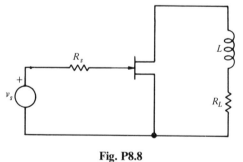

Fig. P8.8

8.9 For the values given in Example 8.7, calculate the mid-frequency gain and upper break frequency for $R_s = 0$; (b) $R_s = 10$ K; and (c) $R_s = 100$ K. Compare results.

8.10 Referring to Fig. P8.10, assume that capacitors C_1 and C_2 act as shorts to the signal. The transistor has the following parameters: $r_{bb'} =$

50 ohms, $r_{b'e} = 400$ ohms, $g_m = 0.2$ mho, $C_{b'c} = 5\,\text{pF}$, $C_{b'e} = 100\,\text{pF}$, and r_{ce} is much greater than the load resistance. Determine (a) the mid-frequency voltage gain and (b) the upper break frequency.

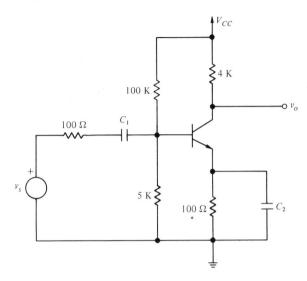

Fig. P8.10

8.11 Repeat Prob. 8.10 assuming that the load resistance is 1 K. Compare results.

8.12 A cascaded transistor amplifier stage with shunt compensation may be represented by the model of Fig. P8.12. (a) Derive an expression for current gain i_2/i_1. (b) How should the value of L be specified in terms of the other circuit parameters for the critically-damped case?

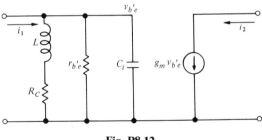

Fig. P8.12

8.13 Another method for achieving wide bandwidth is called *emitter degeneration*. In this procedure the emitter resistance is not perfectly bypassed for high frequencies. Referring to Fig. 8.20A and assuming that C_E affects the amplifier response at high frequencies, (a) derive an expression for voltage gain. (b) What happens to the gain for $C_E = 0$ and $C_E = \infty$? Neglect $C_{b'e}$, C_{os}, and make other simplifications.

8.14 Verify equations (a) (8.58); (b) (8.60); and (c) (8.65).

8.15 For a transistor $f_T = 400$ MHz, $C_{b'e} = 150$ pF, $I_C = 10$ mA, and $h_{fe} = 100$. Calculate the values of g_m, $r_{b'e}$, $C_{b'c}$, f_α, and f_β.

8.16 What is the half-power frequency if the transistor of Prob. 8.15 is terminated by a 20-K load resistance? How does this compare with the value of f_β? Assume that $r_{ce} \gg 20$ K and $r_{bb'} = 0$.

8.17 Setting the reference impedance to unity, derive expressions for the y parameters in terms of the s parameters.

Cascading Amplifier Stages

In Chapter 8 models for solid-state and vacuum tube amplifiers operating at high frequencies were developed, and the frequency response of a single-stage amplifier was studied. The gain obtained from a single-stage voltage or current amplifier is, however, not sufficient for many applications. For this reason it is seldom that an amplifier has only one stage; it is common practice to connect a number of stages in cascade so that the total required gain is realized.

In this chapter the gain and frequency response of cascaded amplifiers will be studied and analyzed. The analysis is simplified if the loading effect of stages on each other can be considered negligible. As considered in Chapter 3, if $G_1, G_2, \ldots, G_n$ represent the gain of each stage without loading, the total amplification G for n stages in cascade is

$$G = G_1 \times G_2 \times G_3 \times \cdots \times G_n. \tag{9.1}$$

The modeling of an amplifier satisfying (9.1) is quite simple, because loading effects are neglected, and each stage is treated separately. Generally, all stages except the first and the last have the same transfer function. The input stage might differ from the remaining stages because of the nature of the input source impedance Z_s; the output stage could be different because of the load impedance Z_L.

If the loading effect of each stage is not negligible, (9.1) no longer applies. Because of loading, the transfer function of the amplifier must be calculated from the model of the entire amplifier rather than on a single-stage basis and thus involves lengthy calculations.

Cascading amplifier stages may be accomplished in different ways. If the stages are coupled directly, we obtain *direct-coupled*, or dc amplifiers. In the case of ac amplifiers, however, the dc portion of the output of each stage is eliminated. One method of accomplishing this is to use a capacitor in series with the output of each stage. An amplifier using this interconnection is called an *RC-coupled* amplifier. A third method, *transformer coupling*, will be considered in Chapter 10, Power Amplifiers.

9.1   Cascaded Stages with Negligible Loading

As a first example, consider the two-stage transistor amplifier of Fig. 9.1: the output of a common-emitter stage feeds into an emitter follower. Because the input impedance of an emitter follower is generally high, the loading effect may be considered negligible. It should be noted that the input impedance of the emitter follower also includes the bias resistance R'_1.

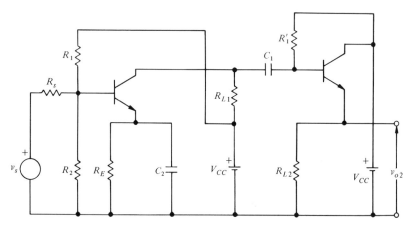

Fig. 9.1   Two-stage cascaded amplifier with an emitter follower output stage.

With the assumption of negligible loading, the high-frequency model for the first stage is shown in Fig. 9.2; this figure is the same as Fig. 8.20 with capacitance C_{os} assumed negligible and bias resistance $R_B = R_1 // R_2$ included.

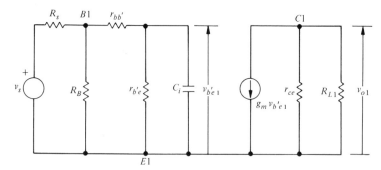

Fig. 9.2   High-frequency model for the first transistor stage of Fig. 9.1.

From the figure,

$$v_{o1} = -g_m v_{b'e1}[r_{ce}R_{L1}/(r_{ce} + R_{L1})] \tag{9.2}$$

With

$$r_{bb'} \ll \left| r_{b'e} \middle/\!\middle/ \frac{1}{j\omega C_i} \right| \text{ assumed,}$$

$$V_{b'e1} = V_s Z/(R_s + Z), \tag{9.3}$$

where

$$Z = R_T/(1 + j\omega C_i R_T)$$

and

$$R_T = R_B/\!/r_{b'e}.$$

Therefore,

$$A_{v1} = V_{o1}/V_s = -g_m Z r_{ce} R_{L1}/(R_s + Z)(R_{L1} + r_{ce}). \tag{9.4}$$

Expression (9.4) is the voltage gain of the first stage.

With the loading effect of the second stage assumed to be negligible, (9.4) is multiplied by the gain of the second stage to obtain the overall gain of the amplifier. A high-frequency model for the emitter follower is given in Fig. 9.3.

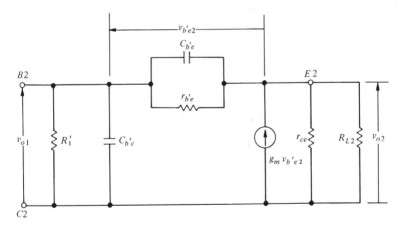

Fig. 9.3 High-frequency model for the emitter follower of Fig. 9.1.

Because $v_{b'e2} = v_{o1} - v_{o2}$, by the substitution theorem, Fig. 9.3 is replaced by Fig. 9.4. From Fig. 9.4 one may write the following expressions:

$$V_{o2} = \frac{g_m V_{o1} + (V_{o1} - V_{o2})(j\omega C_{b'e} + g_{b'e})}{g_m + h_{oe} + G_{L2}}, \tag{9.5}$$

where $h_{oe} = 1/r_{ce}$, $G_{L2} = 1/R_{L2}$, and $g_{b'e} = 1/r_{b'e}$.

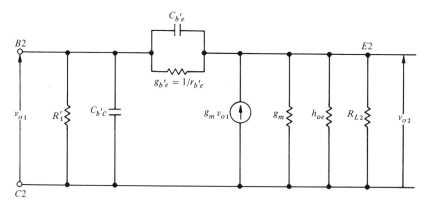

Fig. 9.4 A simplification of Fig. 9.3 obtained with the aid of the substitution theorem.

Solving (9.5) for $A_{v2} = V_{o2}/V_{o1}$, one obtains

$$A_{v2} = \frac{g_m + g_{b'e} + j\omega C_{b'e}}{g_m + h_{oe} + G_{L2} + g_{b'e} + j\omega C_{b'e}}. \tag{9.6}$$

Expression (9.6) may be written as

$$A_{v2} = A_{MF2}\left(\frac{1 + j\omega/\omega_1}{1 + j\omega/\omega_2}\right), \tag{9.7}$$

where

$$A_{MF2} = \frac{g_m + g_{b'e}}{g_m + h_{oe} + G_{L2} + g_{b'e}}$$

is the mid-frequency gain of the emitter follower, and

$$\omega_1 = \frac{g_m + g_{b'e}}{C_{b'e}},$$

$$\omega_2 = \frac{g_m + h_{oe} + G_{L2} + g_{b'e}}{C_{b'e}}.$$

Logarithmic plots of the amplitude and the phase of (9.7) are shown in Fig. 9.5. Note that A_{MF2} is also equal to ω_1/ω_2 and $\omega_2 > \omega_1$.

The total voltage gain is obtained by multiplying expressions (9.4) and (9.7). Before we do this, however, (9.4) will be expressed in a simpler form. Substituting the expression for Z in (9.4) yields

$$A_{v1} = \frac{-g_m R_T r_{ce} R_{L1}}{R_s(R_{L1} + r_{ce})(1 + j\omega C_i R_T) + R_T(R_{L1} + r_{ce})},$$

or

$$A_{v1} = A_{MF1}/(1 + j\omega/\omega_3),$$

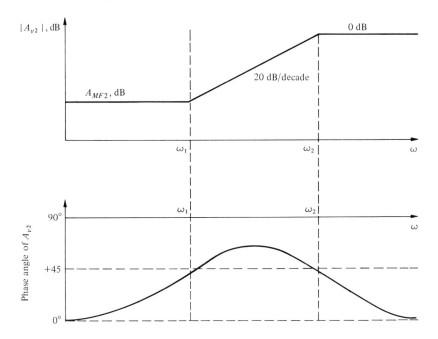

Fig. 9.5. Logarithmic plots of (9.7).

where $A_{MF1} = -g_m r_{ce} R_T R_{L1}/(R_s + R_T)(R_{L1} + r_{ce})$ (9.8)

and $\omega_3 = (R_T + R_s)/C_i R_T R_s.$

The voltage gain of the entire amplifier is therefore equal to

$$A_{vs} = \frac{V_{o2}}{V_s} = \frac{A_{MF}(1 + j\omega/\omega_1)}{(1 + j\omega/\omega_3)(1 + j\omega/\omega_2)},$$ (9.9)

where $A_{MF} = A_{MF1}A_{MF2}$. Logarithmic plots of the amplitude and the phase of (9.9) are shown in Fig. 9.6.

If the loading effect of the second stage on the first stage is not negligible, the input impedance of the second stage must be calculated first, becoming part of the load of the first stage.

Example 9.1

In Fig. 9.1, each transistor has the following parameters:

$$h_{fe} = 50, \qquad\qquad r_{bb'} = 40 \text{ ohms},$$

$$r_{b'e} = 500 \text{ ohms}, \qquad C_{b'c} = 10 \text{ pF},$$

$$r_{ce} \approx \infty, \qquad\qquad C_{b'e} = 100 \text{ pF}.$$

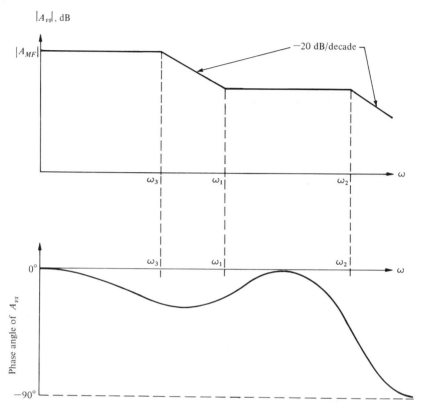

Fig. 9.6 Complete logarithmic plots (amplitude and phase) for the two-stage amplifier of Fig. 9.1.

With the following source, load, and bias resistances:

$$R_1 = 200 \text{ K}, \qquad R_2 = 7 \text{ K}, \qquad R_{L1} = 10 \text{ K},$$
$$R_s = 1 \text{ K}, \qquad R_{L2} = 10 \text{ K}, \qquad R'_1 = 100 \text{ K},$$

(a) derive an expression for the voltage gain at high frequency. (b) Draw the logarithmic plots of voltage gain and phase response at high frequencies.

Solution

(a) Because we are analyzing the circuit at high frequencies, the coupling and bypass capacitors act as shorts. Using (9.8) we calculate the response of the first stage at high frequencies. The hybrid-pi parameters are first calculated:

$$g_m = h_{fe}/r_{b'e} = 50/500 = 100 \text{ millimhos},$$

$$g_{b'e} = 1/500 = 2 \text{ millimhos,}$$

$$R_B = R_1 R_2/(R_1 + R_L) = 7 \times 200/207 = 6.75 \text{ K,}$$

$$R_T = \frac{0.5 \times 6.75}{7.25} \approx 0.46 \text{ K,}$$

$$g_m R_L = 1000,$$

$$C_i \approx C_{b'e} + C_{b'c} g_m R_L = 100 + 10 \times 1000 \approx 10^4 \text{ pF.}$$

With $r_{ce} \approx \infty$,

$$A_{MF1} = -\frac{g_m R_T R_{L1}}{R_T + R_s}$$

$$= -\frac{0.1 \times 10^4 \times 460}{10^3 + 0.46 \times 10^3} = -315,$$

$$\omega_3 = \frac{R_T + R_s}{C_i R_T R_s} = \frac{1.46}{10^{-8} \times 0.46 \times 10^3} \approx 3.17 \times 10^5 \text{ rad/s.}$$

Then, for the first stage,

$$A_{v1} = \frac{-315}{1 + j\omega/(3.17 \times 10^5)}.$$

For the second stage, using (9.7) and substituting the given values in the expressions, one obtains

$$A_{MF2} \approx 1, \qquad \omega_1 = 10^9 \text{ rad/s,} \quad \text{and} \quad \omega_2 \approx 10^9 \text{ rad/s.}$$

Because $10^9 \gg 3.17 \times 10^5$, we see that the second stage approximates a flat response. In the case of the emitter follower, a flat response is possible, but the voltage gain is less than unity. The transfer function of the amplifier, for all practical purposes, therefore is

$$A_{vs} = \frac{-315}{1 + j\omega/(3.17 \times 10^5)}.$$

(b) Plots of voltage gain and frequency response have the same form as Fig. 8.3.

Cascaded RC-Coupled Pentode Amplifier

A high-frequency model of a two-stage RC-coupled pentode amplifier is shown in Fig. 9.7. In the case of pentode amplifiers the loading effect of stages is negligible; thus, the voltage gain of each stage can be calculated separately.

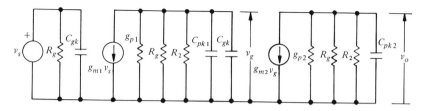

Fig. 9.7 High-frequency model of a two-stage pentode amplifier.

For the first stage, we have

$$V_g = -g_{m1}V_s/(g_{p1} + G_L + j\omega C_T),$$

where
$$C_T = C_{pk1} + C_{gk}$$

and
$$R_L = R_2//R_g; \qquad G_L = 1/R_L.$$

Then,

$$A_{v1} = V_g/V_s = -g_{m1}/(g_{p1} + G_L + j\omega C_T) = A_{MF1}/(1 + j\omega/\omega_1), \qquad (9.10)$$

where
$$A_{MF1} = -g_{m1}/(g_{p1} + G_L)$$

and
$$\omega_1 = (g_{p1} + G_L)/C_T.$$

For the second stage, similar relations may be written:

$$V_o = \frac{-g_{m2}V_g/(g_{p2} + G_L)}{1 + j\omega C_{pk2}/(g_{p2} + G_L)}.$$

Therefore,

$$A_{v2} = A_{MF2}/(1 + j\omega/\omega_2), \qquad (9.11)$$

where
$$A_{MF2} = -g_{m2}/(g_{p2} + G_L)$$

and
$$\omega_2 = (g_{p2} + G_L)/C_{pk2}.$$

The high-frequency expression for the voltage gain of the amplifier is the product of (9.10) and (9.11).

$$A_{vs} = \frac{V_o}{V_s} = \frac{A_{mF}}{(1 + j\omega/\omega_1)(1 + j\omega/\omega_2)}, \qquad (9.12)$$

where
$$A_{MF} = A_{MF1}A_{MF2}.$$

Let us draw a low-frequency model for the amplifier. In this model we assume that the input coupling and cathode bypass capacitors act as short circuits. Shunting capacitances C_T and C_{pk} of the high-frequency model act as open circuits at low frequencies. The corresponding low-frequency model therefore obtained is shown in Fig. 9.8. Expressions for the voltage gains of the first and second stages are similar, the differences being in the values of load and tube parameters.

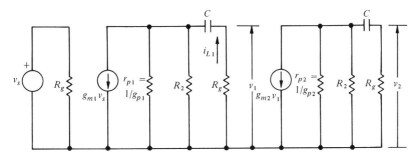

Fig. 9.8 Low-frequency model of two-stage amplifier.

For the first stage of Fig. 9.8, current I_{L1} is

$$I_{L1} = g_{m1} V_s R'_L/(R'_L + R_g + 1/j\omega C)$$

$$= R'_L g_{m1} j\omega C V_s/[1 + j\omega C(R'_L + R_g)],$$

where
$$R'_L = r_{p1}//R_2.$$

Then,

$$A_{v1} = V_1/V_s = -R'_L R_g g_{m1} j\omega C/[1 + j\omega C(R'_L + R_g)]. \qquad (9.13)$$

Expression (9.13) is of the form

$$A_{v1} = (A_{MF1} j\omega/\omega_3)/(1 + j\omega/\omega_3), \qquad (9.14)$$

where
$$\omega_3 = 1/C(R'_L + R_g).$$

The expression for A_{MF1} is the same as that obtained for the high-frequency model. On the assumption that both tubes as well as their loads and coupling impedances are the same, the overall voltage gain for the amplifier at low frequency becomes

$$A_{vs} = V_2/V_s = [A^2_{MF1}(j\omega/\omega_3)^2]/(1 + j\omega/\omega_3)^2. \qquad (9.15)$$

Logarithmic plots of voltage gain over the band of frequencies from 0 to ∞ are shown in Fig. 9.9.

A figure of merit for the pentode amplifier under discussion is the gain-bandwidth product ω_b. The gain-bandwidth product for one stage of amplification is

$$\omega_b = -A_{MF1}\omega_1 = \left(\frac{g_{m1}}{g_{p1} + G_L}\right)\left(\frac{g_{p1} + G_L}{C_T}\right) = \frac{g_{m1}}{C_T}.$$

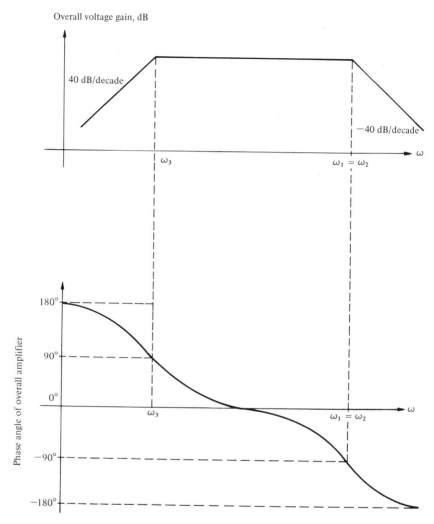

Fig. 9.9   Overall (low- and high-frequency) response of a pentode amplifier.

The gain-bandwidth product is a function of the tube characteristics and is independent of the external circuit. If the gain is increased (decreased) by variation in the output or input elements, the bandwidth will decrease (increase). The gain of the amplifier may be increased by decreasing G_L.

Cascaded Field-Effect Transistor (FET) Amplifiers

A cascaded field-effect transistor amplifier is shown in Fig. 9.10. The high-frequency performance of this amplifier is analyzed in a manner similar

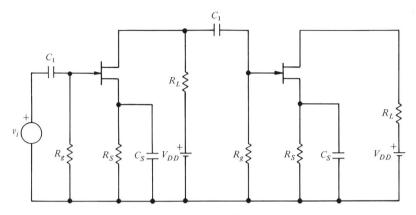

Fig. 9.10 Cascaded FET amplifier.

to that of the pentode amplifier discussed in the previous section. A simplified high-frequency model developed in Chapter 8 (Fig. 8.14) may be drawn for each FET. The low-frequency analysis, however, is more involved and is the subject of the following discussion. Because the input impedance of the FET is very large, the loading effect is neglected. Figure 9.11 shows the low-frequency model for the amplifier of Fig. 9.10. Assuming $i_{g1} \ll i_{d1}$, from Fig. 9.11 one obtains

$$I_{d1} = \mu V_{g1}/(r_p + Z_S + R_L),$$

where

$$Z_S = R_S/(1 + sR_SC_S).$$

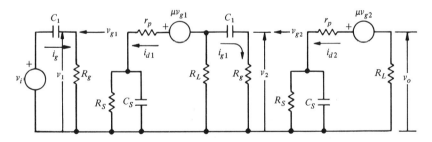

Fig. 9.11 Low-frequency model for the FET amplifier.

Also,

$$V_2 = \frac{-\mu V_{g1}R_LR_g}{(r_p + R_L + Z_S)(1/sC_1 + R_g)},$$

$$V_{g2} = \frac{-\mu V_{g1}R_LR_g}{(r_p + R_L + Z_S)(1/sC_1 + R_g)} - Z_SI_{d2},$$

or

$$V_{g2} = \frac{-\mu V_{g1} R_L R_g}{(r_p + R_L + Z_S)(1/sC_1 + R_g)} + \frac{R_S V_0}{R_L(1 + sR_S C_S)} \tag{9.16}$$

and

$$V_o = \frac{-\mu V_{g2} R_L}{r_p + R_L + Z_S}. \tag{9.17}$$

Combining (9.16) and (9.17), we obtain the voltage gain

$$A'_v = \frac{V_o}{V_{g1}} = \frac{(\mu R_L)^2 R_g(1 + sR_S C_S)^2 sC_1}{[(r_p + R_L)(1 + sR_S C_S) + R_S][1 + sR_g C_1]} . \tag{9.18}$$
$$\times [(r_p + R_L)(1 + sR_S C_S) + (1 + \mu)R_S]$$

Also,

$$V_{g1} = V_1 - [\mu V_{g1} Z_S/(r_p + Z_S + R_L)], \tag{9.19}$$

where

$$V_1 = V_i sR_g C_1/(1 + sR_g C_1). \tag{9.20}$$

Combining (9.18), (9.19), and (9.20) yields the overall voltage gain $A_v = V_o/V_i$ for a two-stage FET amplifier:

$$A_v = \frac{(\mu R_L)^2 R_g^2 (sC_1)^2 (1 + sR_S C_S)^2}{(1 + sR_g C_1)^2 [(r_p + R_L)(1 + sR_S C_S) + (1 + \mu)R_S]^2}. \tag{9.21}$$

Equation (9.21) is of the form:

$$A_v = \frac{K^2 (j\omega/\omega_1)^2 (1 + j\omega/\omega_2)^2}{(1 + j\omega/\omega_1)^2 (1 + j\omega/\omega_3)^2}, \tag{9.22}$$

where $K = \dfrac{\mu R_L}{(1 + \mu)R_S + r_p + R_L}$, $\omega_1 = \dfrac{1}{R_g C_1}$, $\omega_2 = \dfrac{1}{R_S C_S}$,

and

$$\omega_3 = \frac{(1 + \mu)R_S + r_p + R_L}{R_S C_S(r_p + R_L)}.$$

Equation (9.21) shows that at low frequencies the gain of the amplifier decreases. The break frequencies depend on the characteristics of the FET and the circuit parameters. The above is true for any amplifier, regardless of the type of active device used in the circuit. As we have seen, the gain also drops at very high frequencies. The useful range of operation of an amplifier is between the low- and high-frequency breakpoints.

9.2   RC-Coupled Common Emitter Stages with Loading

Consider the two-stage common-emitter amplifier of Fig. 9.12. It is desired to calculate the high-frequency incremental current gain $A_i = I_3/I_s$.

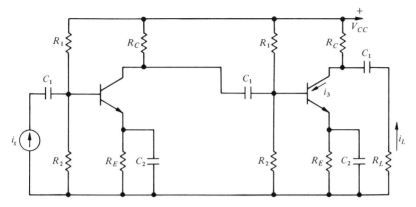

Fig. 9.12   Two-stage *RC*-coupled transistor amplifier.

A high-frequency model of the circuit is given in Fig. 9.13. In this model, the parameters are defined as

$$R_B = R_1//R_2;$$

$$R_{t1} = R_B//r_{b'e}; \quad G_{t1} = 1/R_{t1};$$

$$R_{t2} = R_B//r_{b'e}//R_C; \quad G_{t2} = 1/R_{t2};$$

$$R_{t3} = R_C//R_L; \quad G_{t3} = 1/R_{t3};$$

$$r_{bb'} \approx 0;$$

$$r_{ce} \approx \infty.$$

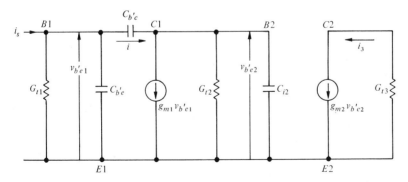

Fig. 9.13   Simplified high-frequency model for the two-stage transistor amplifier.

In the analysis we shall let $g_{m1} = g_{m2} = g_m$. The Miller effect on the output stage is similar to that found for the transistor in Chapter 8, relation (8.57).

For the first stage, because of the capacitor load, the Miller effect becomes more complicated and is calculated below. From Fig. 9.13,

$$I = j\omega C_{b'c}(V_{b'e1} - V_{b'e2}). \tag{9.23}$$

Neglecting I with respect to $g_m V_{b'e2}$, one obtains

$$V_{b'e2} = -g_m R_{t2} V_{b'e1}/(1 + j\omega C_{i2} R_{t2}).$$

The voltage gain of the first stage is

$$A_{v1} = V_{b'e2}/V_{b'e1} = -g_m R_{t2}/(1 + j\omega/\omega_2), \tag{9.24}$$

where

$$\omega_2 = 1/(R_{t2}C_{i2})$$

and

$$C_{i2} = C_{b'e} + g_m R_{t3} C_{b'c}.$$

From (9.23) and (9.24), one obtains

$$I = j\omega C_{b'c}\left(1 + \frac{g_m R_{t2}}{1 + j\omega/\omega_2}\right) V_{b'e1} \tag{9.25}$$

Equation (9.25) shows that capacitor $C_{b'c}$ of Fig. 9.13 may be replaced at the input by $C_{b'c}$ in parallel with a series resistance R and a capacitance C (see Fig. 9.14), considered in Chapter 8. The impedance value Z_2 of the series resistance and capacitance is

$$Z_2 = (1/j\omega C_{b'c}g_m R_{t2}) + (1/C_{b'c}g_m R_{t2}\omega_2).$$

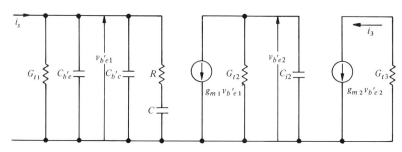

Fig. 9.14 Modification of Fig. 9.13.

In Fig. 9.14 the value of R is generally negligible with respect to $1/j\omega C$. With this assumption, the model of Fig. 9.14 reduces to that of Fig. 9.15. From the circuit, the expression for the current gain is

$$I_3 = g_m V_{b'e2},$$

$$V_{b'e2} = -g_m V_{b'e1}[R_{t2}/(1 + j\omega R_{t2}C_{i2})],$$

$$V_{b'e1} = I_s R_{t1}/(1 + j\omega R_{t1}C_{i1}),$$

$$C_{i1} = C_{b'e} + C_{b'c} + C,$$

where
$$C = g_m R_{t2} C_{b'c}.$$

Then,

$$A_i = -g_m^2 R_{t1} R_{t2}/(1 + j\omega/\omega_{H1})(1 + j\omega/\omega_{H2}), \quad (9.26a)$$

where
$$\omega_{H1} = 1/(R_{t1}C_{i1}) \quad \text{and} \quad \omega_{H2} = 1/(R_{t2}C_{i2}). \quad (9.26b)$$

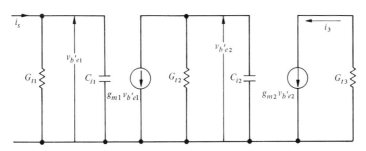

Fig. 9.15 Final simplified model of transistor amplifier.

Let us now consider the low-frequency response of the circuit of Fig. 9.12. The corresponding low-frequency model is given in Fig. 9.16 where the reduction theorem was applied to reflect R_E and C_2 across the input. Because we have both coupling and shunting capacitances present, there exists a number of break frequencies. To simplify the analysis, and at the same time obtain meaningful results, we can take one of two approaches:

1. Let C_1 determine the dominant lower break frequency, that is, the first break frequency encountered in coming from high to low frequencies. For this condition, $C_2/(1 + h_{fe})$ is assumed to act as a short circuit. As the frequency is further decreased, however, C_1 will act as an open circuit. An examination of Fig. 9.16 reveals that no output current will flow; the break frequency is therefore primarily determined by C_1.

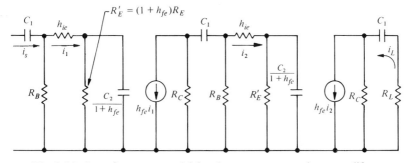

Fig. 9.16 Low-frequency model for the two-stage transistor amplifier.

2. If we let $C_2/(1 + h_{fe})$ determine the dominant lower break frequency, C_1 is assumed initially to behave as a short circuit. As we go farther down in frequency, $C_2/(1 + h_{fe})$ acts as an open circuit and C_1 determines the lower break frequency. Because this approach shows the effect of both types of capacitances, it will serve as a basis for our analysis.

The output stage of Fig. 9.16 is considered first, and C_1 is assumed to act as a short circuit, the expression for i_L/i_2 is

$$i_L/i_2 = h_{fe}R_C/(R_C + R_L) = A_1. \tag{9.27a}$$

At lower frequencies, C_1 must be considered; for this case,

$$\frac{I_L}{I_2} = \left(\frac{h_{fe}R_C}{R_C + R_L}\right)\left(\frac{j\omega C_1(R_C + R_L)}{1 + j\omega C_1(R_C + R_L)}\right)$$

or

$$I_L/I_2 = (A_1 j\omega/\omega_{L0})/(1 + j\omega/\omega_{L0}), \tag{9.27b}$$

where

$$\omega_{L0} = 1/C_1(R_C + R_L). \tag{9.28}$$

Note that when C_1 is assumed to act as a short circuit, $\omega_{L0} \to \infty$ and (9.27b) reduces to (9.27a). Therefore, (9.27b) is a general expression and the one to use for the output stage.

Assuming now that C_1 acts as a short circuit in the interstage, we obtain

$$I_2 = \frac{-h_{fe}I_1 R'_{t2}}{R'_{t2} + h_{ie} + R'_E/(1 + j\omega C_2 R_E)},$$

where $R'_{t2} = R_B//R_c$ and $R'_E = R_E(1 + h_{fe})$. Therefore,

$$\frac{I_2}{I_1} = A_2\left(\frac{1 + j\omega/\omega_{L1}}{1 + j\omega/(\alpha_1 \omega_{L1})}\right), \tag{9.29}$$

where

$$A_2 = -h_{fe}R'_{t2}/(R'_E + R'_{t2} + h_{ie}),$$

$$\alpha_1 = (R'_E + R'_{t2} + h_{ie})/(R'_{t2} + h_{ie}), \tag{9.30}$$

and

$$\omega_{L1} = 1/(R_E C_2). \tag{9.31}$$

Letting $C_2/(1 + h_{fe})$ act as an open circuit, we obtain

$$I_2/I_1 = (A_2 j\omega/\omega_{L2})/(1 + j\omega/\omega_{L2}), \tag{9.32}$$

where

$$\omega_{L2} = 1/C_1(R_B//(h_{ie} + R'_E) + R_C). \tag{9.33}$$

For the input circuit,

$$\frac{I_1}{I_s} = \frac{R_B(1 + j\omega R_E C_2)}{(1 + j\omega R_E C_2)(R_B + h_{ie}) + R_E(1 + h_{fe})}$$

$$= A_3\left(\frac{1 + j\omega/\omega_{L1}}{1 + j\omega/(\alpha_2 \omega_{L1})}\right), \tag{9.34}$$

where $$A_3 = R_B/[R_E(1 + h_{fe}) + (R_B + h_{ie})]$$

and $$1/\alpha_2 = (R_B + h_{ie})/[R_E(1 + h_{fe}) + (R_B + h_{ie})]. \qquad (9.35)$$

The overall current gain at low frequencies therefore becomes

$$A_i = \frac{I_L}{I_s} = A\left(\frac{1 + j\omega/\omega_{L1}}{1 + j\omega/(\alpha_1\omega_{L1})}\right)\left(\frac{j\omega/\omega_{L0}}{1 + j\omega/\omega_{L0}}\right)\left(\frac{j\omega/\omega_{L2}}{1 + j\omega/\omega_{L2}}\right)\left(\frac{1 + j\omega/\omega_{L1}}{1 + j\omega/(\alpha_2\omega_{L1})}\right),$$
$$(9.36)$$

where $A = A_1 A_2 A_3$. At mid frequencies,

$$A_i = A_1 A_2 A_3 \alpha_1 \alpha_2 = -g_m^2 R_{t1} R_{t2} R_C/(R_L + R_C).$$

A typical plot of A_i is illustrated in Fig. 9.17. The important thing to observe from Fig. 9.17 and expression (9.36) is the highest break frequency: Below this frequency range the amplifier is not useful.

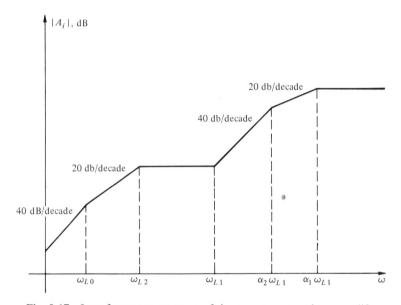

Fig. 9.17   Low-frequency response of the two-stage transistor amplifier.

Example 9.2

Two identical silicon transistors are used in the amplifier of Fig. 9.12. The parameter and component values are

$h_{fe} = 50$	$r_{bb'} = 40$ ohms,	$r_{b'e} = 500$ ohms,
$C_{b'c} = 10\,\text{pF}$,	$C_{b'e} = 100\,\text{pF}$,	$r_{ce} \approx \infty$,
$R_1 = 200\,\text{K}$,	$R_2 = 7\,\text{K}$,	$R_C = 10\,\text{K}$

$$R_L = 20 \text{ K}, \qquad R_E = 2 \text{ K}, \qquad C_2 = 10 \,\mu\text{F},$$

$$C_1 = 2 \,\mu\text{F}.$$

Calculate the expression for the high-frequency current gain.

Solution

$$g_m = h_{fe}/r_{b'e} = 100 \text{ millimhos},$$

$$R_B = 6.75 \text{ K},$$

$$R_{t1} = 6.75 \text{ K}//0.5\text{K} = 0.46 \text{ K},$$

$$R_{t2} = 6.75 \text{ K}//0.5 \text{ K}//10 \text{ K} \approx 0.44 \text{ K},$$

$$\omega_{H2} = 1/R_{t2}C_{i2},$$

where

$$C_{i2} = C_{b'e} + g_m R_{t3} C_{b'c} \quad \text{and} \quad R_{t3} = R_C//R_L.$$

Therefore, $C_{i2} = 100 + 100 \times 10^{-3} \times 6.6 \times 10^3 \times 10 = 6700 \,\text{pF},$

$$R_{t3} = R_C R_L/(R_C + R_L) = 200/30 = 6.6 \text{ K},$$

$$\omega_{H2} = \frac{1}{6700 \times 10^{-12} \times 0.44 \times 10^3} = 0.34 \times 10^6 \text{ rad/s},$$

$$C_{i1} = 560 \,\text{pF}; \qquad R_{t1} = 0.46 \text{ K},$$

$$\omega_{H1} = \frac{1}{560 \times 10^{-12} \times 0.46 \times 10^3} \approx 3.85 \times 10^6 \text{ rad/s},$$

$$g_m^2 R_{t1} R_{t2} R_C/(R_C + R_L) = 0.01 \times 0.46 \times 10^3 \times 0.44 \times 10^3 \times 10/30 = 675.$$

Then

$$A_i = \frac{-675}{(1 + j\omega/0.34 \times 10^6)(1 + j\omega/3.85 \times 10^6)}.$$

The plot of the amplitude response is shown in Fig. 9.18.

Example 9.3

Using the data given in Example 9.2, calculate the lower break frequencies. What is the dominant lower break frequency?

Solution

Using expressions (9.28), (9.30), (9.31), (9.33), and (9.35) we obtain

$$\omega_{L0} \approx 16.6 \text{ rad/s},$$

$$\omega_{L1} = 50 \text{ rad/s},$$

$$\alpha_1 \omega_{L1} \approx 1100 \text{ rad/s},$$

$$\omega_{L2} \approx 30 \, \text{rad/s},$$

$$\alpha_2 \omega_{L1} \approx 700 \, \text{rad/s}.$$

The dominant frequency is $1100 \, \text{rad/s}$.

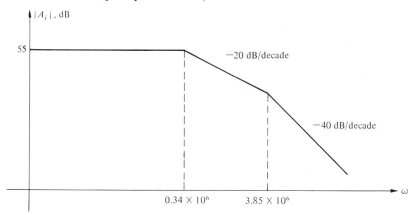

Fig. 9.18 High-frequency amplitude response obtained in Example 9.2.

9.3 Summary

Cascading stages is a practical method to increase the gain of an amplifier. In this chapter, the frequency response of RC-coupled amplifiers was studied. Owing to the coupling capacitor there is no transmission of signals at zero frequency. The interstage network reduces the gain to zero at zero frequency, and the device and parasitic capacitances reduce the gain to zero at infinite frequency. Cascaded RC-coupled amplifiers are examples of networks where the gain is greater than unity. These amplifiers are also called wideband amplifiers. The design of wideband amplifiers is concerned with obtaining a large and fixed gain in an appropriate band of frequencies.

Analysis of cascaded amplifiers becomes complicated if the loading effect of stages are not neglected. For this case a computer solution is most practical (see Chapter 17). If the loading effect is neglected, however, analysis of the overall gain reduces to the analysis of a single stage used in the overall amplifier multiplied by the number of stages. Examples of junction transistor, FET, as well as vacuum tube amplifiers, were considered in this chapter.

References

ALLEY, C. L., and K. W. ATWOOD, *Electronic Engineering*, Wiley, New York, 2nd ed., 1966.

ANGELO, JR., E. J., *Electronic Circuits*, McGraw-Hill, New York, 2nd ed., 1964.

SCHILLING, D. L., and C. BELOV, *Electronic Circuits, Discrete and Integrated*, McGraw-Hill, New York, 1968.

Problems

9.1 Repeat Example 9.1 for $h_{fe} = 100$; the other component values remain the same. Compare results.

9.2 In Example 9.1 it is desired to increase the upper break frequency by 20%. The midband gain and passive component values are to remain the same. What parameter values should the transistors now have? Are the values realistic?

9.3 A 6AU6-A pentode is used in a two-stage amplifier whose model is given in Fig. 9.7. Assume that $g_m = 2.5$ mmhos, $r_p = 10$ M, $C_{gk} = 6$ pF, $C_{pk} = 5$ pF, $C_{gp} = 0$, and the stray capacitance is 10 pF across the input of the first tube and 5 pF across the output load. If $R_g = 200$ K, $V_{bb} = 300$ V, and the Q-point is at $V_b = 150$ V, $V_{C1} = -1.5$ V, and $V_{C2} = 150$ V, (a) derive an expression for voltage gain at high frequencies. (b) Plot the Bode (amplitude and phase) response curves for the amplifier.

9.4 In Prob. 9.3 coupling capacitor $C = 10$ μF. (a) Referring to Fig. 9.8, derive an expression for voltage gain at low frequencies. (b) Plot the Bode response curves.

9.5 Derive an expression for voltage gain at low frequencies for the amplifier of Fig. P9.5. Assume that only capacitance C_c acts as a short to the signal.

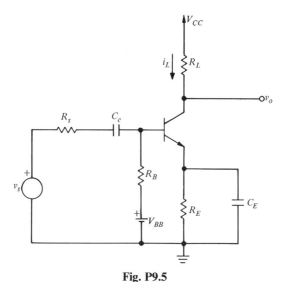

Fig. P9.5

9.6 Repeat Prob. 9.5 assuming that capacitor C_E acts as a short to the signal. Compare results.

9.7 In Fig. P9.5, $h_{ie} = 1.5$ K, $h_{fe} = 50$, $h_{re} = h_{oe} \approx 0$, $R_L = R_s = 1$ K, $R_E = 100$ ohms, and $R_B = 10$ K. Assuming that capacitance C_c acts as a short to the signal, calculate the value of C_E for a lower break frequency of 40 Hz.

9.8 Repeat Prob. 9.7 assuming that C_E acts as a short and C_c determines the lower break frequency of 40 Hz.

9.9 The parameters for the field-effect transistors in Fig. 9.10 are $g_m = 5$ mmhos, $C_{gs} = 10$ pF, $C_{gd} = 2$ pF, $C_{ds} = 0$, $g_p = 10^{-6}$ mho; $R_g = 100$ K. (a) Is it possible to obtain an upper break frequency ≥ 1 MHz? (b) If your answer to (a) is affirmative, calculate the value of R_L.

9.10 In Prob. 9.9, assume that $R_S = 1$ K, $R_L = 50$ K, $C_1 = 10$ μF, and $C_S = 100$ μF. (a) Derive an expression for the low-frequency voltage gain. (b) Plot the logarithmic amplitude and phase angle response curves.

9.11 In Fig. P9.5 replace voltage source v_s in series with R_s by an ideal current source i_s. Derive an expression for current gain at low frequencies. Assume that $h_{ie} = 1.5$ K, $h_{fe} = 50$, $h_{re} = h_{oe} = 0$, $R_E = 300$ ohms, $R_B = 10$ K, $R_L = 1$ K, and $C_E = C_c = 10$ μF.

9.12 Repeat Example 9.2 for $h_{fe} = 100$, all other parameter and component values remaining the same. Compare results.

9.13 Design a two-stage current amplifier with an upper break frequency of 1 MHz and a lower break frequency of 100 Hz. Choose device, operating points, etc.

9.14 In Example 9.3 calculate the dominant lower break frequency if $C_2 = 1$ μF and the other parameters remain the same.

9.15 For the cascode amplifier of Fig. P9.15 attempt to derive an expression for voltage gain v_o/v_s at high frequencies. Why is the circuit useful?

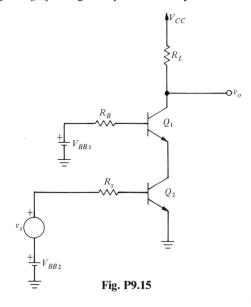

Fig. P9.15

Power Amplifiers

A power amplifier is used where appreciable output power (usually greater than 1 W) is required to drive a transducer, such as a loudspeaker or a servo motor. Voltage gain is relatively unimportant in characterizing the performance of a power amplifier; what is important is its output power, distortion, efficiency, stability, power gain, reliability, and cost. The stages preceding the power amplifier, the *preamplifier*, furnish the necessary voltage gain.

In this chapter we shall consider the analysis of low- and audio-frequency power amplifiers, our attention being directed primarily to transistor circuits. Vacuum tubes are seldom used in new amplifier designs. Because the transistor is temperature sensitive, the thermal behavior of power transistors will also be considered.

The analysis of power amplifier performance is an example of *large-signal* analysis. One cannot use the incremental model that was so useful in analyzing small-signal amplifiers; instead, graphical and piecewise-linear methods have to be employed. Our study will emphasize graphical techniques.

During large-signal swings the transistor operates over its nonlinear regions and produces distortion. A method for predicting distortion that is based on graphical analysis will also be considered.

10.1 Classes of Operation and Efficiency

As discussed in Chapter 3 and reviewed here, there are three basic classes of operation suitable for audio-frequency amplifiers: A, AB, and B. Based on a sinusoidal input signal, in class A operation the transistor is biased at approximately the center of the load line, and collector current flows for each 2π radians ($360°$) of the input signal. In class AB operation the transistor may be biased near cutoff, and collector current flows for more than π ($180°$) but less than 2π radians ($360°$). For class B the transistor is at cutoff, and collector current flows for only π radians ($180°$).

Some thought will convince the reader that a single-transistor power amplifier, often referred to as *single-ended operation*, biased class *AB* or *B* will produce appreciable distortion. In operating active devices in either class *AB* or *B*, *push-pull* operation to be described later, is used. In push-pull operation two active devices are required, in contrast to single-ended operation, where one active device is used.

Because the transistor is biased beyond cutoff in class *C*, collector current flows for less than π radians. This mode of operation is unsuitable for audio applications. Class *C* operation, however, is used often in tuned amplifiers which is the subject of Chapter 12.

One of the many parameters that characterize a power amplifier is the *conversion*, or *collector efficiency*, η_c. It is defined as the ratio of the ac signal output power P_o to the dc input power P_{dc}:

$$\eta_c = P_o/P_{dc}. \tag{10.1}$$

In applying (10.1), the idealized collector characteristics of Fig. 10.1B will be used. The collector curves are horizontal, equally-spaced, parallel lines.

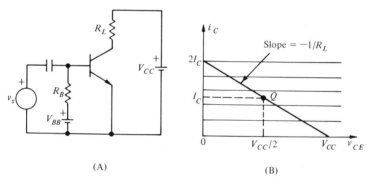

(A)   (B)

Fig. 10.1 Load R_L connected directly in the collector circuit. (A) Circuit. (B) Graphical construction.

Results obtained from these ideal characteristics for largest possible signal swings yield maximum conversion efficiency. Note that the characteristics given are for the common-emitter configuration—an often used connection for power amplifiers. Because the collector current is approximately equal to the emitter current, the common-emitter collector characteristics may also be used in the analysis of the emitter follower stage.

Consider the single transistor power amplifier of Fig. 10.1A which is biased at the center of the load line for class *A* operation. Resistance R_L is the load to which ac power is supplied. The result of superimposing the load line on the ideal collector characteristics is given in Fig. 10.1B. For a sinusoidal input to the circuit, the largest value of the rms collector current is $I_C/\sqrt{2}$.

The corresponding rms voltage is $V_{CC}/2\sqrt{2}$ and the output power P_o is

$$P_o = (I_C/\sqrt{2})(V_{CC}/2\sqrt{2}) = I_C V_{CC}/4. \tag{10.2}$$

The dc input power P_{dc} is

$$P_{dc} = I_C V_{CC}, \tag{10.3}$$

neglecting the input power to the bias network, which is much less than $I_C V_{CC}$. Substitution of (10.2) and (10.3) in (10.1) yields

$$\eta_c = (I_C V_{CC}/4)/I_C V_{CC} = 0.25 = 25\%.$$

An efficiency of 25% is considered poor.

Instead of connecting load R_L of Fig. 10.1A directly in series with the source V_{CC} and the transistor, an output transformer can be used to isolate the load from the collector circuit as shown in Fig. 10.2A. Turns ratio $n:1$ is chosen such that resistance R'_L reflected to the collector side yields the best compromise between maximum output power and minimum distortion. Because we are assuming idealized collector characteristics, distortion is not present. In physical devices with nonlinear characteristics, however, distortion can be appreciable.

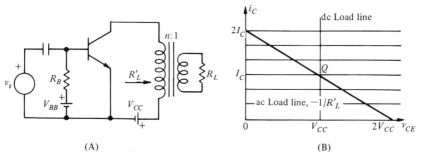

(A)   (B)

Fig. 10.2 Transformer coupled load. (A) Circuit. (B) Superposition of dc and ac load lines on collector characteristics.

In Fig. 10.2B the dc, or *static* load line, which represents the dc winding resistance of the transformer primary side, is plotted as a vertical line and intersects the v_{CE}-axis at V_{CC} volts. A physical transformer has dc winding resistance which is not zero like that of an ideal transformer. The static load line is then not a vertical line, but one with a slope equal to $-1/R_p$, where R_p is the dc primary winding resistance. The ac, or *dynamic*, load line represents the reflected load resistance. Its slope is $-1/R'_L$ and it passes through the Q-point. For maximum output power the dynamic load line intersects the v_{CE}-axis at $2V_{CC}$ volts. The ac output power is, therefore,

$$P_o = (I_C/\sqrt{2})(V_{CC}/\sqrt{2}) = I_C V_{CC}/2.$$

The dc input power, as before, is given by

$$P_{dc} = I_C V_{CC}.$$

Substitution of these expressions in (10.1) yields the maximum conversion efficiency for the class A transformer-coupled amplifier:

$$\eta_c = (I_C V_{CC}/2)/I_C V_{CC} = 0.5 = 50\%.$$

For a square-wave input the maximum conversion efficiency is 100%.

It is seen that, for sinusoidal signals, the conversion efficiency for class A operation with a transformer load is 50%—twice as much as for a load connected directly to the collector. This difference results from dc power being wasted in the load resistance that is connected directly in the collector circuit. In a physical transformer the dc power dissipated in the winding is generally negligible. It should be noted that for the transformer load the voltage across the collector-emitter junction, is equal to the signal plus the collector supply voltage; the maximum value is therefore equal to $2V_{CC}$ volts.

As mentioned earlier, in class B operation the device is biased at cutoff, that is, without an input signal the collector current is zero. For a sinusoidal signal, output current flows only during the positive half cycle, and the output resembles that of a half-wave rectifier. One cannot, therefore, use a single transistor stage operating class B because the output is badly distorted. Two transistors are required in push-pull, or *double-ended*, operation as shown in Fig. 10.3. Transformer $T1$ provides equal signals that are 180° out of phase at the bases of transistors $Q1$ and $Q2$; $T2$ is a center-tapped output transformer which couples R_L to the collectors. Each transistor sees the

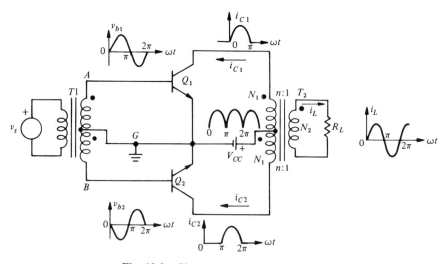

Fig. 10.3   Class B push-pull amplifier.

ac reflected load resistance R'_L, where

$$R'_L = n^2 R_L \qquad (10.4)$$

and $n = N_1/N_2$.

When point A is positive with respect to point G, point B is negative; transistor $Q1$ therefore conducts and $Q2$ is cut off. During the next half cycle, point B is positive and point A negative; now $Q2$ conducts and $Q1$ is cut off. The output will be a replica of the input signal. As seen from Fig. 10.3, the collector supply current has the same waveform as that obtained from the full-wave rectification of a sinusoidal input.

The complete idealized characteristics and the superimposed ac load line for the class B push-pull amplifier are shown in Fig. 10.4. The characteristics of Fig. 10.4 were obtained by inverting the collector family of curves for one transistor and aligning its V_{CC} point with the one above it. Actually, these characteristics are not required because all necessary information is obtained from the normal collector characteristic curves. The total characteristics are shown here to assist the reader in understanding class B push-pull operation.

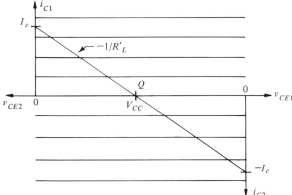

Fig. 10.4 Graphical analysis of a class B push-pull amplifier.

From Fig. 10.4 the ac output power is

$$P_o = (I_c/\sqrt{2})(V_{CC}/\sqrt{2}) = I_c V_{CC}/2.$$

The average, or dc, current for each transistor I_{av} is

$$I_{av} = I_c/\pi.$$

The value of average current is the same as that obtained from a half-wave rectifier for a sinusoidal input. This should not be surprising, because the output of each transistor in a class B push-pull amplifier resembles a half-wave rectified waveform, as indicated in Fig. 10.3. The average current for the two transistors is $2I_c/\pi$ and the total dc input power is

$$P_{dc} = 2I_c V_{CC}/\pi \quad \text{and} \quad \eta_c = 0.785 = 78.5\,\%.$$

Class B is the most efficient type of operation for low- and audio-frequency amplifiers.

In class AB push-pull operation, each transistor is slightly forward biased. Because physical transistors are nonlinear, pure class B operation is seldom used. The efficiency of class AB is between 50 and 78.5 percent. If each transistor is forward biased slightly and is operating close to class B, the efficiency of class AB is of the order of 70 %; if biased close to class A it is approximately 60 %. For straight class A push-pull operation the maximum conversion efficiency is 50 %.

10.2   Power Transistors

The ideal power transistor, in addition to having the ideal collector characteristics defined previously, would also exhibit

1. Infinite current and voltage ratings.
2. Collector dissipation that is independent of temperature.
3. No localized hot spots which may cause the transistor to break down; this is referred to as *second breakdown*.
4. Infinite frequency response.

Physical power transistors exhibit nonlinear characteristics, are voltage and current limited, have thermal losses which increase with temperature, suffer from second breakdown, and generally have a poorer frequency response than small-signal transistors.

The maximum collector current rating of a power transistor is based on the value of current the transistor can safely withstand or on the minimum current gain specified by the manufacturer. As collector current increases, the collector-base junction temperature rises and produces localized hot spots that can possibly damage the transistor. The value of the current gain is also a function of collector current; h_{fe} increasing, and then decreasing, with current. In explaining this behavior *silicon* transistors will be assumed.

Recombination centers existing in the base region tend to reduce the effective emitter current. As the emitter current increases, however, more recombination centers are filled and a greater number of carriers cross the base and reach the collector. This explains the rising value of current gain for increasing collector current, starting from zero. When the recombination centers are filled, the value of current gain attains a broad plateau for an appreciable range of collector current.

The principal reason for the decrease in current gain as the collector current is further increased is an increase in majority carriers in the base. These carriers are injected into the emitter region and reduce the emitter and collector currents. The ratio of collector to base current is therefore reduced. If, for a particular transistor, the current gain falls off at values of collector current levels less than required to destroy the transistor, the maximum collector current rating for the device will be limited by the minimum value of current gain specified by the manufacturer.

Multiplication of Collector Current

For a transistor operated as an amplifier, the collector-base junction is reverse biased. As the reverse bias is increased a voltage is reached where avalanche breakdown may occur, similar in behavior to that of a junction diode. The multiplication of current carriers M during avalanche breakdown is given by the following relationship:

$$M = 1/[1 - (V/V_b)^n],$$

where V_b represents the breakdown voltage, V is a given voltage, and n has a value of from 2 to 6. If we let V_b equal the breakdown voltage for a transistor in the common-base configuration with the emitter left open, that is, $V_b = BV_{CBO}$, the preceding equation can be written as

$$M = 1/[1 - (V/BV_{CBO})^n]. \tag{10.5}$$

With the common-emitter configuration considered, the reverse saturation current with the base open I_{CEO} is given by

$$I_{CEO} = I_{CBO}/(1 - h_{FB}), \tag{10.6}$$

where I_{CBO} is the reverse saturation current of the transistor in the common-base configuration with the emitter open and h_{FB} is the average value (dc value) of the forward current gain. At the onset of avalanche, I_{CEO} approaches infinity. For this to happen, h_{FB} is multiplied by the multiplication factor M (the carriers are increasing and therefore the current gain increases) such that $h_{FB}M = 1$. Substituting $M = 1/h_{FB}$ in (10.5) and solving for $V = BV_{CEO}$, one obtains the breakdown voltage of the transistor in the common-emitter configuration with the base open:

$$M = 1/h_{FB} = 1/[1 - (BV_{CEO}/BV_{CBO})^n]$$

or $$BV_{CEO} = BV_{CBO}(1 - h_{FB})^{1/n}. \tag{10.7}$$

Example 10.1

Assume a silicon transistor has the following values: $n = 4, h_{FB} = 0.98$, and $BV_{CBO} = 50$ V. Find BV_{CEO}.

Solution

Substitution of the given values in (10.7) yields

$$BV_{CEO} = 50(1 - 0.98)^{1/4} = 19 \text{ V}.$$

The result obtained indicates that a transistor in the common-emitter configuration has a breakdown voltage considerably less than that of a transistor in the common-base configuration; in this example it is less than one-half the value.

Instead of the base-emitter circuit being open, what happens if the circuit is terminated by a resistance R_B? Figure 10.5 shows the transistor cut off until the base-emitter voltage is equal to the offset voltage V_o; for voltages less than V_o the base-emitter junction resistance is extremely high, much higher than any practical value for R_B. Hence, we can assume that I_{CBO} flows through R_L, across the collector-base junction, and through R_B.

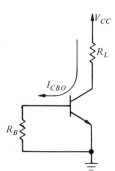

Fig. 10.5   Determining the value of BV_{CER}.

When $MI_{CBO}R_B = V_o$, the current will begin to flow through the emitter-base junction. Letting $M = V_o/(I_{CBO}R_B)$ and the collector-emitter breakdown voltage equal to BV_{CER} for this condition, from (10.5), we have

$$BV_{CER} = BV_{CBO}(1 - I_{CBO}R_B/V_o)^{1/n}. \tag{10.8}$$

For $R_B = 0$, the breakdown voltage is defined as BV_{CES}; (10.8) therefore reduces to

$$BV_{CES} = BV_{CBO}. \tag{10.9}$$

If resistance R_B in Fig. 10.5 is returned to a negative (back-bias) voltage V_{BB}, the breakdown voltage is denoted by BV_{CEX} and is given by

$$BV_{CEX} = BV_{CBO}[1 - I_{CBO}R_B/(V_{BB} + V_o)]^{1/n}. \tag{10.10}$$

The preceding equations neglected the base spreading resistance $r_{bb'}$. When resistance R_B is external to the base, the total resistance in the base circuit is actually $R_B + r_{bb'}$. If $R_B = 0$, the net resistance in the base circuit is $r_{bb'}$; consequently, BV_{CES} is somewhat less than BV_{CBO}. In general,

$$BV_{CEO} < BV_{CER} < BV_{CEX} < BV_{CES} < BV_{CBO}.$$

These results are summarized in Fig. 10.6. Note that the breakdown curves are asymptotic to the BV_{CEO} curve; for this reason BV_{CEO} is sometimes referred to as the *sustaining voltage*, $V_{CE(sus)}$.

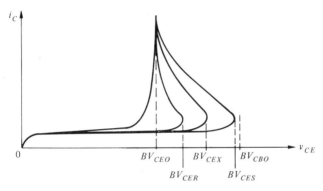

Fig. 10.6   Idealized curves of breakdown voltages.

Punch Through

Another possible breakdown mechanism in transistors is *punch through*, also referred to as *reach through*. As the collector-base voltage increases (remember, the collector-base junction is reverse biased) the depletion region of the collector-base junction extends farther into the base region. Because the base width of a transistor is small, the collector depletion region will ultimately meet the emitter-base depletion region. When this happens, it is as though the emitter is shorted to the collector and useful transistor action ceases. If the punch-through voltage is less than the avalanche breakdown voltage, the maximum voltage rating of the transistor will be the punch-through voltage.

10.3   Thermal Effects and Second Breakdown

Because of the large amounts of power dissipated, thought must be given to means for removing the generated heat from a power transistor. If this is not done, a regenerative condition, called *thermal runaway*, may occur in which the thermally intrinsic generation of electron-hole pairs approaches the impurity carrier concentration. This can lead to irreversible changes in the transistor's characteristics or to the actual destruction of the device.

The collector of a power transistor is usually soldered or gold plated to a copper header for heat dissipation. The effectiveness in dissipating heat in steady state is characterized by a parameter called *thermal resistance* with the unit of degrees Centigrade per watt of dissipated power (°C/W). It is symbolized by the Greek letter theta (θ) and represents the rise in temperature for a watt of dissipated power. For example, the thermal resistance between the collector junction and transistor case θ_{JC} is typically 0.5°C/W to 1°C/W.

If one considers only steady-state conditions, a simple thermal equivalent circuit may be drawn which relates dissipated power P_C, thermal resistance θ, and temperature T. Such a circuit is shown in Fig. 10.7; note that T, θ, and P_C are analogous to V, R, and I, respectively. Ohm's law yields $I = (V_A - V_B)/R_{AB}$; the analogous equation for the thermal circuit is

$$P_C = (T_J - T_A)/\theta_{JA}. \tag{10.11}$$

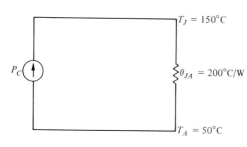

Fig. 10.7 Thermal circuit for a power transistor without a heat sink.

To ensure that the maximum allowable junction temperature T_J of a transistor is not exceeded (approximately 150°C for silicon and 100°C for germanium), the transistor is mounted on a heat sink. A heat sink, normally made of aluminum and anodized or painted black for good radiation characteristics, of suitable size and shape helps dissipate the heat to the surrounding environment, or *ambient*, maintaining the junction temperature at a safe value. For example, if a heat sink is not used, a thermal resistance between the junction and ambient θ_{JA} is defined. A possible value for θ_{JA} is 200°C/W. Assuming the maximum temperature $T_J = 150°C$ and the ambient $T_A = 50°C$, from (10.11) one obtains

$$P_C = (150 - 50)/200 = 0.5 \text{ W}.$$

If a heat sink were used, the total thermal resistance of the equivalent thermal circuit could be as low as 1°C/W permitting a power dissipation of 100 W— 200 times as great.

Because the collector is generally connected to the transistor case, suitable electrical insulation must be provided between the transistor and the heat sink. The insulating material must also have a low thermal resistance. Although these are conflicting requirements, since a good electrical insulator is also a poor conductor of heat, the materials listed in Table 10.1 provide a good compromise. The thermal resistance between case and heat sink is designated θ_{CS}. The metal transistor case, separated from the heat sink by the insulating material, or dielectric, forms a capacitor. This capacitor is between the collector and ground and consequently limits the high-frequency response of the transistor. If the heat sink is ungrounded, the insulating material is not required.

Table 10.1 Comparison of Insulating Materials.[a] (Courtesy of RCA)

Material	Thickness (in.)	θ_{CS} (°C/W)	Capacitance (pF)
Mica	0.002	0.4	90
Anodized aluminum	0.016	0.35	110
Beryllia	0.063	0.25	15

[a] Based on a TO-3 case whose mounting area is approximately 1 square inch.

Heat sinks are also characterized by a thermal resistance θ_{SA}. The value of θ_{SA} depends on the type of material, its thickness and area, and if forced air cooling is used. A sample curve for a square heat sink of a given thickness is shown in Fig. 10.8. As the area of the sink is increased, a larger area of radiation is realized and θ_{SA} is reduced.

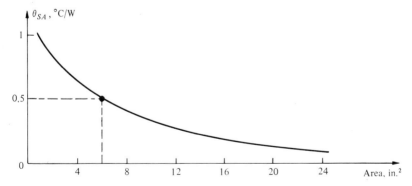

Fig. 10.8 Characteristic curve for a particular heat sink.

An example of mounting a stud-type power transistor on a heat sink is illustrated in Fig. 10.9. The stud is insulated from the sink by a fiber, or similar material, shoulder bushing. To ensure good thermal contact, silicone grease or a zinc oxide filler (for example, Dow-Corning No. 340) is applied to the transistor and the heat sink surface in contact with the insulating washer, which is typically mica.

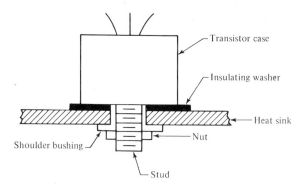

Fig. 10.9 Cross-sectional view of a stud-mounted transistor on a heat sink.

The thermal equivalent circuit for a configuration like that of Fig. 10.9 is shown in Fig. 10.10. Writing the "Ohm's Law" equivalent for the circuit, we obtain

$$P_C = (T_J - T_A)/(\theta_{JC} + \theta_{CS} + \theta_{SA})$$
$$= (T_J - T_A)/\theta_{JA}, \tag{10.12}$$

where $\theta_{JA} = \theta_{JC} + \theta_{CS} + \theta_{SA}$.

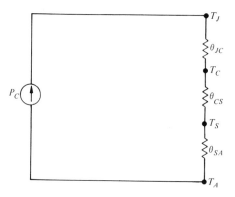

Fig. 10.10 A complete thermal equivalent circuit for a transistor mounted on a heat sink.

To determine, for instance, the case temperature T_C, from (10.12) we write

$$T_J = P_C\theta_{JA} + T_A. \tag{10.13}$$

Also,
$$P_C = (T_J - T_C)/\theta_{JC}. \tag{10.14}$$

Substituting (10.13) in (10.14) and solving for T_C, we obtain

$$T_C = T_A + P_C(\theta_{JA} - \theta_{JC}).$$

But $\theta_{JA} - \theta_{JC} = \theta_{CS} + \theta_{SA} = \theta_{CA}$; therefore,

$$T_C = T_A + P_C\theta_{CA}. \tag{10.15}$$

Example 10.2

A silicon power transistor (TO-3 case) is mounted on a 6-square-inch heat sink described by the characteristic curve of Fig. 10.8. A 0.002-inch thick mica washer is used. The thermal resistance for the transistor is $\theta_{JC} = 0.6°C/W$; the maximum junction temperature $T_J = 150°C$. (a) If the ambient temperature is $T_A = 50°C$, find the maximum allowable power the transistor can dissipate. (b) For the condition of (a) what is the case temperature T_C?

Solution

(a) From Fig. 10.8, $\theta_{SA} = 0.5°C/W$; Table 10.1 yields $\theta_{CS} = 0.4°C/W$ for the mica washer. Therefore $\theta_{JA} = 0.6 + 0.4 + 0.5 = 1.5°C/W$. From (10.12) $P_{C(max)} = (150 - 50)/1.5 = 66.6$ W.

(b) $\theta_{CA} = \theta_{CS} + \theta_{SA} = 0.4 + 0.5 = 0.9°C/W$. Substituting in (10.15), one obtains $T_C = 66.6 \times 0.9 + 50 = 110°C$.

Second Breakdown

A power transistor may be viewed as consisting of many small transistors in parallel. Because a transistor structure can never be strictly uniform, each of the small transistors has different forward current gains. When the transistor is forward biased, the current flowing in each of the equivalent transistors will depend on their respective current gains—the greater the gain, the greater the current. The higher gain units, therefore, will heat up sooner than the lower gain units. This results in localized hot spots, which can destroy the transistor. The mechanism is referred to as *second breakdown*.

If one defines a current level I_{SB} at which second breakdown begins, it is found that second breakdown current varies inversely with the cutoff frequency f_T and the collector-emitter voltage V_{CE}. This behavior suggests that a transistor with the lowest value of f_T required for a given application should be selected and reduced collector-emitter voltage should be used.

Experimentally, thermal rating and second breakdown of a transistor can be combined in a single rating curve, the *safe-area rating curve*. An example of such a curve is shown in Fig. 10.11, where the collector dissipation for a given transistor case temperature is plotted as a function of collector-emitter voltage. To ensure reliable transistor operation, the value of P_C must not be exceeded for a given value of V_{CE} determined from the curve.

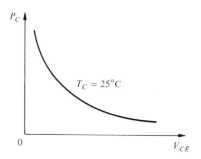

Fig. 10.11   An example of a safe-area rating curve.

10.4   Class A Power Amplifier

Consider the single-ended class *A* power amplifier of Fig. 10.12. For an optimum choice of transformer turns ratio n, the resistance reflected by the transformer to the collector circuit will provide greatest output power at lowest possible distortion. Resistances R_1 and R_2, as discussed in Chapter 5, determine the quiescent-operating (Q) point for the transistor. We shall consider the operation of the amplifier at mid frequencies where capacitors C_c and C_E are assumed to act as shorts to the signal frequencies.

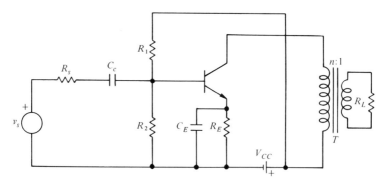

Fig. 10.12   A typical class A power amplifier with transformer output.

With the amplifier of Fig. 10.12 considered on a dc basis, the circuit reduces to that of Fig. 10.13A where resistance $R_B = R_1//R_2$ and voltage $V_B = V_{CC}R_2/(R_1 + R_2)$. Voltage $V_{EE} \approx I_C R_E$, where I_C is the quiescent collector current. Collector resistance R_p is the dc resistance of the transformer primary winding; if an ideal transformer is assumed, $R_p = 0$. The superposition of the dc load line of zero ohms appears as a vertical line in Fig. 10.14 where the Q-point is located at $i_C = I_C$ and $v_{CE} = V_{CC}$. Since the value of V_{EE} is generally much less than V_{CC}, it is neglected in Fig. 10.14. Base current $I_B = (V_B - V_{BE})/R_B$.

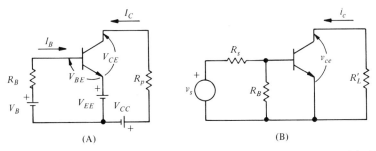

Fig. 10.13 Viewing the power amplifier on a dc and ac basis. (A) Dc model. (B) Ac model.

From an ac standpoint the amplifier appears as shown in Fig. 10.13B. The dc sources have been set to zero. The collector circuit sees the reflected ac load resistance $R'_L = n^2 R_L$. If a line having a slope of $-1/R'_L$ is drawn through the Q-point (see Fig. 10.14), the ac load line is superimposed on the collector characteristics.

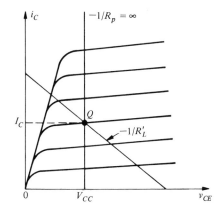

Fig. 10.14 Superimposing the dc and ac load lines on the collector characteristics.

The total dc input power (P_{dc}) delivered by the collector source V_{CC} equals the power dissipated in the transformer winding resistance (P_T) *plus* the power dissipated in the emitter resistance (P_E) *plus* the power dissipated in the collector-base junction (P_C) *plus* the power absorbed by the reflected load resistance (P_L). By the law of conservation of energy, we have

$$P_{dc} = P_T + P_E + P_C + P_L, \tag{10.16}$$

where $P_{dc} = V_{CC} I_C$, $P_T = I_C^2 R_p$, $P_E = I_E^2 R_E \approx I_C^2 R_E$, and $P_L = I_{rms}^2 R'_L$ (I_{rms} is the rms value of the ac component). The average power dissipated in the collector is, from (10.16),

$$P_C = V_{CC} I_C - I_{rms}^2 R'_L - I_C^2 R_p - I_C^2 R_E. \tag{10.17a}$$

The winding resistance R_p of an ideal transformer is zero and for many physical transformers it may be assumed to be zero. Generally, R_E is of a very small value and P_E can be ignored. Hence, (10.17a) reduces to

$$P_C \approx V_{CC}I_C - I_{\text{rms}}^2 R_L'. \tag{10.17b}$$

From (10.17b) it is evident that maximum collector dissipation occurs when no input signal is present and consequently $I_{\text{rms}} = 0$; hence,

$$P_{C(\text{max})} = P_{\text{dc}} = V_{CC}I_C. \tag{10.18}$$

Because the maximum theoretical conversion efficiency for class A operation is 50%, the maximum load power $P_{L(\text{max})} = P_{C(\text{max})}/2$.

Maximum collector dissipation, as just shown, occurs when no signal is present. A chosen transistor must be capable of dissipating, and be rated for, $P_{C(\text{max})} = V_{CC}I_C$. Manufacturers sometimes superimpose a maximum dissipation curve for a particular transistor case temperature on the collector characteristics, as illustrated in Fig. 10.15. (Also shown are the maximum values of collector current and voltage.) If the dissipation curve is not provided, it may be generated by choosing a series of values for v_{CE} and calculating the corresponding values for $i_C = P_{C(\text{max})}/v_{CE}$. A few values of v_{CE} should suffice; the resulting curve will be an equilateral hyperbola.

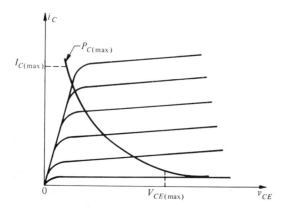

Fig. 10.15 Plot of the maximum dissipation curve on the collector characteristics.

An advantage is gained if the quiescent operating point is located somewhat to the left of center of the point of tangency between the ac load line R_L' and the maximum dissipation curve $P_{C(\text{max})}$. In Fig. 10.16, two dissipation curves are shown: curve $P_{C(\text{max})1}$ for 25°C and curve $P_{C(\text{max})2}$ for 125°C. The 125°C-curve is below the 25°C curve, because as the operating temperature is increased the transistor must dissipate less power for reliable operation. Quiescent point $Q1$ corresponds to the operating point at 25°C. As the temperature rises, the Q-point moves to higher values of collector current.

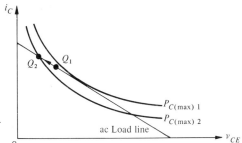

Fig. 10.16 The shifting of the Q-point with rising temperatures.

(How far it moves will depend on the stability factor for the amplifier.) At 125°C it is seen that the quiescent point, now designated $Q2$, intersects the $P_{C(max)2}$ curve and operation is considered to be safe. If the initial location of $Q1$ was at the point of tangency or to the right of it, as the temperature rose the operating point would find itself above the $P_{C(max)2}$ curve. This may result in overheating of the collector-base junction and ultimate destruction of the device because $P_{C(max)1} > P_{C(max)2}$.

Graphical Determination of Output Power and Gain

Assume that for the class A power amplifier of Fig. 10.12 the dc and ac load lines superimposed on the collector characteristics appear as shown in Fig. 10.17. Also plotted on the figure are the resultant collector current and voltage waveforms for a signal base current $i_b = I_b \cos \omega t$. A cosinusoidal input is used to simplify the analysis. Neglecting distortion in the output waveform (it will be shown that the results based on this assumption are valid even for appreciable distortion), the rms values of ac collector current and voltage, I_{rms} and V_{rms}, respectively, are

$$I_{rms} = (I_{c(max)} - I_{c(min)})/2\sqrt{2} \quad \text{and} \quad V_{rms} = (V_{c(max)} - V_{c(min)})/2\sqrt{2}.$$

Since $P_o = V_{rms} I_{rms}$, then

$$P_o = [(V_{c(max)} - V_{c(min)})(I_{c(max)} - I_{c(min)})]/8. \tag{10.19}$$

To determine the signal input power P_i required to develop the output power P_o, consider Fig. 10.18A. Examining the network from the dc standpoint, one sees that capacitor C_c is an open circuit. The equation for the dc input load line may be written as

$$V_B = i_B R_B + v_{BE}, \tag{10.20}$$

where V_B and R_B are Thevenin values of the dc input circuit. The dc load line is superimposed (dashed curve) on the input characteristics of Fig. 10.19.

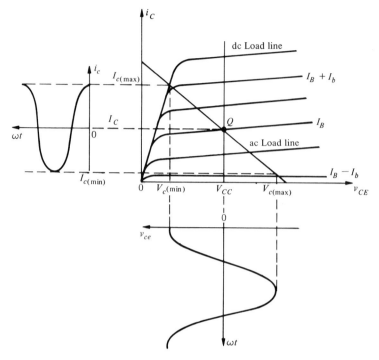

Fig. 10.17 Graphical determination of output power for a class A power amplifier.

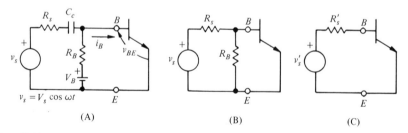

Fig. 10.18 Determining the input power. (A) Base-emitter circuit. (B) Ac model (C) Thevenin equivalent taken with respect to terminals B–E.

If one assumes that C_c acts as a short, the circuit of Fig. 10.18A reduces to Fig. 10.18B for ac signals. Forming the Thevenin equivalent circuit with respect to terminals B–E produces Fig. 10.18C, where $R'_s = R_s // R_B$ and $v'_s = R_B v_s / (R_B + R_s)$. If $R_B \gg R_s$, then $R'_s \approx R_s$ and $v'_s \approx v_s$.

Load line R'_s (solid line in Fig. 10.19) having a slope of $-1/R'_s$ intersects the Q-point. If $v_s = V_s \cos \omega t$ is plotted about V_{BE}, the base current swings between $I_{b(max)}$ and $I_{b(min)}$. The ac input power P_i is, therefore, given by

$$P_i = [V_s(I_{b(max)} - I_{b(min)})]/4. \tag{10.21}$$

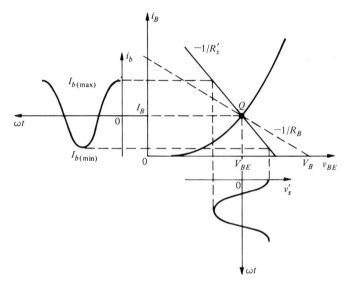

Fig. 10.19 Graphical determination of input power.

If the input characteristics are not available, the ac input power to the amplifier may be estimated with the aid of Fig. 10.18C. The ac rms value of the base current I_b is

$$I_{brms} = V_s'/\sqrt{2}/(h_{ie} + R_s').$$

Therefore,

$$P_i = (V_s')^2/2(h_{ie} + R_s'). \tag{10.22}$$

The signal power gain A_p is

$$A_p = P_o/P_i. \tag{10.23}$$

10.5 Distortion

By their very nature power amplifiers are required to handle large-signal swings. The resulting collector current and voltage swings cover the nonlinear regions of the collector characteristics. Generally, the distortion produced is primarily second-harmonic distortion. A graphical method for predicting distortion, based on a *three-point schedule*, will now be described.

Assume that for the amplifier of Fig. 10.12 the resultant collector characteristics with the superimposed ac load line appear as shown in Fig. 10.17. The *dynamic transfer curve* of Fig. 10.20, which in this case is a plot of collector current i_C versus base current i_B, is obtained by plotting the points of intersection of the ac load line and the base current curves. For example, the intersection of the ac load line with, say, the base current curve for I_{B1} corresponds to collector current I_{C1}. Other points are determined in the same manner to yield the transfer curve of Fig. 10.20.

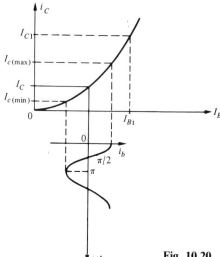

Fig. 10.20 Resultant transfer curve.

Note that the transfer curve is *nonlinear*; for an ideal device, the transfer curve would be a straight line and there would be no need for predicting distortion since it would not exist. Although the transistor is the basis for our discussion, the results obtained are perfectly general and can be used to predict distortion for any active device.

A nonlinear curve, like the transfer curve of Fig. 10.20, can be approximated by the following simple power series:

$$i_C = I_C + Ai_b + Bi_b^2. \tag{10.24}$$

Substitution of $i_b = I_b \cos \omega t$ in (10.24) yields

$$i_C = I_C + AI_b \cos \omega t + BI_b^2 \cos^2(\omega t). \tag{10.25}$$

But $\cos^2(\omega t) = 1/2 + \cos 2\omega t/2$; using this identity in place of $\cos^2(\omega t)$ in (10.25) and simplifying, we have

$$i_C = I_C + A_0 + A_1 \cos \omega t + A_2 \cos 2\omega t. \tag{10.26}$$

Examination of (10.26) reveals that the output expression contains an additional frequency term, $\cos 2\omega t$, that was not present at the input ($i_b = I_b \cos \omega t$) to the amplifier. Term $A_2 \cos 2\omega t$, of twice the frequency of the input signal, represents *second-harmonic distortion* owing to the nonlinear collector characteristics. In addition, a dc term A_0 which may add to or subtract from the quiescent collector current I_C is also present. The desired output, of course, is the *fundamental* term $A_1 \cos \omega t$.

To evaluate coefficients A_0, A_1, and A_2 of (10.26), it is convenient to choose points that yield easy-to-read values of collector current from the collector characteristics. Referring to Fig. 10.20, one can see that for $\omega t = 0$, $i_C = I_{c(max)}$; at $\omega t = \pi/2$, $i_C = I_C$; and for $\omega t = \pi$, $i_C = I_{c(min)}$. Substitution of these values in (10.26) yields

$$I_{c(max)} = I_C + A_0 + A_1 + A_2, \tag{10.27a}$$

$$I_C = I_C + A_0 - A_2, \tag{10.27b}$$

$$I_{c(min)} = I_C + A_0 - A_1 + A_2. \tag{10.27c}$$

Solving the preceding equations for A_0, A_1, and A_2, we obtain

$$A_0 = A_2 = (I_{c(max)} + I_{c(min)} - 2I_C)/4, \tag{10.28}$$

$$A_1 = (I_{c(max)} - I_{c(min)})/2. \tag{10.29}$$

Because $A_0 = A_2 \neq 0$, the change in quiescent collector current due to distortion is a function of the amount of distortion present. This may serve as a rough indication of the degree of distortion in an amplifier.

There is no need to draw the dynamic transfer characteristic curve in using the three-point schedule. The values of $I_{c(max)}$, $I_{c(min)}$, and I_C can be read directly from the collector family of curves, as will be illustrated in Example 10.3.

The percentage of second-harmonic distortion D_2 is given by

$$D_2 = \frac{|A_2|}{|A_1|} \times 100\%. \tag{10.30}$$

Example 10.3

The collector characteristics for a germanium transistor used in the single-ended class A power amplifier of Fig. 10.12 are given in Fig. 10.21. The transistor has the following ratings: $BV_{CER} = 30$ V, $P_{C(max)} = 10$ W, $V_{BE} = 0.3$ V, and $h_{ie} = 25$ ohms. Load resistance $R_L = 8$ ohms. Select V_{CC} and the transformer turns ratio n to ensure maximum possible output power with less than 5% second-harmonic distortion. Determine the values of R_1 and R_2, the output power, power gain, collector efficiency, and collector dissipation. Assume the peak-to-peak signal swing is 40 mA and neglect R_E. $R_s = 60$ ohms.

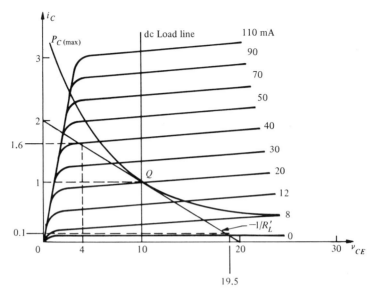

Fig. 10.21   Graphical construction for Example 10.3.

Solution

Because the maximum collector voltage swing can equal $2V_{CC}$ and $BV_{CER} = 30$ V, a value of $V_{CC} = 10$ V is chosen for conservative operation. (In practice it is not at all unusual to have the power supply voltage V_{CC} specified for you. The transistor is then selected such that twice the supply voltage does not exceed the breakdown voltage rating.) Neglecting the dc primary winding resistance, the dc load line appears as a vertical line in Fig. 10.21. Superimposed on the collector characteristics is the maximum dissipation curve. This was plotted by choosing various values for v_{CE} and calculating i_C such that their product is 10 W. Three points were sufficient for plotting the curve.

The Q-point is located at $V_{CE} = V_{CC} = 10$ V and $I_C = 1$ A; the magnitude of the base current $I_B = 20$ mA. Because $h_{ie} = 25$ ohms, the parallel combination of $R_1//R_2 = R_B$ should be at least equal to 10 times the value of h_{ie}, or 250 ohms to prevent any significant loading of the signal source by the bias network. A value of $R_2 = 600$ ohms is chosen; therefore, $I_{R2} = 0.3/600 = 0.5$ mA, and $I_{R1} = I_B + I_{R2} = 20.5$ mA. Hence, $R_1 = (10 - 0.3)/(20.5 \times 10^{-3}) = 470$ ohms; $R_B = 470//600 = 264$ ohms. This value is greater than 250 ohms and therefore $R_1 = 470$ ohms and $R_2 = 600$ ohms will be used.

To ensure maximum output power, the ac load line is made to intersect the Q-point and $v_{CE} = 20$ V. The slope $-1/R'_L = -1/10$. Since $R'_L = n^2 R_L, n = (R'_L/R_L)^{1/2} = (10/8)^{1/2} = 1.12$.

For a peak-to-peak signal swing of 40 mA, from Fig. 10.21 $I_{c(max)} =$ 1.6 A, $I_{c(min)} = 0.1$ A, $V_{c(min)} = 4$ V, and $V_{c(max)} = 19.5$ V. Using (10.19), we have

$$P_o = (19.5 - 4)(1.6 - 0.1)/8 \approx 3 \text{ W}.$$

Also,

$$P_{dc} = 10 \times 1 = 10 \text{ W},$$

$$\eta_c = (3/10) \times 100\% = 33.3\%,$$

$$P_{C(max)} = 10 \text{ W}.$$

From (10.28) and (10.29),

$$A_2 = (1.6 + 0.1 - 2 \times 1)/4 = -0.075,$$

$$A_1 = (1.6 - 0.1)/2 = 0.75,$$

$$D_2 = (0.075/0.75) \times 100\% = 10\%.$$

(Because $A_2 = A_0 = -0.075$ A is much less than $I_C = 1$ A, it is neglected and P_{dc} does not have to be recalculated.)

Since the second-harmonic distortion turns out to be twice as great as the specified 5% for the given signal swing, a trial-and-error approach is required in the selection of a new Q-point and load line, repeating the preceding calculations. A tradeoff will be made, obtaining less distortion at the expense of lower output power. This tradeoff process is rather typical in engineering design. If the input signal swing is reduced, the distortion will also be less.

The rms value of the base current is $40/(2\sqrt{2}) = 14.14$ mA. The value of $R'_s = 60//264 = 49$ ohms; $V'_s = (14.14 \times 10^{-3})(49 + 25) = 1.05$ V. Therefore, $V_s = 1.05 \times 324/264 = 1.23$ V, and $P_i = 1.23 \times 14.14 \times 10^{-3} = 17.3$ mW. $A_P = 3/(17.3 \times 10^{-3}) = 174 = 10\log_{10}(174) = 22.4$ dB.

For a germanium transistor, stability factor $S_i = \partial I_C / \partial I_{CO}$ is significant. If $S_i = 6$ is selected, it is found that $R_E = 52.5$ ohms is needed for current feedback stabilization. For the given Q-point, the voltage drop across the resistance would be $52.5 \times 1 = 52.5$ V, and the power dissipated in R_E would be equal to 52.5 W. Furthermore, an inordinately large value bypass capacitor would be required. Because of these practical difficulties, no attempt would be made to stabilize this particular amplifier in this manner. Instead, the power transistor would be mounted on a heat sink to ensure stable operation of the amplifier.

If an input transformer with a low value of secondary dc winding resistance is used, then it becomes feasible to use current feedback stabilization. For example, if the secondary resistance $R_s = 5$ ohms, then a value of $R_E = 1$ ohm is all that is required for $S_i = 6$. Since $R_E = 1$ ohm, no attempt would be made to use a bypass capacitor across the resistance.

Effect of Distortion on Output Power

A more accurate approximation of the dynamic transfer curve is based on a power series containing five terms, leading to a *five-point schedule*. Let

$$i_C = I_C + Ai_b + Bi_b^2 + Ci_b^3 + Di_b^4. \tag{10.31}$$

Substituting $i_b = I_b \cos \omega t$ and simplifying yields

$$i_C = I_C + A_0 + A_1 \cos \omega t + A_2 \cos 2\omega t + A_3 \cos 3\omega t + A_4 \cos 4\omega t. \tag{10.32}$$

Two new terms are present in (10.32), the *third* and *fourth* harmonics $A_3 \cos 3\omega t$ and $A_4 \cos 4\omega t$, that were not present in the expression based on the three-point schedule. Generally, these additional terms are quite small compared to the second harmonic and may be neglected in many applications.

The power produced by the fundamental term P_1 may be expressed as $A_1^2 R_L'/2$; in the general case, the total power P_t contributed by the fundamental and harmonic terms is

$$P_t = (A_1^2 + A_2^2 + A_3^2 + \cdots)R_L'/2. \tag{10.33}$$

But $D_2 = |A_2|/|A_1|$, $D_3 = |A_3|/|A_1|$, etc.; therefore,

$$P_t = (1 + D_2^2 + D_3^2 + \cdots)P_1. \tag{10.34}$$

If the total distortion D_T is defined as

$$D_T = (D_2^2 + D_3^2 + \cdots)^{1/2}, \tag{10.35}$$

then
$$P_t = (1 + D_T^2)P_1. \tag{10.36}$$

Assume that $D_T = 10\% = 0.1$; substitution of $0.1^2 = 0.01$ in (10.36) yields $P_t = 1.01P_1$. Note that 10% distortion represents only 1% of the total power delivered to the load. For this reason our previous analysis for determining output power that resulted in (10.19), where fundamental current and voltage terms were assumed, is valid even if appreciable distortion exists.

10.6   Class B Push-Pull Amplifier

It was demonstrated earlier that the maximum collector efficiency for a class *B* amplifier is 78.5%. Because such an amplifier is biased at cutoff, single-ended operation results in excessive distortion; for a sinewave input the output would appear as a half-wave rectified waveform. By connecting two transistors in a push-pull circuit, distortion is minimized and high collector efficiency is realized. In such applications as aerospace and hearing aids, class B operation is highly desirable. Since each transistor is biased at cutoff, the quiescent power is zero. Furthermore, the high efficiency permits transistors of smaller power ratings to be used than if operated as class A. Another advantage of push pull, regardless of the class of operation, is that all even-harmonic distortion terms are greatly reduced.

The class B push-pull amplifier was examined briefly in the beginning of the chapter. In this section we shall analyze the circuit in considerable detail. As shown in Fig. 10.3, from 0 to π radians transistor $Q1$ is forward biased and $Q2$ reverse biased. Therefore, collector current flows in $Q1$, and $Q2$ is cut off and behaves like an open switch. From π to 2π radians the transistors reverse their roles; now $Q2$ conducts and $Q1$ appears as an open switch.

With currents flowing away from the transformer polarity dots assumed positive, the net magnetomotive force H_n is

$$H_n = N_1(i_{C1} - i_{C2}) + N_2 i_L,$$

or
$$N_2 i_L - H_n = N_1(i_{C2} - i_{C1}). \qquad (10.37)$$

For a well-designed output transformer, $N_2 i_L \gg H_n$; therefore, (10.37) becomes

$$i_L = (N_1/N_2)(i_{C2} - i_{C1}). \qquad (10.38)$$

Equation (10.38) and the waveforms of Fig. 10.3 demonstrate that output current i_L is a sinewave if the input signal is a sinewave.

Because the load current i_L is a function of the difference in collector currents $i_{C2} - i_{C1}$, all even harmonic distortion terms cancel. Let

$$i_{C1} = I_c + A_0 + A_1 \cos \omega t + A_2 \cos 2\omega t + A_3 \cos 3\omega t + A_4 \cos 4\omega t + \cdots,$$
$$(10.39a)$$

$$i_{C2}(\omega t) = i_{C1}(\omega t + \pi)$$
$$i_{C2} = I_c + A_0 - A_1 \cos \omega t + A_2 \cos 2\omega t - A_3 \cos 3\omega t + A_4 \cos 4\omega t + \cdots.$$
$$(10.39b)$$

Replacing (10.39a, b) in (10.38) yields

$$i_L = (2N_1/N_2)(A_1 \cos \omega t + A_3 \cos 3\omega t + \cdots). \qquad (10.40)$$

Although the odd harmonic terms are doubled, these are generally small to begin with; the even harmonic terms, especially the second harmonic, predominate.

The preceding analysis assumed identical transistors. In practice, this can only be approximated, and consequently perfect cancellation of even harmonic terms is never realized.

Since one transistor is cut off while the other transistor is conducting, an examination of the "on" transistor is sufficient for finding the output power of a class B push-pull amplifier. With $N_1/N_2 = n$, the reflected impedance across the conducting transistor is $R'_L = n^2 R_L$. This is shown graphically in Fig. 10.22 where the ac load line is drawn through the Q-point at $v_{CE} = V_{CC}$ volts with a slope equal to $-1/R'_L$. When a transistor conducts, its voltage may swing between 0 and V_{CC} volts. The output power P_o, assuming the collector current swing reaches $I_{c(max)}$, is therefore equal to

$$P_o = I^2_{c(max)} R'_L/2. \tag{10.41}$$

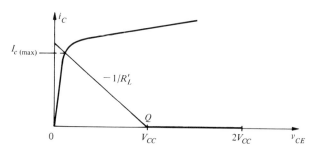

Fig. 10.22   Graphical determination of output power for a class B push-pull amplifier.

The dc input power per transistor is $I_{c(max)} V_{CC}/\pi$; for both transistors it is $2I_{c(max)} V_{CC}/\pi$. The total dc input power, in terms of collector dissipation per transistor P_C and output power P_o, is

$$P_{dc} = 2P_C + P_o \quad \text{or} \quad P_C = (P_{dc} - P_o)/2. \tag{10.42}$$

Substitution of the expressions for P_{dc} and P_o in (10.42) yields

$$P_C = I_{c(max)} V_{CC}/\pi - I^2_{c(max)} R'_L/4. \tag{10.43}$$

From (10.43) it is seen that without a signal, that is, $i_C = 0$, the collector dissipation is equal to zero. This is the opposite of class A operation where maximum collector dissipation occurs when no signal is present. To determine at what value of collector current I_{CM} maximum dissipation occurs in a class B push-pull amplifier, (10.43) is differentiated with respect to the collector current and equated to zero. The result obtained is

$$I_{CM} = 2I_{c(max)}/\pi, \tag{10.44}$$

which shows that maximum collector dissipation occurs at approximately two-thirds the value of the maximum collector current.

Because the base-emitter junction of a transistor is like that of a semiconductor diode, there is a deadband region where hardly any input current flows. This results in *crossover distortion*, as shown in Fig. 10.23. It is seen that the sinewave is flattened for small values of collector current as it crosses the ωt-axis. Crossover distortion may be removed by operating the transistor in class A or AB, to be described in the next section, or by introducing negative feedback around the amplifier (see Chapter 11). Another technique is to use a forward-biased diode of the same material as the transistor, illustrated in Fig. 10.24. The forward-bias voltage across the diode tends to cancel the base-emitter junction voltage. As was shown in Chapter 5, the diode also serves to stabilize the amplifier.

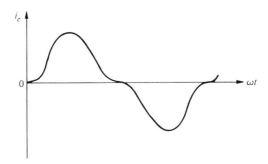

Fig. 10.23 An example of cross-over distortion.

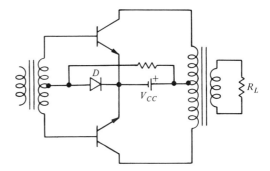

Fig. 10.24 Using a diode D to provide a turn-on bias for the elimination of crossover distortion.

Example 10.4

Assume the transistors in the class B push-pull amplifier of Fig. 10.3 have the characteristics given in Fig. 10.21. The collector supply voltage $V_{CC} = 10$ V and $R_L = 8$ ohms. The collector current should not exceed a peak value of 2 A. Determine the values of n, P_o, P_{dc}, η_c, and $P_{C(max)}$.

Solution

From Fig. 10.25, the ac load line intersects the v_{CE}-axis at $V_{CC} = 10$ V and the i_C-axis at 2 A. Therefore, $R'_L = 10/2 = 5$ ohms, and $n = N_1/N_2 = (5/8)^{1/2} = 0.79$.

From Fig. 10.25 it is estimated that $I_{c(max)} = 1.9$ A. By (10.41) $P_o = (1.9)^2 \times 5/2 = 9$ W. The dc input power $P_{dc} = 2 \times 1.9 \times 10/\pi = 12.1$ W; $\eta_c = (9/12.1) \times 100\% = 74.5\%$. At maximum collector dissipation, from (10.44), $I_{CM} = 2 \times 1.9/\pi = 1.21$ A. Substitution of this value in (10.43) yields the value for maximum collector dissipation:

$$P_{C(max)} = 1.21 \times 10/\pi - (1.2)^2 \times 5/4 = 2.03 \text{ W}.$$

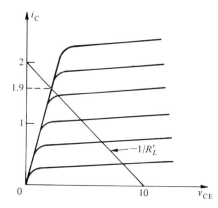

Fig. 10.25   Determining output power in Example 10.4.

A comparison of these results with those obtained in Example 10.3 for a single-ended class A power amplifier shows that class B operation provides three times the output power with a maximum dissipation equal to one-fifth that obtained from class A operation.

10.7   Class A and AB Push-Pull Operation

Although class B push-pull operation enjoys a high collector efficiency, crossover distortion results when transistors are used for the active device, and the power supply source V_{CC} generally has to be regulated for good results. The need for regulation arises because the average value of collector current fluctuates with the signal amplitude. Furthermore, one can never obtain a pair of perfectly matched transistors and consequently, in class B operation, there will be greater distortion than in either class A or AB push-pull operation. For these reasons we shall examine class A push-pull operation. It will be seen that classes AB and B are special cases of class A operation.

It was relatively simple to analyze the class B push-pull amplifier because when one transistor was conducting the other transistor was turned off. In class A push-pull operation each transistor is always conducting and thereby interacting with each other. Either a piecewise-linear analysis or a graphical analysis based on the composite characteristics of the transistors, to be described later, may be used.

If we use a piecewise-linear analysis, we are forced to linearize the collector characteristics. The analysis will yield only an approximate value of output power and no distortion value because of the linearization of the collector characteristics. The method, however, will be described since it permits a relatively quick estimate of output power.

The schematic of a class A push-pull amplifier is given in Fig. 10.26. By means of an ac linear model, the output circuit appears in Fig. 10.27A, where h_{OE} and h_{FE} are the average values of output admittance and short-circuit current gain, respectively. Because base currents I_{b1} and I_{b2} are 180° out of phase, the two controlled-current sources appear in series. Therefore, connection AB may be removed and the circuit redrawn as in Fig. 10.27B. Finally, by source transformation, Fig. 10.27C is obtained, where $R'_L = 4n^2 R_L$. From the figure,

$$I_L = h_{FE} I_b / (1 + h_{OE} R'_L / 2) \tag{10.45}$$

and

$$P_o = I_L^2 R'_L. \tag{10.46}$$

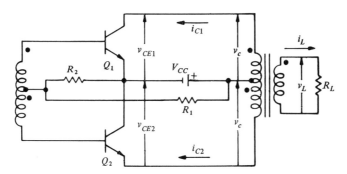

Fig. 10.26 A class A push-pull amplifier.

A graphical analysis will be undertaken now that provides distortion information and a more accurate value of output power than that obtainable from the piecewise-linear model. The basis for this approach is a derived set of *composite characteristics*, which is a family of curves relating $(i_{C1} - i_{C2})$ and v_{CE} for different values of signal base current i_b. From Fig. 10.26,

$$v_L = i_L R_L = (i_{C1} - i_{C2}) n R_L. \tag{10.47}$$

Also,

$$v_c = n v_L = (i_{C1} - i_{C2}) n^2 R_L.$$

But $R'_L = 4n^2 R_L$; hence, $n^2 R_L = R'_L / 4$ and

$$v_c = (i_{C1} - i_{C2}) R'_L / 4. \tag{10.48}$$

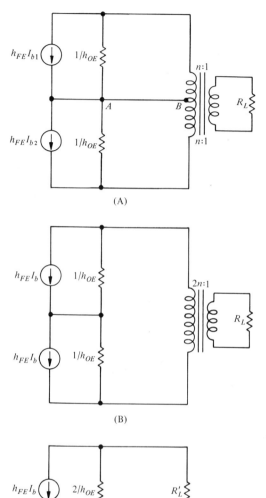

(A)

(B)

Fig. 10.27 Development of an ac-linear model for a class A push-pull amplifier. (A) Directly obtained model. (B) Removing connection AB. (C) Final simplification.

(C)

When the base current, say of $Q1$, is increased, the collector voltage of $Q1$ decreases. At the same time, the base current of $Q2$ decreases, and the collector voltage increases. These statements may be summarized in the following expressions:

$$i_{B1} = I_B + i_b, \tag{10.49a}$$

$$v_{CE1} = V_{CE} - v_c, \tag{10.49b}$$

$$i_{B2} = I_B - i_b, \tag{10.49c}$$

$$v_{CE2} = V_{CE} + v_c. \tag{10.49d}$$

The application of (10.49) yield the composite characteristics, as will now be explained.

In Fig. 10.28A, the collector characteristics for transistor $Q1$ are shown and the Q-point is located on the curves for class A operation. With a value for v_c chosen arbitrarily, that is, v_{ca}, point $X1$ corresponds to $V_{CE} - v_{ca}$ and $I_B + I_{b1}$, and point $Y1$ to $V_{CE} + v_{ca}$ and $I_B - I_{b1}$. If the ordinate of $Y1$ is subtracted from the ordinate of $X1$, we obtain point $Z1$. The ordinate of point $Z1$ is equal to $i_{C1} - i_{C2}$ for signal current I_{b1} and an arbitrary value of v_{ca}. By selecting other values of v_C, such as v_{cb}, we obtain points $X2$, $Y2$, and $Z2$ for I_{b1}. Repeating this procedure for other values of i_b, we have the composite characteristics of Fig. 10.28B, where $i_{C1} - i_{C2}$ versus v_{CE1} for different values of signal current i_b is plotted.

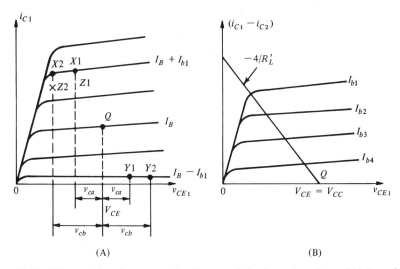

Fig. 10.28 Determining the composite characteristics for a transistor. (A) Location of points $Z1$ and $Z2$. (B) Final set of composite characteristics.

Now, substituting (10.48) in (10.49b), we obtain

$$v_{CE1} = V_{CE} - (i_{C1} - i_{C2})R_L'/4. \tag{10.50}$$

Expression (10.50) is an equation of the ac load line having a slope equal to $-4R_L'$ and intersecting $i_{C1} - i_{C2} = 0$ and $v_{CE1} = V_{CE} = V_{CC}$. This load line is plotted in Fig. 10.28B. Because of symmetry, one can determine the output power and distortion from the composite characteristics of a single transistor.

For example, the maximum value of load voltage v_L expressed by (10.47) can be determined from the maximum value of $i_{C1} - i_{C2}$ found graphically from Fig. 10.28B.

The described procedure can also be used for the analysis of class AB push-pull amplifiers. Some reflection will convince the reader that for class B operation the composite and static collector characteristics are identical and thus it is unnecessary to generate the composite characteristics.

10.8 Effects of Transformer Coupling on Frequency Response

The advantages of using coupling transformers include load matching and isolation, and the realization of greater collector efficiencies. On the debit side are cost, size, weight, and limited frequency response. In this section we examine the effects of the coupling transformer on the frequency response of an amplifier. To simplify the analysis, we shall consider the output transformer and neglect both the device and transformer capacitances. These restrictions, however, will not detract from the analysis, because the obtained results will point up the significant transformer parameters that limit frequency response.

In Fig. 10.29 the transistor output circuit is represented by a Thevenin equivalent, where the Thevenin resistance is equal to output resistance R_o, and the transformer is represented by its model. Resistance R_p is the primary dc winding resistance; $n^2 R_s$ is the reflected secondary dc winding resistance; $n^2 R_L = R'_L$; and R_m accounts for the transformer hysteresis and eddy current losses. Because resistance R_m in a well-designed transformer is very large compared with the other resistances in the circuit, it will be neglected in the analysis.

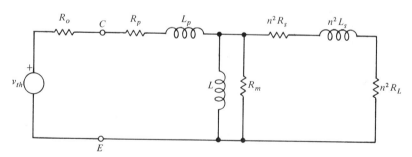

Fig. 10.29   Model of a coupling transformer.

Inductance L is the magnetizing inductance; L_p and $n^2 L_s$ are the primary and reflected secondary leakage inductances, respectively. The leakage inductances are very much less in value than the magnetizing inductance.

At low frequencies the leakage reactances are negligible compared with the magnetizing reactance. The lower break frequency ω_L occurs at the frequency for which the inductive reactance $\omega_L L$ equals the net resistance in the circuit R:

$$\omega_L L = R$$

or
$$\omega_L = R/L, \qquad (10.51)$$

where $R = (R_o + R_p)//n^2(R_L + R_s)$.

At high frequencies the leakage reactances are dominant, and the effects of the magnetizing inductance may be neglected. Again equating the reactance to the resistance in the circuit, we obtain the upper break frequency ω_H:

$$\omega_H = \frac{R_o + R_p + n^2(R_L + R_s)}{L_p + n^2 L_s}. \qquad (10.52)$$

Equations (10.51) and (10.52) indicate the transformer parameters required for good frequency performance. A large magnetizing inductance is essential for good low-frequency response, and low leakage inductance is necessary for good high-frequency response. A transformer with these characteristics can be bulky and expensive. Although we neglected the capacitance present in the circuit, these will have a pronounced effect at the resonant frequency determined by the net capacitance and inductance. At the resonant frequency a peak in the output response will be seen. In practice, the transformer selected will have the resonant peak well beyond the useful frequency range of the amplifier.

10.9 Transformerless Operation

It has been seen that a center-tap transformer is required at the input, as well as the output, for push-pull operation. The question one is tempted to ask is : Can the transformers be eliminated? Besides the obvious advantages of reduced weight, size, and cost in eliminating transformers, there is also the prospect of improved amplifier frequency response.

The center-tap input transformer for a push-pull amplifier provides equal amplitude and 180° out-of-phase signals to the bases of the transistors. An example of an electronic circuit which duplicates this action, the *split-load phase inverter*, is shown in Fig. 10.30A. Output 1 from the collector is 180° out of phase with respect to the input signal, whereas output 2, derived from the emitter, is in phase with the signal. Resistors R_1 and R_2 provide the bias for class A operation of the transistor. A hybrid model, neglecting h_{re}, h_{oe}, and $R_1//R_2$ as shown in Fig. 10.30B, will be analyzed to determine the relationship between R_E and R_C for equal signal gains.

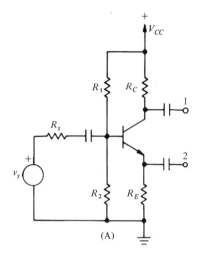

(A)

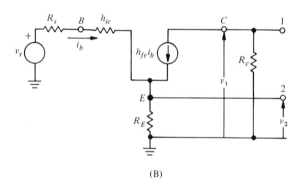

(B)

Fig. 10.30 Split-load phase inverter. (A) Circuit. (B) Small-signal model.

For the input circuit, we obtain

$$v_s = (R_s + h_{ie})i_b + (1 + h_{fe})i_b R_E$$

or

$$i_b = \frac{v_s}{R_s + h_{ie} + (1 + h_{fe})R_E}, \tag{10.53}$$

$$v_2 = R_E(1 + h_{fe})i_b$$

$$= \frac{(1 + h_{fe})v_s R_E}{R_s + h_{ie} + (1 + h_{fe})R_E}.$$

Solving for the voltage gain A_{v2}, we obtain

$$A_{v2} = \frac{(1 + h_{fe})R_E}{R_s + h_{ie} + (1 + h_{fe})R_E}. \tag{10.54}$$

From $v_1 = -h_{fe}i_b R_C$, we obtain A_{v1}:

$$A_{v1} = \frac{-h_{fe}R_C}{R_s + h_{ie} + (1 + h_{fe})R_E}. \tag{10.55}$$

For equal voltage gains, $(1 + h_{fe})R_E = h_{fe}R_C$; therefore,

$$R_E = h_{fe}R_C/(1 + h_{fe}). \tag{10.56}$$

Since $h_{fe} \gg 1$, $R_E \approx R_C$.

Inspection of (10.54) and (10.55) reveals that the voltage gains are less than unity and the voltage at the collector is 180° out of phase with respect to the voltage at the emitter. Since the output resistance is much less for the emitter output than for the collector output, a resistor is sometimes placed in series with output 2 to equalize the output resistance. Another circuit that is used for phase inversion, the difference amplifier, will be analyzed in Chapter 16.

Complementary Symmetry

A push-pull amplifier that does not require input or output transformers, referred to as the *complementary symmetry amplifier*, is shown in Fig. 10.31. Note that transistor $Q1$ is *n-p-n* and $Q2$ is *p-n-p*. Also, each transistor behaves as an emitter follower. If class B operation is assumed, for the source polarity indicated in Fig. 10.31, $Q1$ is forward biased and $Q2$ is cut off. Transistor $Q1$ conducts from 0 to π radians like the transformer version of the amplifier.

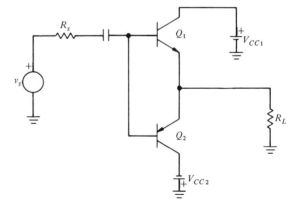

Fig. 10.31 Complementary symmetry class B push-pull amplifier.

On the negative-half input cycle, π to 2π radians, $Q2$ conducts and $Q1$ is off. Because $I_e \approx I_c$, the equations derived for the transformer class B push-pull amplifier also apply to the complementary symmetry circuit. The circuit can be also adapted for class A or AB operation.

There are two significant disadvantages to the complementary symmetry circuit of Fig. 10.31: (1) High-power *n-p-n* and *p-n-p* transistors having the same electrical characteristics are difficult to obtain and are expensive. (2) Two separate power supplies may be required. The *quasi-complementary* circuit, shown in basic form in Fig. 10.32, removes these objections. Note that power transistors $Q2$ and $Q4$ are both *n-p-n* and the low-level driving transistors are complementary, that is, $Q1$ is *n-p-n* and $Q3$ is *p-n-p*. On the positive half cycle of the input signal $Q1$ and $Q2$ conduct, while $Q3$ and $Q4$ are cut off. During the negative half cycle, $Q1$ and $Q2$ are cut off, and $Q3$ conducts. The collector current of $Q3$ is the base current for $Q4$ and output current flows through load resistance R_L.

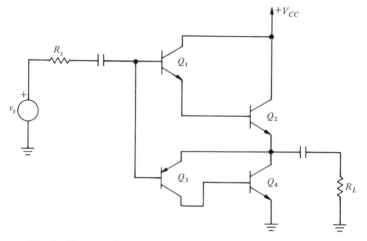

Fig. 10.32   Quasi-complementary class B push-pull amplifier.

10.10   Voltage-Operated Power Amplifiers

Our discussion of power amplifiers to this point has considered only a current-operated device, that is, the junction transistor. The restriction to junction transistor circuits was for very good reasons; vacuum tubes are rarely used in new low- and audio-frequency power amplifier designs and the field-effect transistor is presently limited in output power. The techniques derived for the analysis of junction transistor power amplifiers, however, apply to vacuum tubes, as well as FET circuits.

Examples of vacuum tube power amplifiers are illustrated in Fig. 10.33. Note that for class *B* operation a separate bias source V_{cc} is required to operate the device in cutoff. Complementary symmetry operation is not possible with vacuum tubes; field-effect transistors, however, may be operated as complementary-symmetry amplifiers.

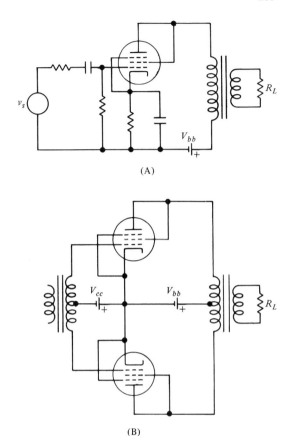

Fig. 10.33 Examples of vacuum tube power amplifiers. (A) Class A single-ended amplifier. (B) Class B push-pull amplifier.

10.11   Summary

Because of the widespread use of junction transistors for low- and audio-frequency power amplifiers, our discussion was limited to this device. The methods of analysis developed for the junction transistor circuit, however, also apply in general to vacuum tube and FET power amplifiers. Class *B* push-pull operation yields maximum collector efficiency of 78.4%, whereas class *A* operation with output transformer coupling exhibits 50% maximum collector efficiency.

The significant parameters for characterizing a power amplifier are output power, distortion, efficiency, power gain, and thermal resistance. Junction transistors are generally mounted on a heat sink of suitable dimensions to dissipate the heat arising primarily in the collector-base junction. A thermal equivalent circuit was derived and a procedure for determining heat sink dimensions given. Other factors, such as avalanche, punch through, and second breakdown, were also considered.

A graphical method based on the three-point schedule was developed for predicting distortion. In single-ended operation, second-harmonic distortion usually predominates. Graphical methods were also developed for finding the output power of single-ended class *A* and of class *A*, *AB*, and *B* push-pull amplifiers. For matched devices, all even harmonics cancel in push-pull operation. Whereas maximum collector dissipation occurs with no signal in class *A*, collector dissipation is zero in absence of a signal for class *B* operation.

The coupling transformers used in power amplifiers affect the frequency response. For good response a coupling transformer should have large magnetizing inductance and small leakage inductance. Complementary symmetry and quasi-symmetry power amplifiers are examples of circuits that require neither input nor output transformers. The split-load phase inverter is an electronic circuit that can replace the input phase-inverting transformer required for push-pull operation.

References

ANGELO, JR., E. J., *Electronics: BJTs, FETs, and Microcircuits*, McGraw-Hill, New York, 1969.
MILLMAN, J., *Vacuum-Tube and Semiconductor Electronics*, McGraw-Hill, New York, 1958.
PIERCE, J. F., *Transistor Circuit Theory and Design*, Charles E. Merrill, Ohio, 1963.
RCA Silicon Power Circuits Manual SP-50, 1967.

Problems

10.1   In the circuit of Fig. 10.2A, assume that the transistor and transformer are ideal. If $R_L = 8$ ohms, $V_{CC} = 30$ V, and the power dissipated in R_L is 10 W for maximum signal swing, calculate (a) turns ratio n; (b) Q-point; and (c) the maximum collector current and voltage. (d) What is the collector efficiency?

10.2   Assume that a dc meter is placed in the collector circuit of an ideal single transistor amplifier operating class *B*. If the meter reads 100 mA and the collector load resistance is 100 ohms, what is the average signal power dissipated in the load resistance?

10.3   Referring to Fig. 10.3, assume that the transistor and transformers are ideal. If $V_{CC} = 30$ V, $R_L = 25$ ohms, $n = 2$, and the peak voltage of the output signal swing is V_{CC} volts, calculate (a) output signal power; (b) collector efficiency; and (c) power dissipated in each transistor.

10.4   Repeat Prob. 10.3 for $n = 4$. Compare results.

10.5 Verify equation (10.10).

10.6 If $I_{CBO} = 0.1\,\mu A$, $V_o = 0.6$ V, $BV_{CBO} = 50$ V, $V_{BB} = 2.4$ V, $R_B = 500$ K, and $n = 4$, calculate the values of BV_{CER} and BV_{CEX}.

10.7 Repeat Prob. 10.6 for $I_{CBO} = 1\,\mu A$. Compare results.

10.8 A value of $\theta_{JC} = 5°C/W$ is specified for a 2N3879 power transistor. Assuming that the data of Table 10.1 and Fig. 10.8 are applicable, calculate the heat sink size if the transistor dissipates 17 W at 100°C ambient and a mica washer is used. The maximum junction temperature is 200°C.

10.9 Repeat Prob. 10.8 for 25 W dissipation at 50°C. Compare results.

10.10 A silicon power transistor (TO-3 case) is mounted on a 8-square inch heat sink described by Fig. 10.8. The insulating materials is beryllia (see Table 10.1). Assuming that $T_J = 150°C$ and $\theta_{JC} = 1°C/W$ (a) if the ambient temperature is 75°C, find the maximum allowable power the transistor can dissipate. (b) For the conditions of (a), what is the case temperature?

10.11 Assume that a load line is just tangent to the 35-W dissipation curve for a 2N3879 at $V_{CE} = 10$ V. Is this a good Q-point? Why? (b) If your answer to (a) is negative, how should the Q-point be located?

10.12 For the class A power amplifier of Fig. 10.12, a 2N3879 power transistor is used. The transistor is biased at $V_{CE} = 7$ V and $I_C = 2.4$ A. (a) What base current is required? If $n^2 R_L = 2.9$ ohms and the peak-to-peak base current swing due to a sinusoidal signal is 60 mA, determine (b) output power; (c) input power; (d) power gain; (e) collector efficiency; and (f) second-harmonic distortion. Assume that the transformer is ideal, $R_E = 0$, and $R_s = 50$ ohms.

10.13 A 2N3879 power transistor is used in the amplifier of Fig. 10.12 and the Q-point is specified at 10 V and 3.5 A; $R_L = 4$ ohms and $R_s = 50$ ohms. Design the amplifier for maximum output power. Determine the value of (a) n; (b) R_1 and R_2; (c) output power; (d) collector efficiency; and (e) second-harmonic distortion.

10.14 Choosing the values of $\omega t = 0$ for $i_c = I_{c(max)}$; $\omega t = \pi/3$ for $i_c = I_{c1}$; $\omega t = \pi/2$ for $i_c = I_C$; $\omega t = 2\pi/3$ for $i_c = I_{c2}$; and $\omega t = \pi$ for $i_c = I_{c(min)}$, derive the coefficients of (10.32) for a five-point schedule.

10.15 The transistor type used in a class B push-pull amplifier is a 2N3879. The collector supply voltage is 8 V and $R_L = 4$ ohms. The collector current should not exceed 5 A. Determine the value of (a) n; (b) P_o; (c) P_{dc}; (d) η_c; and (e) $P_{C(max)}$.

10.16 Repeat Prob. 10.15 for a collector-supply voltage of 10 V. Compare results.

10.17 Repeat Prob. 10.15 for class AB operation. Each transistor is biased at $V_{CE} = 8$ V and $I_C = 0.5$ A. Compare results.

10.18   Calculate (a) the maximum output power and (b) collector efficiency for a class A push-pull amplifier. Each transistor is biased at 6 V and 3 A; assume ideal transistor characteristics.

10.19   In Fig. 10.29, assume that $R_o = 1$ K, $R_p = 4$ ohms, $R_s = 0.9$ ohm, $n = 2$, and $R_L = 4$ ohms. If the low-break frequency is 50 Hz, determine the minimum value of magnetizing inductance L.

10.20   If, in Prob. 10.19, the upper break frequency is 10 kHz, calculate the maximum total leakage inductance $L_p + n^2 L_s$.

10.21   Referring to Fig. 10.31, assume that p-n-p version of the 2N3879 is available and used for $Q2$; $V_{CC1} = V_{CC2} = 6$ V; $R_L = 4$ ohms; and the peak collector current does not exceed 1 A. (a) Plot the load voltage across R_L for one cycle of a sinusoidal input signal. (b) Determine the output power and collector efficiency of the amplifier.

10.22   Carefully analyze the circuit of Fig. 10.32 by drawing signal waveforms at the base and collector of each transistor.

10.23   A 6L6-GC, connected as a triode, is operated class A in a single-ended transformer-coupled power amplifier. For a Q-point of 200 V and 60 mA, determine the output power and second-harmonic distortion for a sinusoidal signal swing of 30 V peak-to-peak for a reflected load R_L' of (a) 3.5 K and (b) 5 K.

The Feedback Amplifier

The performance characteristics of an amplifier may be altered considerably by the use of feedback. The input to a feedback amplifier consists of the input signal and a portion, *or* all, of the output signal. The algebraic sign of the feedback signal with respect to the input determines whether the feedback is called *positive* or *negative*. Also, the manner by which the feedback signal is derived enables one to speak of *current* or *voltage* feedback.

The feedback amplifier may be considered a special case of a general feedback loop. For this reason it is appropriate to study a single loop system and relate the feedback amplifier to this case.

11.1   Definition of the Transfer Function

In feedback systems, an element is normally represented by its block diagram, as illustrated in Fig. 11.1. The ratio of the output to the input signal is the transfer function signified by symbol $G(s)$. The relationship between output and input of an element as a function of time may be expressed by an integro-differential equation. The transfer function, however, is usually given in terms of the complex variable s.

Fig. 11.1   Block diagram of a circuit element.

Consider a series RC highpass circuit, which was also discussed in Chapter 8. The differential equation relating input $v_1(t)$ and output $v_2(t)$ may be expressed as

$$C\frac{dv_2(t)}{dt} + \frac{v_2(t)}{R} = C\frac{dv_1(t)}{dt}. \tag{11.1}$$

Taking the Laplace transform of (11.1) and assuming zero initial conditions, one obtains

$$G(s) = \frac{V_2(s)}{V_1(s)} = \frac{sRC}{1 + sRC}. \tag{11.2}$$

The block diagram of the RC network may therefore be represented as in Fig. 11.1 where $G(s)$ is given by (11.2), $V_1(s) =$ input, and $V_2(s) =$ output. With the aid of the transfer function, the transient or steady-state response of a circuit may be studied. The transfer function of cascaded elements is the product of the transfer function of each element (providing the loading effect of the elements can be neglected). For example, in a field-effect transistor amplifier, the loading effect of the gate may usually be neglected. Figure 11.2A shows a one-stage RC-coupled amplifier, and Fig. 11.2B gives the transfer function of each element. The overall transfer function $G(s)$, valid for low frequencies, is

$$G(s) = \frac{V_3(s)}{V_1(s)} = G_1(s)G_2(s) = -\left(\frac{\mu R_L}{r_p + R_L}\right)\left(\frac{sR_g C}{1 + sR_g C}\right). \tag{11.3}$$

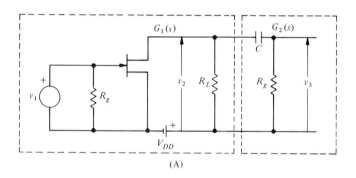

(A)

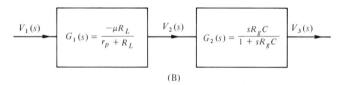

(B)

Fig. 11.2   An RC-coupled FET amplifier. (A) Circuit. (B) Block diagram.

11.2   Negative Feedback

When the returned signal subtracts from the input, negative feedback is obtained. For the case in which the output signal is added to the input, positive feedback is said to exist. In this chapter, our concern will be with negative feedback. Positive feedback will be considered in the chapter on oscillators.

In an electronic amplifier, negative feedback is generally utilized to stabilize the circuit against component or power supply changes, to extend amplifier bandwidth, and to minimize distortion. An example is the emitter resistor used in transistor amplifiers for stabilizing the dc operating point. In some cases, however, negative feedback is introduced as a result of other considerations. An illustration of this is the source resistor used in FET amplifiers for biasing.

Figure 11.3 indicates a feedback-loop system. The box denoted by $H(s)$ represents the feedback element. It may take the form of a simple resistive voltage divider or a sophisticated circuit. More will be said about the feedback element later in the chapter.

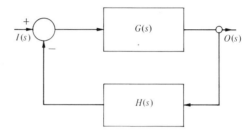

Fig. 11.3 Block diagram of a system with feedback.

The loop of Fig. 11.3 introduces negative feedback because the signal fed back is *subtracted* from the input signal. Let us compare the performance of this system with an open-loop type, that is, a system with no feedback. Assume both systems have the same transfer function $G(s)$; for the case without feedback, the output is

$$O(s) = G(s)I(s), \tag{11.4}$$

where $O(s)$ and $I(s)$ are the output and input signals, respectively. The signals may represent voltage or current.

Let us assume that the amplitude and the phase of the input signal remain constant, but G changes.* For example, if G represents the block diagram of a FET amplifier, aging could change the μ and r_p of the device. The open-loop gain will consequently change as follows:

$$dO = I\,dG,$$

or the ratio of change is

$$dO/O = dG/G. \tag{11.5}$$

* At this point we can write G instead of $G(s)$, H instead of $H(s)$, etc., without any misunderstanding.

If G varies by 10%, the output will also change by the same amount.
For the closed loop, one obtains

$$O = (I - OH)G$$

or
$$O(1 + GH) = IG.$$

Therefore,

$$O = \frac{G}{1 + GH}I. \tag{11.6}$$

If I and H are constant and if G varies as in the previous case, one obtains

$$dO = \left[\frac{(1 + GH)\,dG - GH\,dG}{(1 + GH)^2}\right]I$$

or
$$\frac{dO}{dG} = \left(\frac{O}{G}\right)\left(\frac{1}{1 + GH}\right).$$

Therefore,

$$\frac{dO}{O} = \frac{dG}{G}\left(\frac{1}{1 + GH}\right). \tag{11.7}$$

Equation (11.7) states that the change in O is divided by $1 + GH$. If $1 + GH = 10$, then a 10% change in G produces only a 1% change in the output.
From (11.6), if $GH \gg 1$, then

$$O = I/H. \tag{11.8}$$

In other words, if $GH \gg 1$, the output remains virtually independent of the characteristics of the forward loop. For feedback electronic amplifiers, G depends on the characteristics of the active device being used. The feedback element, on the other hand, is usually composed of passive elements and its transfer function $H \leqslant 1$. Highly stable components for the feedback element can be chosen to ensure stable amplifier operation. We then see that feedback has the advantage of making the output independent of variable parameter elements included in G.
If $H = 1$, we have 100% feedback and

$$O/I = G/(1 + G). \tag{11.9}$$

The Effect of Negative Feedback on Gain and Bandwidth

Consider again the RC-coupled amplifier (without feedback) of Fig. 11.2. The overall transfer function may be written as

$$G = -Ks/(1 + sT), \tag{11.10}$$

where $K = \mu R_L R_g C/(r_p + R_L)$ and

$$T = R_g C.$$

With $s = j\omega$, (11.10) becomes

$$G(j\omega) = -j\omega K/(1 + j\omega T). \tag{11.11}$$

The same circuit with unity feedback ($H = -1$) is shown in Fig. 11.4. Then,

$$O/I = G_f = G/(1 - G) \tag{11.12a}$$
$$= -Ks/[1 + s(K + T)].$$

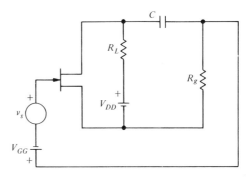

Fig. 11.4 RC-coupled amplifier with unity feedback.

With $s = j\omega$, (11.12a) becomes

$$G_f = -j\omega K/[1 + j\omega(K + T)]. \tag{11.12b}$$

The asymptotic plots of the amplitudes of (11.11) and (11.12b) are given in Fig. 11.5. Referring to curve B, we see the break frequency is lowered and the midband gain decreased. Curve A represents the response of the circuit without feedback. Negative feedback reduces the gain and increases the bandwidth. If an output equal to that obtained without feedback is desired, a greater signal is necessary. With feedback, increasing the midband gain K itself would modify the lower break frequency, as may be seen from (11.12b).

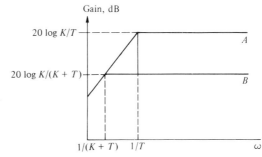

Fig. 11.5 Gain as a function of frequency. Curve A: without feedback. Curve B: with unity feedback.

Example 11.1

The first stage of an RC-coupled amplifier has a midband gain of 20 dB and a lower break frequency of 10 rad/s. The transfer function for the amplifier is $G = s/(1 + 0.1s)$. An output of 20 mV is required at mid-frequencies. (a) Without feedback, find the required input signal for 20 mV of output and calculate the output at 10 rad/s. (b) Is it possible to lower the break frequency to 5 rad/s? (c) If the condition imposed in part (b) is possible, calculate the required input signal for a midband output of 20 mV.

Solution

(a) A gain of 20 dB corresponds to a numerical value of gain $= 10$. Therefore,

$$v_{in} = 20/10 = 2 \text{ mV}.$$

The output at the break frequency of 10 rad/s is

$$v_o = 20/\sqrt{2} \text{ mV}.$$

(b) To lower the break frequency to 5 rad/s, negative feedback will be used. If H is made equal to unity, 100 % feedback is obtained. The transfer function of the amplifier without feedback is

$$G = s/(1 + 0.1s).$$

With unity feedback, we have

$$G_f = s/[1 + (1 + 0.1)s].$$

The minimum break frequency is $\omega_b \approx 1$ rad/s. Therefore it is possible to lower the break frequency to 5 rad/s.

(c) The value of H required for $\omega_b = 5$ rad/s is now calculated. From

$$G_f = s/[1 + (0.1 + H)s]$$

$$1/(0.1 + H) = 5 \text{ rad/s}.$$

Solving for H, one obtains

$$H = 0.1.$$

The midband gain is

$$G_f = 10/(1 + 10 \times 0.1) = 5.$$

Consequently, 4 mV is required for an output of 20 mV at mid-frequencies.

Effect of Negative Feedback on Distortion and Noise

Negative feedback reduces greatly amplitude (nonlinear) distortion which may be present at the output of an amplifier. For an amplifier output of v volts, assume that d represents the amount of distortion present without feedback. With negative feedback and a sufficient input signal, it is possible to produce the same output voltage v with less distortion d.

A portion of the output distortion is returned to the amplifier input through the feedback network and reamplified in such a manner as to cancel the distortion present in the amplifier. Let D be the distortion of the amplifier with feedback. The distortion returned to the input of the amplifier is therefore HD. This is amplified and the total distortion at the output will be $D = d - HDG$. Solving for D, one obtains

$$D = d/(1 + GH). \qquad (11.13)$$

Equation (11.13) shows that amplitude distortion is reduced by the factor $(1 + GH)$. We also observe that distortion is reduced by the same amount as the gain of the amplifier without feedback. For example, if a 20 dB reduction in distortion is required, the input signal must be 20 dB greater than required without feedback. If the input cannot be increased, the amplifier is designed so its gain without feedback is 20 dB greater than the actual required gain.

The reader may wonder if increasing the input signal also increases the distortion. Generally, this will not be the case. Amplitude distortion normally occurs in the last, or power stage, of an amplifier where large signal swings exist. Raising the gain of the voltage stages preceding the power stage, or increasing the amplitude of the input signal, will not result in an increase in distortion for a properly designed circuit.

Hum and other spurious noise introduced externally into the amplifier will be reduced also by the factor $(1 + GH)$. Internal noise in the device itself or from passive components, however, will not be reduced by negative feedback.

11.3 Current and Voltage Feedback

With current feedback we can achieve somewhat different results than with voltage feedback. For this reason it is important to be able to distinguish between these two types. In current feedback the voltage returned to the input is proportional to the output, or load, current. In voltage feedback the voltage fed back is proportional to the output, or load, voltage. An amplifier with current feedback tends to maintain constant output current regardless of the load; the amplifier therefore appears as a current source. Voltage feedback will tend to make the amplifier behave as a voltage source.

An example of current feedback is a FET amplifier with its source resistance R_S unbypassed. One effect of this type of feedback is to increase the effective value of the drain resistance r_p. The incremental model of the amplifier is given in Fig. 11.6, and the block diagram of the circuit is shown in Fig. 11.7.

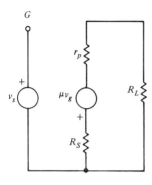

Fig. 11.6 Incremental model of a FET amplifier with current feedback.

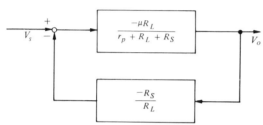

Fig. 11.7 Block diagram of circuit of Fig. 11.6.

The output is taken across R_L, that is, between drain and ground. Consequently, the transfer function of the amplifier without feedback, is

$$G = -\mu R_L/(r_p + R_L + R_S).$$

The feedback factor is

$$H = -R_S/R_L.$$

The transfer function of the amplifier, including feedback, becomes

$$G_f = -\mu R_L/[r_p(1 + R_S g_m) + R_L + R_S]. \tag{11.14}$$

Equation (11.14) indicates that the amplifier with current feedback may be viewed as an amplifier without feedback but with a drain resistance equal to $r_p(1 + R_S g_m)$. Similar results are obtained for a vacuum tube using a cathode resistance.

An example of a transistor amplifier with voltage feedback is given in Fig. 11.8A, and its incremental model is shown in Fig. 11.8B. It is assumed that $h_{re} = 0$. The output admittance will be calculated with feedback and compared to the value without feedback, which is h_{oe}. From Fig. 11.8B, one obtains

$$Y_o = i_c/v_o.$$

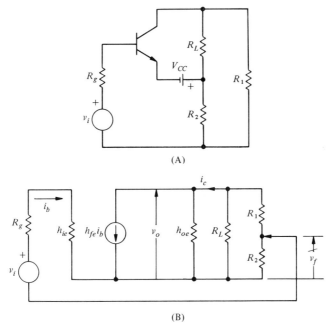

(A)

(B)

Fig. 11.8 Transistor amplifier with voltage feedback. (A) Circuit. (B) Incremental model.

But

$$i_c = h_{fe}i_b + v_o h_{oe}. \tag{11.15a}$$

With $v_i = 0$,

$$i_b = v_f/(R_g + h_{ie}) = R_2 v_o/(R_1 + R_2)(R_g + h_{ie}), \tag{11.15b}$$

where $v_f =$ feedback voltage to the input circuit. Substituting (11.15b) for i_b in (11.15a) and simplifying, one obtains

$$Y_o = h_{oe} + [h_{fe}/(R_g + h_{ie})][R_2/(R_1 + R_2)]. \tag{11.16}$$

Equation (11.16) illustrates that the output admittance is greater (or one can say the output resistance is less) with feedback than without feedback, for which $Y_o = h_{oe}$.

The transfer function representing the gain of a feedback amplifier is easily obtained if the feedback factor is identified. In this example, the feedback factor H is found by inspection of Fig. 11.8:

$$H = -R_2/(R_1 + R_2). \tag{11.17}$$

The gain G without feedback is easily obtained:

$$G = v_o/v_i = -h_{fe}(r_o//R_L)/(R_g + h_{ie}), \tag{11.18}$$

where $r_o = 1/h_{oe}$. The gain with feedback is calculated from (11.6):

$$G_f = \frac{-h_{fe}(r_o//R_L)(R_1 + R_2)}{(R_g + h_{ie})(R_1 + R_2) + h_{fe}(r_o//R_L)R_2}. \qquad (11.19)$$

In some cases, however, one cannot identify the feedback factor by inspection, and the gain is calculated by other methods. The feedback factor is then identified from the expression for gain. As an example, consider the FET amplifier of Fig. 11.9. The gain for this configuration will be found with the aid of four-terminal theory developed in Chapter 6. If $Z_1 = 0, Z_f = \infty$, and $Z_g = \infty$, the feedback is eliminated and we obtain the following y-matrix:

$$[Y]_1 = \begin{bmatrix} 0 & 0 \\ g_m & Y_o \end{bmatrix},$$

where g_m = transconductance of the FET in mhos; $Y_o = g_p + Y_L$; $g_p = 1/r_p$; and $Y_L = 1/Z_L$. The voltage gain G_1 of the stage is, therefore,

$$G_1 = v_L/v_i = -g_m/Y_o. \qquad (11.20)$$

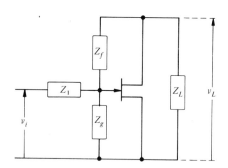

Fig. 11.9 Example of a feedback amplifier.

With finite values for Z_f and Z_g, the following matrix is obtained:

$$[Y]_2 = \begin{bmatrix} Y_f + Y_g & -Y_f \\ g_m - Y_f & Y_o + Y_f \end{bmatrix},$$

where $Y_f = 1/Z_f$ and $Y_g = 1/Z_g$. In order to add Z_1 to the circuit of Fig. 11.9, we transform the Y elements to Z elements:

$$\Delta Y = Y_f Y_o + Y_f g_m + Y_g Y_o + Y_f Y_g. \qquad (11.21)$$

The corresponding Z-matrix with Z_1, Z_f, and Z_g will have the following values:

$$Z_{11} = (Y_o + Y_f + Z_1 \Delta Y)/\Delta Y, \qquad (11.22)$$

$$Z_{21} = (-g_m + Y_f)/\Delta Y. \qquad (11.23)$$

The overall voltage gain of the network will be

$$G_f = v_L/v_i = Z_{21}/Z_{11} = (-g_m + Y_f)/(Y_o + Y_f + Z_1\Delta Y). \quad (11.24)$$

Dividing the numerator and denominator of (11.24) by Y_o, letting $G_1 = -g_m/Y_o$, and expressing ΔY by (11.21), one obtains

$$G_f = \frac{G_1 + Y_f/Y_o}{(1 + Y_f/Y_o)(1 + Z_1Y_g) + (1 - G_1)Z_1Y_f}. \quad (11.25)$$

Expressing (11.25) in Z-parameters, one obtains

$$G_f = \frac{G_1 + Z_o/Z_f}{(1 + Z_o/Z_f)(1 + Z_1/Z_g) + (1 - G_1)Z_1/Z_f}. \quad (11.26)$$

For the conditions that $|Z_o/Z_f| \ll 1$ and $|G_1| \gg 1$, (11.26) reduces to

$$G_f = \frac{G_1}{1 + G_1(Z_1/G_1Z_g - Z_1/Z_f)} \quad (11.27)$$

The feedback factor H from (11.27) is

$$H = Z_1/G_1Z_g - Z_1/Z_f. \quad (11.28)$$

In general, H will be a complex quantity. If a second approximation is made that Z_1/G_1Z_g is negligible with respect to Z_1/Z_f, (11.28) reduces to

$$H = -Z_1/Z_f \quad (11.29)$$

For H to be real when $Z_f = R_f$, Z_1 must also be resistive.

11.4   The Operational Amplifier

An operational amplifier is a high-gain (e.g., 10^6) dc voltage amplifier. With feedback this amplifier is used widely in electronic circuits and is a basic element of analog computers. The circuit is also manufactured as an integrated circuit in large numbers (see Chapter 16). The following is an introduction to the operational amplifier; the schematic symbol for the amplifier is shown in Fig. 11.10A.

(A)

Fig. 11.10 High-gain operational amplifier. (A) Schematic symbol. (B) Impedances Z_1 and Z_f inserted in the forward and feedback paths of the amplifier.

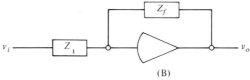

(B)

An operational amplifier, with impedance elements in its forward and feedback paths, is shown in Fig. 11.10B. The general feedback equation for the configuration is

$$V_o/V_i = G/(1 + GH).$$

As $G \to \infty$,

$$V_o/V_i = 1/H.$$

From (11.28), if $G \to \infty$, $H = -Z_1/Z_f$. Therefore,

$$V_o/V_i \approx -Z_f/Z_1. \tag{11.30}$$

Equation (11.30) shows that the output voltage equals the negative of the input voltage time the ratio of the feedback to the input impedance. The negative sign exists because there is a sign reversal between the output and input voltages.

If the impedances are pure resistances, that is, $Z_f = R_f$ and $Z_1 = R_1$, then

$$v_o = -v_i R_f/R_1. \tag{11.31}$$

An operational amplifier with pure resistances at the input and feedback paths multiplies the input by the coefficient $-R_f/R_1$.

Making Z_f capacitive ($Z_f = 1/sC$) and letting $Z_1 = R_1$ we obtain

$$V_o = (-1/sR_1C_f)V_i, \tag{11.32a}$$

where s is interpreted as the Laplace operator. Equation (11.32a) shows that the output is the integral of the input and the circuit behaves like an *integrator*. If now we make Z_1 capacitive and Z_f resistive, we get

$$V_o = -sR_f C_1 V_i. \tag{11.32b}$$

The output is equal to minus the derivative of the input, and the network is called a *differentiator*.

With the operational amplifier it is possible to multiply, integrate, and differentiate. These operations serve as the basis for solving integro-differential equations on the analog computer. Because the operational amplifier when used as a differentiator tends to be sensitive to noise, differentiation is seldom used.

11.5   Stability of Feedback Systems

As mentioned earlier, the transfer function of a circuit expressed as a function of the complex variable s is derived from the integro-differential equation describing the circuit. The roots of the characteristic equation, which determine the transient response, may be real or complex. The solution of the differential equation is of the form:

$$y(t) = C_1 \exp(p_1 t) + C_2 \exp(p_3 t) + \cdots + C_n \exp(p_n t), \qquad (11.33)$$

where $p_1, p_2, \ldots, p_n$ are roots of the characteristic equation and $C_1, C_2, \ldots,$ C_n are constants that depend on the initial conditions of the system.

For the transient terms to vanish with increasing values of time, it is necessary that the real part of all the roots of the characteristic equation be negative in sign; this represents a stable system. If the roots are complex, they occur in conjugate pairs and thus ensure real coefficients. For complex roots with positive real values the response will be sinusoidal with rising amplitude (which will be generally limited to a finite value by the saturation of the active device). The condition of rising amplitude with time represents an unstable system and is to be avoided in feedback amplifiers.

In the next section we study the mathematical requirements for stability of a feedback amplifier. The basic expression derived for a feedback system was

$$0 = [G/(1 + GH)]I. \qquad (11.6)$$

The characteristic equation to be examined is $1 + GH$, because $(1 + GH)0 = GI$.

Nyquist Stability Criterion

The roots of a second-order characteristic equation are readily obtained. If the order is higher, however, the analytical solution becomes quite formidable. For this reason, methods other than those requiring the finding of roots are used for determining the stability of a feedback system. One of these methods is the Nyquist stability criterion. Before defining the criterion, the conditions under which it is applied here will be stated:

1. The system must be capable of being represented by a set of linear differential equations with constant coefficients.

2. The limit of GH must approach a constant or zero as s approaches infinity.

In most applications these two conditions are satisfied. In general G and H of the characteristic equation $1 + GH$ are polynomial fractions of s:

$$G(s) = N_1(s)/D_1(s) \qquad (11.34)$$

and

$$H(s) = N_2(s)/D_2(s). \qquad (11.35)$$

Substituting (11.34) and (11.35) in the characteristic equation, we obtain

$$1 + GH = 1 + N_1(s)N_2(s)/D_1(s)D_2(s)$$

or

$$1 + GH = [D_1(s)D_2(s) + N_1(s)N_2(s)]/D_1(s)D_2(s). \qquad (11.36)$$

The fundamental theorem of algebra states that an nth degree polynomial has n roots and the polynomial may be expressed in terms of its factors. Therefore,

$$1 + GH = [(s - r_{n1})(s - r_{n2}) \cdots (s - r_{nn})]/[(s - r_{d1})(s - r_{d2}) \cdots (s - r_{dn})], \quad (11.37)$$

where $r_{n1}, r_{n2}, \ldots$ are roots of the numerator, and $r_{d1}, r_{d2}, \ldots$ are roots of the denominator.

For a stable feedback amplifier, that is, one that does not oscillate and/or one whose output increases indefinitely, the real part of the roots of the numerator must be negative. Let us plot the roots of the numerator and denominator in the complex plane of Fig. 11.11. A root located on the right-hand side of the $j\omega$-axis (*the right-half plane*) has a positive real value. A closed curve may be drawn around any of these roots. If point P on this curve makes a full clockwise rotation on the curve, vector $s - r_{n4}$ also rotates 360° in the clockwise direction. Then vector $1 + GH$ rotates 360° in the clockwise direction, too. All other vectors, however, $s - r_{n2}$, etc., corresponding to points outside the closed curve, do not rotate at all.

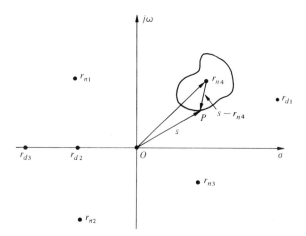

Fig. 11.11 Complex plane plot of the roots of a characteristic equation.

Assume a closed curve is drawn covering the *entire* right-half plane. If a point P on the curve makes one full clockwise rotation, then the total rotation of $1 + GH$ will depend on the number of roots of the numerator and denominator of $1 + GH$ contained in the right-half plane. Let N_n and N_d be the number of roots of the numerator and denominator, respectively, located in the right-half plane. For $N_n > N_d$, vector $1 + GH$ will make $N_n - N_d$ *clockwise* rotations. If $N_d > N_n$, vector $1 + GH$ makes $N_d - N_n$ *counterclockwise* rotations. When $N_d = N_n$, vector $1 + GH$ does not rotate at all. The output of an amplifier will be unstable if, and only if, the numerator has roots located on the right-half plane or on the imaginary axis. Consequently,

1. The system will be stable if the number of counterclockwise rotations of $1 + GH$ is N_d.
2. If vector $1 + GH$ turns clockwise at all, the system will be unstable. Vector $1 + GH$ cannot turn clockwise unless $N_n \neq 0$.
3. Simple roots on the imaginary axis correspond to oscillations of fixed amplitude and frequency.

There is one difficulty to overcome. It is desired that a closed curve be drawn which envelops *all* points in the right-half plane. This requires a curve of infinite radius. It can be proven that a curve of infinite radius covering the right-half plane is equivalent to the $j\omega$-axis itself from $j\omega = -\infty$ to $+\infty$. The proof of this statement is implicit in the second condition imposed on the Nyquist criterion that GH must approach a constant or zero as s approaches infinity. This constant is the same on the $j\omega$-axis as elsewhere. Hence, for counting the rotations of $1 + GH$, covering the $j\omega$-axis from $-\infty$ to $+\infty$ is equivalent to covering the entire right-half plane.

Rather than examine the rotations of $1 + GH$, one can move the point of reference to $-1 + j0$ and deal with the quantity GH instead. This leads to the following statement of Nyquist criterion:

1. The GH function is plotted in the complex plane with $s = j\omega$ for all values of $-\infty \leqslant \omega \leqslant +\infty$. (The plot from $-\infty$ to 0 is the complex conjugate of the plot from $+\infty$ to 0.)
2. The vector from $-1 + j0$ is drawn to a point on the GH curve. The rotation of this vector is observed as ω varies from $-\infty$ to $+\infty$. The system will be stable if the total counterclockwise rotation is equal to N_d, where N_d is the number of roots of the denominator located in the right-half plane; otherwise the system is unstable. This approach requires a knowledge of N_d.

A special case of the Nyquist criterion is given when $N_d = 0$. Here, when there is no net rotation, the system is stable; otherwise it is unstable. The reason for this is that if $N_d = 0$ and $N_n = 0$, there cannot be any rotation.

Example 11.2

Figure 11.12A shows a plot of $G(j\omega)H(j\omega)$ for a stable system; a plot for an unstable system is given in Fig. 11.12B. These statements should be verified by the reader.

The Bode Plot and the Nyquist Criterion

In Chapter 8 the mechanics for drawing asymptotic (Bode) diagrams of transfer functions were developed. The Bode plot is less time consuming

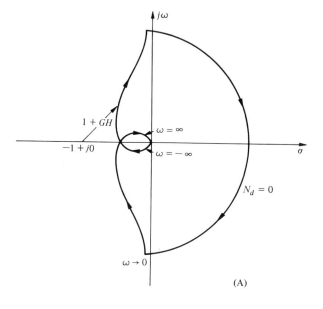

(A)

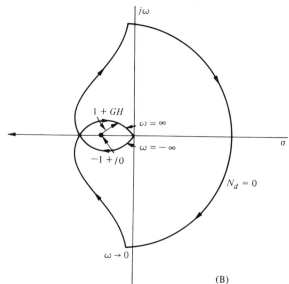

Fig. 11.12 Nyquist plots of a (A) Stable system. (B) Unstable system.

(B)

and easier to manipulate than plotting *GH* on the complex plane. For these reasons it is important to relate the Nyquist criterion to the Bode plot.

Figure 11.13 shows plots of $G(j\omega)H(j\omega)$ from $\omega = 0$ to $\omega = \infty$ for an unstable system (curve *a*) and a stable system (curve *b*). If a circle of unity radius is drawn with the origin as the center, the curve corresponding to an

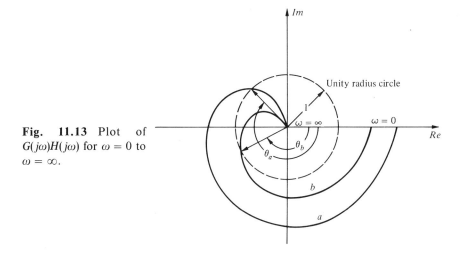

Fig. 11.13 Plot of $G(j\omega)H(j\omega)$ for $\omega = 0$ to $\omega = \infty$.

unstable system cuts the circle at an angle $\theta_a < -180°$ and the curve representing a stable systems cuts at $\theta_b > -180°$. At the intersection of the unity circle and each curve, the amplitude of $GH = 1$, which corresponds to 0 dB. This shows that one may plot the amplitude and phase angle of GH and check the phase angle at 0 dB amplitude, also called *gain crossover*, for system stability. If the phase angle is equal to or less than $-180°$, the system is unstable; if the angle is greater than $-180°$, the system is stable.

We could also explain the result in a different manner. We may check the amplitude of GH corresponding to $-180°$ phase angle, and if $|GH| < 0$ dB the system is stable; otherwise the system is unstable.

Definition of Phase Margin and Gain Margin

The phase margin is defined as

$$\gamma = 180° + \text{phase angle}.$$

For instance, if the phase angle is $-180°$, the phase margin is $0°$. This definition results in a more convenient definition of stability. One may say that *the system is stable if the phase margin is positive at the gain crossover.*

The gain margin is defined as the additional gain that just makes the system unstable. This is then the gain at zero phase margin or at $-180°$ phase angle. This point on the curve of the phase angle is also called *phase crossover*.

Example 11.3

The open-loop transfer function $G(s)H(s)$ is

$$G(s)H(s) = 10/(s + 1)(0.1s + 1)(0.01s + 1).$$

(a) Is the system stable? If so, calculate the phase margin and the gain margin. (b) If the constant 10 is replaced by a constant K, find the maximum value of K for system stability.

Solution

(a) Figure 11.14 shows the Bode plot as a function of the radian frequency ω. The phase angle is approximately $-135°$ at 0 dB, and the system is therefore stable. The phase margin is 45°, and the gain margin is 20 dB.

(b) To find the value of K, we project a line from the 180° point up to the amplitude curve. We obtain $K = 100$ (40 dB).

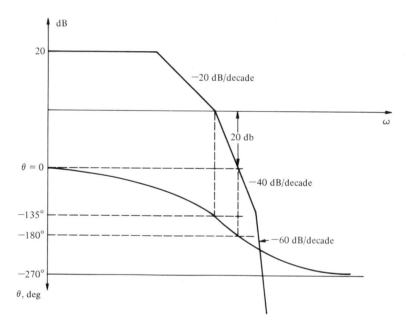

Fig. 11.14 Bode plot for Example 11.3.

Root Locus Method

The Bode plot is very helpful in determining the stability and frequency response of a system. There exists, however, another method, called root locus, for determining stability. In this technique, the locus of the roots of the characteristic equation $1 + GH$ are plotted rather than GH itself. Although this method is more laborious than the Bode plot, additional insight is provided that might be useful in many cases.

As we have seen, the study of system stability begins by writing the characteristic equation $1 + GH = 0$, or

$$GH = N_1(s)N_2(s)/D_1(s)D_2(s) = -1 = 1\underline{/180°}. \qquad (11.38)$$

In the root locus method, the poles and zeros of GH (poles are the roots of the denominator and zeros are the roots of the numerator) are plotted. The locus of points that satisfies (11.38) is then drawn. The parameter used as a variable to plot (11.38) is designated by the symbol K'. As an illustration, K' is related to the constant K of Example 11.3. The difference between K and K' is due to the difference between the representation of GH, as will be clarified in Example 11.5.

The first condition that must be satisfied in plotting (11.38) is that the phase angle be equal to 180°. This requirement is dictated by (11.38) itself, that is, $GH = 1\underline{/180°}$. The second condition is that $|GH| = 1$.

To reduce the work in plotting the root locus, a few rules are offered as guides.

1. The number of branches of the root locus is equal to the number of closed-loop poles. A branch is a separate portion of the root locus which represents a root of $1 + GH = 0$ for all values of K' from zero to infinity. The closed-loop poles are the poles of $G/(1 + GH)$.

2. Each branch of the root locus starts at an open-loop pole (with $K' = 0$) and ends up at an open-loop zero or infinity with $K' = \infty$. The open-loop poles and zeros are the poles and zeros of GH.

3. For a locus to exist on the real axis, the sum of the poles and zeros to the right of the points being considered on the axis must be odd.

4. The root locus is symmetrical with respect to the real axis.

5. The direction of the asymptote lines to the root locus is given by $+180z/(n - m)$ degrees, where n is the number of open-loop poles; m is the number of open-loop zeros; and z is an odd integer, 1, 3, 5, ...

6. The asymptotes intersect the real axis at a distance x given by

$$x = [\Sigma \text{ (real parts of poles)} - \Sigma \text{ (real parts of zeros)}]/(n - m),$$

7. From Rule 1, each branch of the root locus starts from a pole with $K' = 0$ and ends at the zero or at point $s = \infty$. Consider the curve where two branches start from two poles on the real axis and must branch away to go to ∞. This point is called the *breakaway point*, and may be calculated as follows. Let us define

$$W(s) = K'/G(s)H(s).$$

One of the roots of $W'(s) = dW(s)/ds = 0$ would be the breakaway point.

Example 11.4

Draw the root locus for the following expression and calculate the limit of K' for stability.

$$G(s)H(s) = K'/s(s + 10)(s + 100).$$

Solution

Writing the expression for the closed-loop gain, we obtain

$$\frac{G}{1 + GH} = \frac{K'/s(s + 10)(s + 100)}{H + K'H/s(s + 10)(s + 100)}.$$

From Rule 1 there are 3 poles; therefore, 3 branches exist. The plot of zeros and poles are shown in Fig. 11.15. According to Rule 2 the three branches start from the three poles and end at infinity. From Rule 3, the root locus on the real axis can exist only between points 0 and -10, and -100 and infinity.

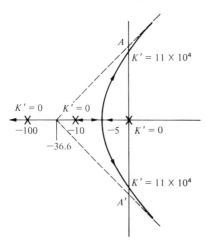

Fig. 11.15 Root locus plot for Example 11.4.

By Rule 5, the angle of the asymptotes are $(z)180°/3 = +60°$ and $180°$. Therefore, one branch starts at -100 and terminates on the real axis at infinity. The other two branches start from 0 and -10, leave the real axis, intersect the $j\omega$-axis, and go to infinity. From Rule 6, the asymptotes intersect the real axis at

$$x = (-10 - 100)/3 = -36.6.$$

The breakaway point is at

$$W(s) = s(s + 10)(s + 100) = s^3 + 110s^2 + 1000s.$$

$$dW(s)/ds = 3s^2 + 220s + 1000 = 0,$$

$$s = -36.6 \pm 31.6.$$

The breakaway point must be between 0 and -10; therefore

$$s = -36.6 + 31.6 = -5.$$

The points of intersection with the $j\omega$ axis may be obtained as follows: On the $j\omega$ axis, $s = 0 + j\omega$; therefore,

$$-1 = K'/j\omega(j\omega + 100)(j\omega + 10).$$

But at points A and A', as well as any other point on the root locus, $GH = -1$; this requires that $G(j\omega)H(j\omega)$ be real. Consequently the imaginary part of the denominator must be zero:

$$j\omega(-\omega^2 + 1000) = 0,$$

or the natural frequency is

$$\omega = \pm\sqrt{1000}.$$

These values of ω correspond to points A and A'. The value of K' is, therefore,

$$-1 = K'/j\omega(10j\omega + 100j\omega) = -K'/110\omega^2$$

or $$K' = 110 \times 1000 = 11 \times 10^4.$$

Example 11.5

Draw the root locus for the circuit of Example 11.3 and calculate the value of K required for system stability.

Solution

Multiplying numerator and denominator of the expression of Example 11.3 by 1000, one obtains

$$G(s)H(s) = K'/(1 + s)(10 + s)(100 + s),$$

where $K' = 10 \times 100 \times K = 1000K$.

The poles of GH are plotted in Fig. 11.16 (no zeros are present). From Rule 1 we see that there should be only 3 branches. According to Rule 2, each branch starts from a pole with $K' = 0$; therefore, the three branches start from -1, -10, and -100.

From Rule 5, the angles of asymptotes are $\pm 60°$ and $180°$. By Rules 6 and 7, $x = -36$, and the breakaway point is at -5.3. Any point, such as A, on the locus represents a value of s_1 corresponding to a particular value of K'. If the roots are located in the right-half plane, the system is unstable. The value of K', which corresponds to the limit of stability, is given by the intersection of the $j\omega$ axis with the branches. At these points $s = 0 + j\omega$; therefore, the preceding equation becomes

$$G(j\omega)H(j\omega) = -1 = K'/(j\omega + 1)(j\omega + 10)(j\omega + 100).$$

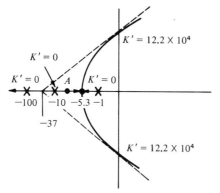

Fig. 11.16 Root locus plot for Example 11.5.

However, as $G(j\omega)H(j\omega) = -1$ anywhere on the locus, then the imaginary part of $G(j\omega)H(j\omega)$ must be zero. Hence,

$$(j\omega)^3 + 10j\omega + 1100j\omega = 0$$

or
$$\omega^2 = 1110; \qquad \omega \approx \pm 33 \text{ rad/s}.$$

This value of ω is the natural frequency of the closed-loop system. The value of K' is calculated by substituting $\omega = 33$ in the equation which yields $K' = 122000$. But $K' = 1000 K$; therefore $K = 122$.

11.6   RC-Coupled Amplifiers with Feedback

The FET amplifier of Fig. 11.17 will now be examined. In Chapter 9 the frequency response of cascaded amplifiers was studied. There the expression for the frequency response of the amplifier stages and coupling networks were obtained. Replacing $j\omega$ by s in those expressions, one obtains equations as a function of s. By representing each element in Fig. 11.17 as a block,

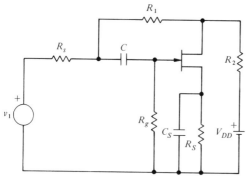

Fig. 11.17 RC-coupled feedback amplifier stage.

Fig. 11.18 is obtained. It is assumed that the amplifier is operating at frequencies where only C_S acts as a short circuit. The block diagram of Fig. 11.18, therefore, corresponds to mid- and high-frequency operation. From the diagram, one may write

$$GH = K's/(s + \omega_1)(s + \omega_2), \qquad (11.39)$$

where $K' = K_1 K_2 H$. The frequency response of GH is given in Fig. 11.19.

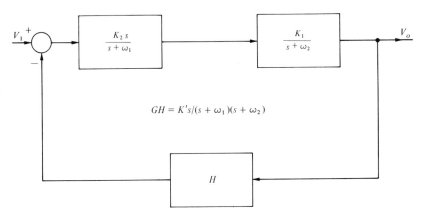

Fig. 11.18 Block diagram for the circuit of Fig. 11.17.

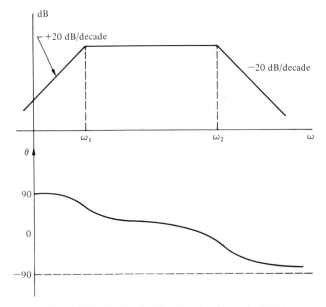

Fig. 11.19 Bode plot for the circuit of Fig. 11.17.

It is seen that the amplifier can not become unstable because the smallest value of the phase angle $\theta = -90°$.

The root locus, shown in Fig. 11.20, corresponds to

$$K's/(s + \omega_1)(s + \omega_2) = -1. \tag{11.40}$$

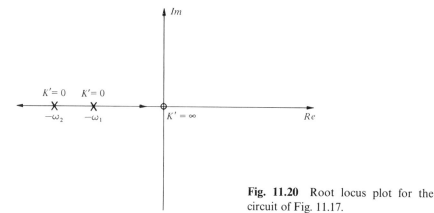

Fig. 11.20 Root locus plot for the circuit of Fig. 11.17.

There are two branches, which are located on the real axis between $-\omega_1$ and zero and $-\omega_2$ and infinity. The angle of the asymptotes is $\pm 180°$. This indicates that the locus will never intersect the $j\omega$-axis or leave the real axis. The amplifier can not oscillate, and it is always stable regardless of the value of K'.

Let us now consider the three-stage feedback amplifier of Fig. 11.21.

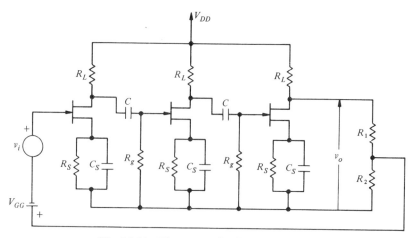

Fig. 11.21 Three-stage feedback amplifier.

Negative voltage feedback is derived from the junction of resistors R_1 and R_2 across the output $[H = -R_2/(R_1 + R_2)]$. The block diagram is given in Fig. 11.22 and the closed-loop transfer function is

$$\frac{V_o(s)}{V_i(s)} = \frac{-Ks^2/(s + \omega_1)(s + \omega_2)^2(s + \omega_3)(s + \omega_4)}{1 + [KR_2s^2/(R_1 + R_2)]/(s + \omega_1)(s + \omega_2)^2(s + \omega_3)(s + \omega_4)}, \quad (11.41)$$

where $\omega_2 = 1/T$ and $K = -K_1K_2K_3$. The open-loop transfer function is

$$GH = [KR_2s^2/(R_1 + R_2)]/(s + \omega_1)(s + \omega_2)^2(s + \omega_3)(s + \omega_4). \quad (11.42)$$

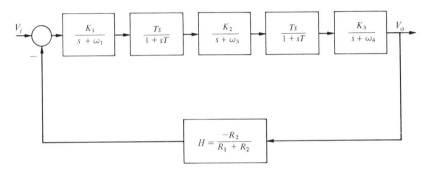

Fig. 11.22 Block diagram for circuit of Fig. 11.21.

Equation (11.42) is plotted in Fig. 11.23. From this plot one sees that the value of K can cause the amplifier to become unstable. For large values of K the angle corresponding to $GH = 0$ dB could become $\theta < -180°$.

For comparison, the root locus plot for the three-stage amplifier of Fig. 11.21 is shown in Fig. 11.24. The plot for this is more complicated than the Bode plot of Fig. 11.23; however, in addition to telling us what the frequency response curve does, the root locus plot can tell us more. For instance, Fig. 11.24 shows that, for values of K greater than K_1, the transient response has vanishing sinewave terms.

The transfer function for a junction transistor amplifier can become rather cumbersome. From Chapter 9 the overall transfer function of one stage of an RC-coupled transistor amplifier may be expressed as

$$G = -Ks\omega_2/(s + \omega_1)(s + \omega_2).$$

This equation is based on the assumption that K is independent of s. At high frequencies, however, the forward short-circuit current gain h_{fe}, which is included in K, is a function of frequency ω. For a more accurate representation, the transfer function should be expressed as

$$G = -K'\omega_2\omega_3s/(s + \omega_1)(s + \omega_2)(s + \omega_3). \quad (11.43)$$

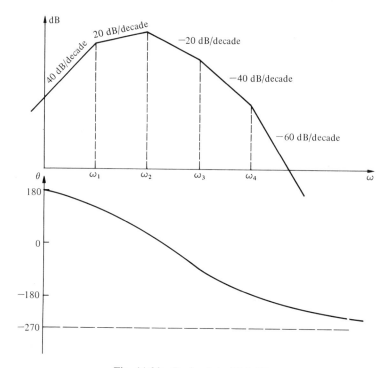

Fig. 11.23   Bode plot of (11.42).

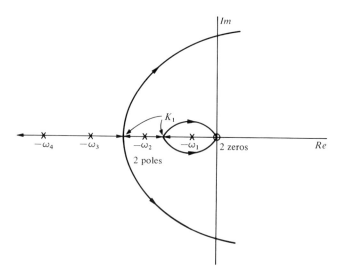

Fig. 11.24   Root locus plot for the circuit of Fig. 11.21.

Equation (11.43) does not assume that the coupling capacitor acts as a short circuit.

Referring to the two-stage RC-coupled amplifier of Fig. 11.25, assume that capacitors C and C_E act as short circuits at high frequencies. Voltage feedback is present only in the second stage. The block diagram of the amplifier is given in Fig. 11.26. The overall transfer function of the last stage is

$$\frac{V_o}{V_1} = \frac{-K_1'/(s + \omega_1)(s + \omega_3)}{1 - K_1'H/(s + \omega_1)(s + \omega_3)} \tag{11.44}$$

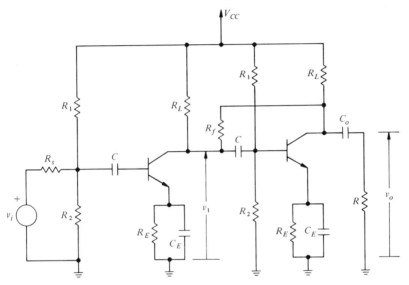

Fig. 11.25 Two stage RC-coupled transistor amplifier.

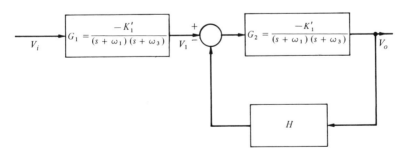

Fig. 11.26 Block diagram of the amplifier of Fig. 11.25.

The root locus plot is illustrated in Fig. 11.27. The diagram shows that the amplifier will always be stable. A further examination, however, reveals the nature of the transient response to a step input which is not apparent

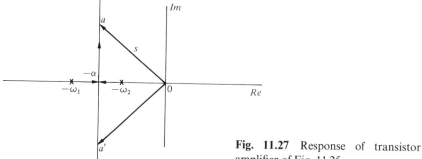

Fig. 11.27 Response of transistor amplifier of Fig. 11.25.

from the Bode diagram. Figure 11.27 shows that s is a complex number at point a. In the time domain, the response will be of the form:

$$A[1 + \exp(-\alpha t)\sin(\omega t + \theta)];$$

the output is said to exhibit ringing (see Fig. 11.28).

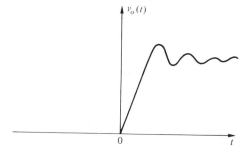

Fig. 11.28 Ringing in an amplifier due to a step input.

11.7 Compensating Networks

In some cases the response of a negative feedback amplifier is not satisfactory. Unsatisfactory conditions exist if the amplifier oscillates, rings, or produces excessive overshoots. These difficulties may be overcome by either of the following methods:

1. Decreasing the open-loop gain.
2. Adding a compensating network in series with the amplifier or in series with the feedback loop.

The first method is not usually desirable because, in most cases, a given amount of gain is required. An example of the second technique will be considered. The addition of a compensating network in the feedback loop can result in complicated calculations. Because of low power levels in the forward path, compensation in the feedback loop is used much less in electronic amplifiers than in other types of feedback systems. We therefore restrict the discussion to the case of a compensating network in series with the amplifier. Consider the following expression:

$$GH = \frac{0.5\,K}{(1 + s/(5 \times 10^4))^2(1 + s/(5 \times 10^5))^3}. \tag{11.45}$$

Assume (11.45) is the open-loop gain of an amplifier. It can be proven that by the addition of a compensating network the limit of stability may be obtained at higher amplifier gain. The Bode diagram of (11.45) is shown in Fig. 11.29. At $\omega = 140 \times 10^3$ rad/s, $\theta = -180°$, and the gain margin is 19 dB.

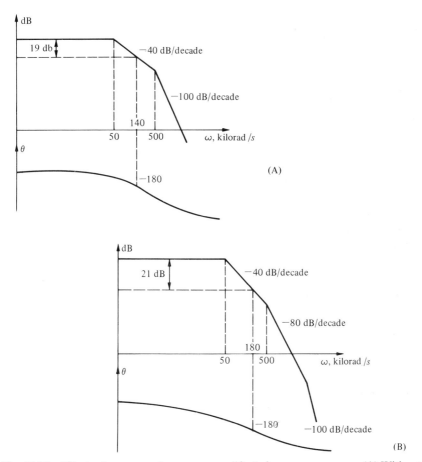

Fig. 11.29 Effects of compensation on an amplifier's frequency response. (A) Without compensation. (B) With compensation.

Let us now add the network shown in Fig. 11.30 in series with the amplifier. This network is known as a *phase-lead network*, because its output voltage leads the input voltage. The transfer function for this circuit is

$$V_o/V_i = (T_2/T_1)[1 + sT_1)/(1 + sT_2)], \qquad (11.46)$$

where $T_1 = R_1 C_1$ and $T_2 = R_1 R_2 C_1/(R_1 + R_2)$.

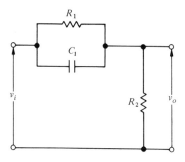

Fig. 11.30   Phase-lead compensation network.

Let $1/T_1 = 500 \times 10^3$ rad/s, and $1/T_2 = 2000 \times 10^3$ rad/s. The new open-loop transfer function becomes

$$GH = \left(\frac{0.5 K}{(1 + s/(5 \times 10^5))^2(1 + s/(5 \times 10^4))^2}\right)\left(\frac{0.25}{1 + s/(2 \times 10^6)}\right). \quad (11.47)$$

The Bode plot of (11.47) is given in Fig. 11.29B. At $\omega = 180 \times 10^3$ rad/s, the phase angle $\theta = -180°$, and at that point the gain margin is 21 dB. This example shows that, without the compensating network, a maximum open loop gain of approximately 80 could be obtained without sustained oscillation. With the network added, however, the gain may be raised to 160 before oscillation occurs.

There are other types of networks that may be used for the same purpose, such as the phase-lag network considered in Chapter 16.

11.8   Summary

The feedback amplifier may be treated as a special case of a general feedback loop. Negative feedback in electronic amplifiers is often used to stabilize the circuit against possible changes in component characteristics and parameters, variations in power supply voltages, and for the reduction of distortion and noise. In addition, negative feedback reduces the gain of the circuit and changes the effective input and output impedances of the active device. Negative feedback may cause an amplifier to break into oscillation. This undesirable condition can be generally prevented by the use of compensating networks, such as the phase-lead network. Nyquist, Bode, and root-locus plots enable the engineer to predict the stability (or instability) of a feedback amplifier.

References

ALLEY, C. L., and K. A. ATWOOD, *Electronic Engineering*, Wiley, New York, 2nd ed., 1966.

ANGELO, JR., E. J., *Electronic Circuits*, McGraw-Hill, New York, 2nd ed., 1966.

CHESTNUT, H., and R. W. MAYER, *Servomechanisms and Regulating System Design*, Wiley, New York, 2nd ed., 1959.

D'AZZO, J. J., and C. H. HOUPIS, *Control System Analysis and Synthesis*, McGraw-Hill, New York, 2nd ed., 1966.

DE PIAN, LOUIS, *Linear Active Network Theory*, Prentice-Hall, Englewood Cliffs, New Jersey, 1962.

RYDER, J., *Electronic Fundamentals and Applications*, Prentice-Hall, Englewood Cliffs, New Jersey, 3rd ed., 1963.

Problems

11.1   The networks of Fig. P11.1 are often used in stabilizing a feedback amplifier. The network of (A) is called a *lead* network; that of (B) a *lag* network. Find their transfer functions $G(s)$.

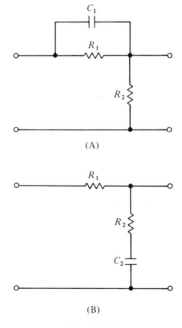

Fig. P11.1

11.2   If $R_1 = 90$ K, $R_2 = 10$ K, and $C_1 = C_2 = 1\,\mu$F, plot the amplitude and phase response curves for the networks of Fig. P11.1.

11.3   Repeat Prob. 11.2 for $R_1 = 75$ K, $R_2 = 15$ K, and $C_1 = C_2 = 2\,\mu$F.

11.4   In a closed-loop system, such as a feedback amplifier, the ratio $(dO/O)/(dG/G)$ is a figure of merit called the *sensitivity* S. For a system that is not sensitive to variations in gain, the value of S is small. For the model of a FET amplifier with feedback (Fig. P11.4), derive an expression for S.

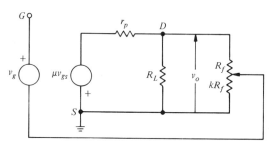

Fig. P11.4

11.5   If a value of $S = 0.09$ is required for the feedback amplifier of Fig. P11.4, calculate the value of k. Assume that $\mu = 50$, $R_L = 10$ K, and $r_p = 20$ K.

11.6   Using the values given in Prob. 11.5, calculate the gain of the amplifier with, and without, feedback.

11.7   Derive an expression for S for the amplifier of Fig. 11.9.

11.8   The gain of an amplifier is expressed by

$$G(s) = 100/(1 + 0.001s).$$

(a) Calculate the dc gain. (b) With negative feedback $(H = 0.1)$, what is the value of dc gain? (c) Plot the logarithmic amplitude and phase response curves with and without feedback. Compare and discuss your results.

11.9   Referring to Fig. 11.3, assume that $G(s) = 100$. Calculate the ratio $O(s)/I(s)$ for $H(s) = 0.01$ and -0.01. Explain your results.

11.10 Referring to Fig. P11.10, (a) What is the feedback ratio $H(s)$? (b) What is the voltage gain with feedback? (c) Without feedback, a change in the dc supply voltage results in a 5 % change in gain. What is the change in gain with feedback?

11.11 It is desired to reduce the distortion in the last stage of a 3-stage amplifier, represented in block form in Fig. P11.11, by a factor of 10. The overall voltage gain with feedback is $v_o/v_s = -600$. Assume that the input resistance of the first stage is of the order of 10 K

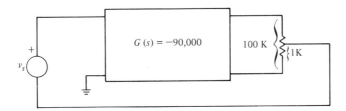

Fig. P11.10

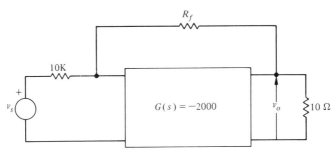

Fig. P11.11

and is much less than R_f. (a) Is an additional amplifier stage necessary? (b) If your answer to (a) is yes, specify the gain. (c) Determine the value of R_f.

11.12   Repeat Prob. 11.11 for $G(s) = -20,000$.

11.13   Calculate the output resistance of the amplifier of Fig. 11.8. Assume that $h_{ie} = 2$ K, $h_{fe} = 50$, $h_{oe} = 2 \times 10^{-5}$ mho, $h_{re} = 0$, $R_g = 1$ K, $R_1 = 40$ K, $R_2 = 20$ K, and $R_L = 2$ K. Compare the values obtained for the amplifier without feedback.

11.14   Repeat Prob. 11.13 for $h_{fe} = 100$. The other component values remain the same.

11.15   Derive equation (11.26).

11.16   The component values for the feedback amplifier of Fig. 11.9 are $Z_1 = 10$ K, $Z_f = (100$ K$)//(1$ pF$)$, $Z_g = (200$ K$)//(2$ pF$)$, $Z_L = (10$ K$)//(2$ pF$)$, $r_p = 100$ K, and $g_m = 4 \times 10^{-3}$ mho. Determine the voltage gain at (a) 1 kHz and (b) 1 MHz.

11.17   The gain of an operational amplifier without feedback can vary greatly. Assume that for the amplifier of Fig. 11.10A the gain is between -2000 and -4000. For stable operation, feedback is used. If $Z_f = 100$ K and $Z_1 = 1$ K, calculate the gain with feedback for the given values of gain without feedback, -2000 and -4000.

11.18   (a) If $N_d = 2$, is it possible for $1 + GH$ (equation 11.37) to make 2 clockwise, 2 counterclockwise, 4 counterclockwise, or no rotations on the *s* plane? Why? (b) Of the above possible cases, which one(s) represents a stable condition? Why?

11.19   Polar plots of $G(j\omega)H(j\omega)$ for three different values of amplifier gain are illustrated in Fig. P11.19. The open-loop amplifier response is stable. Which of the plots in the figure represents an unstable feedback amplifier? Justify your answer.

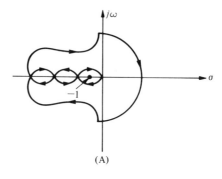

(A)

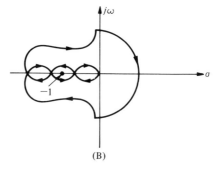

(B)

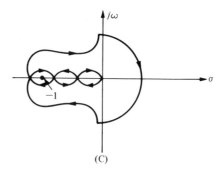

(C)

Fig. P11.19

11.20 For an amplifier with feedback, the low-frequency gain is -2000. The feedback factor is adjusted such that at low frequencies, $GH = 0$ dB. The Bode plot is given in Fig. P11.20. (a) What are the gain and phase margins? (b) At what value of H is the feedback amplifier on the threshold of instability? Assume that the gain without feedback remains constant.

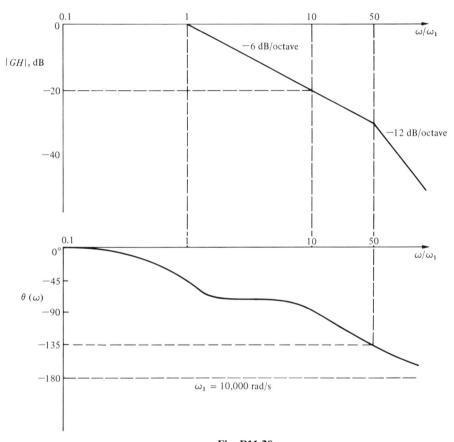

Fig. P11.20.

11.21 For the amplifier of Fig. 11.3

$$G(s) = \frac{-K}{(1 + s/10^5)(1 + s/10^6)(1 + s/10^7)}$$

and $H(s) = -0.1$. Assume that $K = 100$. (a) Plotting the frequency-response (Bode) curve, check the stability of the amplifier. (b) If the amplifier is found to be stable in (a), use the root-locus method to determine if the amplifier rings. (c) Find the limit of K for which the amplifier is unstable.

11.22   In Fig. 11.3 assume that

$$G(s) = \frac{-K}{s(1 + s/10^3)(1 + s/10^4)}$$

and $H(s) = -1$. (a) Plot the root locus. (b) Discuss the possibilities of ringing and instability.

11.23   Design a series-lead network to stabilize a feedback amplifier whose open-loop Bode response is given in Fig. P11.23. Are the calculated component values practical?

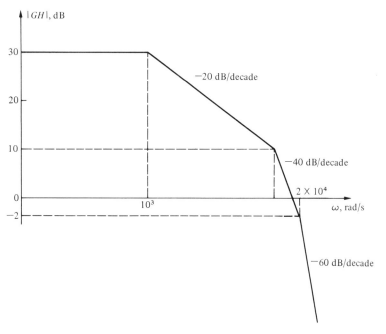

Fig. P11.23.

11.24   (a) From the plot of Fig. P11.23, derive an expression for GH. (b) Using the series-lead network designed in Prob. 11.23, determine the possibility of ringing.

Tuned Amplifiers

An important property required of the amplifiers considered in Chapters 8 and 9 is constant gain over a large bandwidth of frequencies. In some applications, such as radio communications, effective use of the transmission medium requires narrowband amplifiers operating at high frequencies. In commercial radio communications many stations operate between 500 and 1600 kHz at a frequency assigned by the Federal Communications Commission (FCC). For this application, tuned amplifiers using RLC coupling networks must be designed to amplify a small band of frequencies, generally of a few kilohertz, that contain the broadcast information. Preferably, a tuned amplifier should behave like an ideal narrowband filter, with amplification.

In Chapters 14 and 15, modulation and demodulation will be studied; the need for tuned amplifiers in these areas will become further apparent. In this chapter, we shall consider the analysis of tuned amplifiers. An important circuit to study in the tuned amplifier is the RLC network.

12.1 The RLC Coupling Network

The transfer function representing impedance $Z(s) = V(s)/I(s)$ for a parallel RLC circuit is

$$V(s)/I(s) = sL/(s^2LC + sL/R + 1). \tag{12.1}$$

In steady state, $s = j\omega$; therefore (12.1) becomes

$$V(j\omega)/I(j\omega) = (j\omega/C)/(1/LC + j\omega/RC - \omega^2).$$

Let $1/RC = 2\alpha$ and $1/LC = \omega_o^2$; then

$$V(j\omega)/I(j\omega) = (j\omega/C)/(-\omega^2 + j2\alpha\omega + \omega_o^2). \tag{12.2}$$

The logarithmic plot of (12.2) may be constructed as explained in Chapter 8. In the case of tuned amplifiers, values for R, L, and C are chosen so that the roots of the denominator of (12.2) are complex in order to obtain narrow bandwidth characteristics. Assuming complex roots, let us calculate the frequency at which $|V/I|$ reaches a maximum value. To find this maximum we calculate the magnitude of the denominator D of (12.2) as follows:

$$|D|^2 = (\omega_o^2 - \omega^2)^2 + (2\alpha\omega)^2.$$

Letting the derivative of $|D|^2$ with respect to ω equal zero gives the value of ω for which the denominator magnitude is minimum and thus $|V/I|$ is maximum.

$$d|D|^2/d\omega = -2(\omega_o^2 - \omega^2)2\omega + 8\alpha^2\omega = 0,$$

or $$\omega^2 = -2\alpha^2 + \omega_o^2. \tag{12.3}$$

The value of ω determined from (12.3) yields a maximum value for V/I.

In a well-designed amplifier, $2\alpha^2 \ll \omega_o^2$, so that at $\omega \approx \omega_o$ the amplitude of V/I reaches its maximum value. The logarithmic plots of the amplitude and phase of (12.2) are shown in Fig. 12.1. It may be verified that the smaller

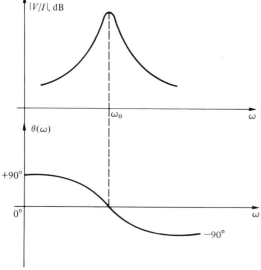

Fig. 12.1 Plots of amplitude and phase response of an RLC circuit.

the value of α the higher is the maximum amplitude. For $\alpha = 0$ we get $\omega = \omega_o$ and $|V/I| = \infty$. (Comparing the above with the universal curves shown in Fig. 8.6, we see that $\alpha = \zeta\omega_o$.) A parallel RLC circuit can therefore be used as a filter to permit the passing of a narrow band of frequencies.

Another circuit of interest is shown in Fig. 12.2; the transfer function representing the impedance V/I is

$$\frac{V(s)}{I(s)} = \frac{L'(s + R'/L')}{C'L'(1/C'L' + sR'/L' + s^2)}.$$

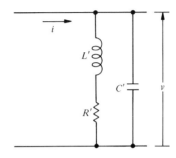

Fig. 12.2 An RLC circuit with the resistance in series with the inductance.

Let $2\alpha = R'/L'$ and $\omega_o = (1/L'C')^{1/2}$; then

$$V(s)/I(s) = (1/C')[(s + 2\alpha)/(s^2 + 2\alpha s + \omega_o^2)]. \tag{12.4}$$

If s is replaced by $j\omega$, (12.4) becomes

$$V(j\omega)/I(j\omega) = (1/C')[(j\omega + 2\alpha)/(-\omega^2 + j2\alpha\omega + \omega_o^2)]. \tag{12.5}$$

For small values of α, expressions (12.2) and (12.5) become virtually identical. The two circuits are equivalent if

$$1/CR = R'/L', \tag{12.6a}$$

$$1/L'C' = 1/LC, \tag{12.6b}$$

$$C' = C, \tag{12.6c}$$

$$L' = L, \tag{12.6d}$$

and, from (12.6a) and (12.6d),

$$R' = L/RC. \tag{12.6e}$$

Depending on the frequency of operation, the model of a practical inductance can be an ideal inductance in series with a resistance, in parallel with a resistance, or both. A capacitance, representing turn-to-turn capacity, may be also shunted across the inductance. Figures 12.3A, B, and C show possible models for a physical inductance. With regard to tuned amplifiers, the RLC circuit may be connected across the input or output of the active device. Because of this, a resistance is always in parallel with the inductance and, in general, the circuit of Fig. 12.3C is a valid representation.

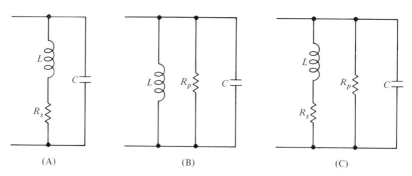

Fig. 12.3 Different models for a physical inductance in parallel with a capacitance.

Example 12.1

For the tuned circuit of Fig. 12.3C, the component values are $C = 200$ pF, $R_p = 200$ K, $R_s = 200$ ohms, and $L = 10^{-3}$ H. Replace the circuit of Fig. 12.3C by the equivalent circuits of Figs. 12.3A and B and calculate the values of their elements.

Solution

In Fig. 12.3C the tuned circuit has a series resistance R_s and a parallel resistance R_p. To find the elements of the equivalent circuit of Fig. 12.3B, we shall first eliminate R_s by finding its equivalent parallel resistance from (12.6e):

$$R'_p = L/R_s C = 10^{-3}/(200 \times 10^{-12} \times 200) = 25 \text{ K.}$$

Resistance R'_p is a parallel resistance equivalent to the 200 ohm series in Fig. 12.3C. As shown in Fig. 12.4A, we now have R'_p and 200 K in parallel; this results in the circuit of Fig. 12.4B, with a parallel resistance of 25 K$//$200 K $= 22.2$ K. The values of L and C remain the same [see (12.6c, d)]

To find the values of elements of Fig. 12.3A, we refer to Fig. 12.4B and transform it to a series equivalent circuit. The capacitance and

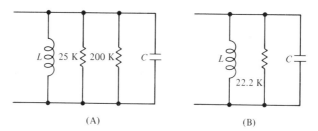

Fig. 12.4 Obtaining the equivalent circuit in Example 12.1.

inductance values remain the same as in Figs. 12.4B and 12.3C. The resistance is calculated with the aid of (12.6e).

$$R_s = 10^{-3}/(200 \times 10^{-12} \times 22.2 \times 10^3) = 225 \text{ ohms.}$$

12.2   Single-Tuned FET and Vacuum Tube Amplifiers

The single-tuned amplifier is the simplest form of a narrowband amplifier. For this circuit the input or output is connected to the RLC network considered in the previous section. A tuned amplifier using a field-effect transistor or a pentode tube is easily analyzed; the circuit is shown in Fig. 12.5A (the dc biasing sources have been omitted), and its incremental model is given in Fig. 12.5B. In Fig. 12.5B, R_p represents the parallel equivalent of the load resistance R_L and the output resistance of the FET. Figure 12.5C shows the transformation of the series resistance R_s to a parallel resistance R'_p in parallel

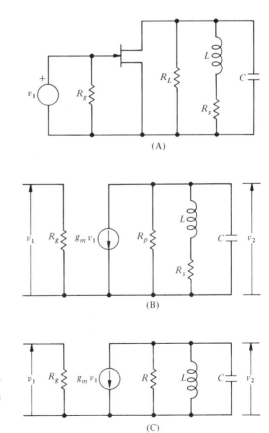

Fig. 12.5 A tuned amplifier using a FET. (A) Circuit. (B) Model. (C) Simplified model.

with R_p; the combination reduces to resistance R. The voltage gain A_v of the circuit is

$$A_v = \frac{V_2}{V_1} = -\frac{g_m}{C}\left(\frac{j\omega}{-\omega^2 + j2\alpha\omega + \omega_o^2}\right),\tag{12.7}$$

where $\alpha = 1/2RC$ and $\omega_o^2 = 1/LC$. Equation (12.7) is similar to that of (12.2) except for the gain of the active device. A plot of (12.7) as a function of frequency has the same shape as that of Fig. 12.1.

In tuned amplifiers the *bandwidth* is defined as the passband of frequencies separating the two half-power frequencies, $\omega_H - \omega_L$, as illustrated in Fig. 12.6. The amplitude of V_2/V_1 at the resonant frequency, from (12.7), is

$$|V_2/V_1| = g_m/C[\omega^2/(2\alpha\omega)^2]^{1/2} = g_m/2\alpha C,$$

or

$$|V_2/V_1| = g_m R.\tag{12.8}$$

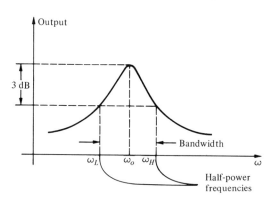

Fig. 12.6 Plot of frequency response of a tuned amplifier.

To calculate the bandwidth, we find the magnitude of V_2/V_1 and equate it to $g_m R/\sqrt{2}$, where $g_m R$ is the gain at the resonant frequency (12.8). Therefore,

$$\frac{g_m R}{\sqrt{2}} = \frac{g_m}{C}\left[\frac{\omega^2}{(\omega_o^2 - \omega^2)^2 + (2\alpha\omega)^2}\right]^{1/2},$$

or

$$\omega^2 = \frac{(RC)^2}{2}[(\omega_o^2 - \omega^2)^2 + (2\alpha\omega)^2].\tag{12.9}$$

It must be remembered that this amplifier is a narrowband amplifier, such that $\omega_o \approx \omega$, where ω_o is the resonant frequency and ω is the half power frequency in (12.9); therefore,

$$(\omega_o + \omega)^2 \approx 4\omega^2.$$

Rewriting (12.9) as

$$\omega^2 = [(RC)^2/2][(\omega_o - \omega)^2(\omega_o + \omega)^2 + 4\alpha^2\omega^2]$$

and substituting $4\omega^2$ for $(\omega_o + \omega)^2$, we obtain

$$2R^2C^2[(\omega_o - \omega)^2 + \alpha^2] = 1,$$

or
$$\omega_o - \omega = 1/(2RC) = \alpha.$$

The bandwidth of the amplifier is

$$BW = 2\alpha = 1/(RC). \tag{12.10}$$

There are three variables in an RLC circuit. If the bandwidth and the required amplification are given, two relations are imposed upon parameters $R, L,$ and $C,$ that is, the bandwidth, $BW = 1/(RC),$ and the gain at resonance, $A = g_m R.$ We then have a choice for the third parameter. Usually, the parameter that is chosen by the designer is the capacitance. This value must be selected such that the variation in the capacitance of the active device has a negligible effect on resonant frequency and bandwidth.

Example 12.2

It is desired to calculate (a) the element values of an RLC network used in a single-tuned FET amplifier and (b) the amplifier gain. The bandwidth is to be 10 kHz and the passband is to be centered at a resonant frequency of 500 kHz. The transconductance $g_m = 10$ milli-mhos.

Solution

(a) The bandwidth is given by

$$BW = 1/RC = 2\pi 10^4 \text{ rad/s}.$$

The relationship between the resonant (or center) frequency and LC is

$$\omega_o^2 = 1/LC = (2\pi)^2 \times 25 \times 10^{10} \approx 10^{13} \text{ (rad/s)}^2.$$

The value of C is chosen such that the variation in capacitance owing to wiring and active device capacitances does not change the center frequency. The capacitance contributed by wiring and the FET is of the order of 10 to 20 pF; with $C = 200$ pF, for example, the center frequency ω_o would remain nearly independent of this variation. Then,

$$L = 1/(200 \times 10^{-12} \times 10^{13}) = 0.5 \text{ mH},$$

and
$$R = 1/(2\pi \times 10^4 \times 2 \times 10^{-10}) = 75 \text{ K}.$$

(b) The gain at the resonant frequency is

$$g_m R = 10 \times 75 = 750.$$

12.3 Single-Tuned Junction Transistor Amplifier

Another example, the common-emitter amplifier with the tuned circuit located at the base, is shown in Fig. 12.7A. If the tuned circuit is part of the collector circuit, the incremental model becomes similar to the FET of Fig. 12.5B, and the voltage gain may be calculated by inspection. In Fig. 12.7B resistance $r_{bb'}$ is neglected. Capacitance C includes the input capacitance of the transistor, $C_i = C_{b'e} + C_{b'c}(1 + g_m R_L)$. Resistance R is the parallel equivalent of $r_{b'e}$, the source, the bias, and the tuned circuit resistances.

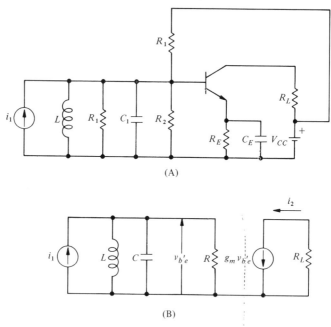

(A)

(B)

Fig. 12.7 Common-emitter tuned amplifier. (A) Circuit. (B) Incremental model.

From Fig. 12.7B we can write

$$I_2 = g_m V_{b'e}$$

$$I_1 = (1/j\omega L + j\omega C + 1/R)V_{b'e}$$

or

$$I_1 = V_{b'e}\left(\frac{1 - \omega^2 LC + j\omega L/R}{j\omega L}\right)$$

and

$$V_{b'e} = \frac{j\omega L I_1}{1 - \omega^2 LC + j\omega L/R}.$$

Therefore,

$$A_i = \frac{I_2}{I_1} = \frac{g_m}{C}\left(\frac{j\omega}{-\omega^2 + j2\alpha\omega + \omega_o^2}\right), \qquad (12.11)$$

where $1/(RC) = 2\alpha$ and $1/(LC) = \omega_o^2$.

In Fig. 12.7A, the input resistance to the common-emitter transistor circuit is generally of the order of 1 kilohm. This value of resistance does not correspond to a low value of α that is required for a narrowband amplifier unless a very large value of C is used; this, however, is not practical. A solution to this problem is to use a transformer between the input of the amplifier and the tuned circuit, as shown in Fig. 12.8. The reflected values of inductance n^2L and capacitance C/n^2, where n is the turns ratio, to the

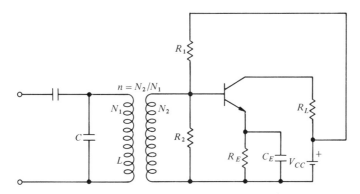

Fig. 12.8 Transformer-coupled, single-tuned transistor amplifier.

secondary side of the transformer result in Fig. 12.9. Resistance R_2' is the equivalent resistance reflected from the primary in parallel with the secondary resistance and is equal to

$$R_2' = n^2 R_p R_s/(n^2 R_p + R_s),$$

where R_p and R_s are the resistances present at the primary and secondary sides, respectively.

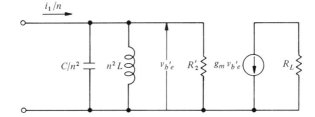

Fig. 12.9 Incremental model of Fig. 12.8.

The effective value of the capacitance is increased by a factor of $1/n^2$. An expression for current amplification is obtained as follows:

$$I_2 = g_m V_{b'e},$$

$$V_{b'e} = \frac{I_1/n}{1/R_2' + 1/n^2 j\omega L + j\omega C/n^2},$$

$$A_i = \frac{I_2}{I_1} = \left(\frac{g_m n}{C}\right)\left(\frac{j\omega}{1/LC + j\omega n^2/R_2'C - \omega^2}\right),$$

or

$$A_i = \frac{g_m n}{C}\left(\frac{j\omega}{\omega_o^2 + j2\alpha\omega - \omega^2}\right). \tag{12.12}$$

Let us now consider the common-base tuned amplifier of Fig. 12.10A. A model is obtained from Fig. 8.23 of Chapter 8, where resistance $r_{bb'}$ is neglected. In this case the transistor is used as a voltage amplifier because the current gain is less than unity. The transistor capacitances are not neglected. The voltage gain may be calculated from the model of Fig. 12.10B.

$$V_{b'e} = -V_1,$$

$$g_m V_{b'e} = -V_2(1/j\omega L + 1/R + j\omega C),$$

$$g_m V_1 = V_2(1/j\omega L + 1/R + j\omega C),$$

or

$$A_v = V_2/V_1 = (g_m/C)[j\omega/(-\omega^2 + j2\alpha\omega + \omega_o^2)]. \tag{12.13}$$

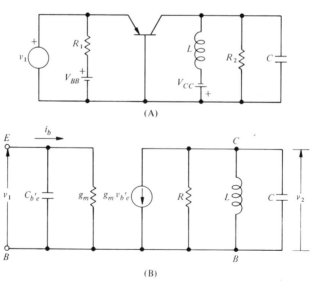

(A)

(B)

Fig. 12.10 (A) Common-base tuned amplifier. (B) Incremental model of common-base amplifier.

Expression (12.13) is the same as (12.11) obtained for the common-emitter tuned amplifier. The common-base configuration, however, behaves as a voltage, rather than a current, amplifier.

12.4 Cascaded Amplifiers with Synchronous and Staggered Tuning

A synchronous-tuned amplifier consists of two cascaded single-tuned stages at the same resonant frequency and with equal gains. If common-emitter stages, with negligible loading are assumed, the overall amplification is the square of the amplification of one stage. Referring to (12.11), we obtain

$$A_i = I_o/I_s = - (g_m/C)^2[\omega^2/(\omega_o^2 - \omega^2 + j2\alpha\omega)^2]. \tag{12.14}$$

Like (12.7), expression (12.14) has a maximum gain at $\omega \approx \omega_o$; at $\omega = \omega_o$, we find

$$A_i = (g_m R)^2.$$

The bandwidth of a synchronous-tuned amplifier will always be less than that of a corresponding single-tuned stage. The reason for this behavior may be glimpsed by examining the denominator of (12.14). Because the denominator is squared, the gain falls off more rapidly than for a single-tuned stage at increasing frequencies.

The response of this amplifier is not ideal; the ideal response is absolutely flat over its bandwidth. The bandwidth for a two-stage synchronous-tuned amplifier will be less than for a single stage and is often undesirable. A better response may be obtained by stagger-tuning the stages. Staggered stages have close, but unequal, resonant frequencies. The amplitude characteristic of a stagger-tuned amplifier may have the form of curve *a* shown in Fig. 12.11.

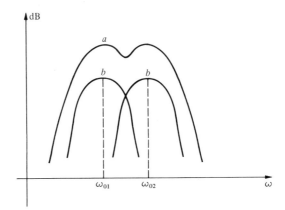

Fig. 12.11 Finding the overall response for a stagger-tuned amplifier.

Its passband is wider and flatter than the passband of a synchronous-tuned amplifier, and therefore a better approximation to the ideal tuned circuit is obtained. The shape of the characteristic curve depends on the spreading between the two resonant frequencies ω_{01} and ω_{02}.

The transfer function of an amplifier having the response of Fig. 12.11 is

$$\frac{V_0}{V_1} = \left(\frac{g_{m1}g_{m2}}{C_1 C_2}\right)\left(\frac{j\omega}{-\omega^2 + j2\alpha_1\omega + \omega_{01}^2}\right)\left(\frac{j\omega}{-\omega^2 + j2\alpha_2\omega + \omega_{02}^2}\right). \quad (12.15)$$

where C_1 and C_2 are the tuned-circuit capacitances of stages 1 and 2, respectively. To find the overall amplitude response (curve a) the amplitude response of each stage (curve b) may be drawn separately and added, as shown in Fig. 12.11.

12.5 Double-Tuned Amplifiers with Inductive Coupling

In the previous section we have demonstrated the superior response and bandwidth characteristics of the stagger-tuned amplifier. Other circuits may also be used to give the same kind of response. A double-tuned amplifier using inductive coupling is an example of such a circuit. It consists of two parallel-tuned circuits loosely coupled by a small mutual inductance L_m, as indicated in Fig. 12.12A. This circuit may be used with junction transistors,

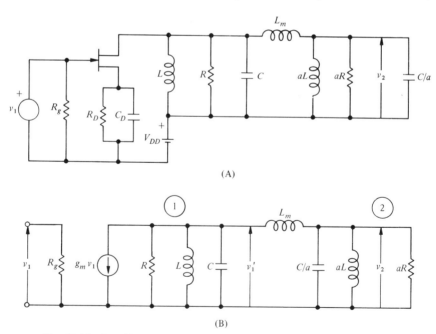

Fig. 12.12 Double-tuned amplifier (A) Circuit. (B) Incremental model.

FETs, or tubes. A model of the circuit of Fig. 12.12A using a FET is shown in Fig. 12.12B.

Voltage gain V_2/V_1 may be calculated from the following two equations written for the model. Letting $Y_m = 1/sL_m = k/sL$ and $Y = sC + 1/R + 1/sL = (C/s)[s^2 + (1/RC)s + 1/LC] = (C/s)(s^2 + 2\alpha s + \omega_o^2) = (C/s)(s - s_1)(s - s_2)$, we can write at node 1,

$$(Y + Y_m)V'_1 - Y_m V_2 = -g_m V_1; \qquad (12.16a)$$

at node 2,

$$- Y_m V'_1 + V_2(1/aY + Y_m) = 0. \qquad (12.16b)$$

Solving (12.16a, b) for V_2/V_1, we obtain

$$A_v = V_2/V_1 = -g_m a Y_m/Y[Y + (1 + a)Y_m],$$

where a is a constant. But

$$Y + (1 + a)Y_m = sC + 1/R + 1/sL + (1 + a)k/sL$$
$$= (C/s)[s^2 + 2\alpha s + \omega_o^2 + (1 + a)k\omega_o^2]$$
$$= (C/s)(s - s_3)(s - s_4).$$

Therefore,

$$A_v = -g_m aks/LC^2(s - s_1)(s - s_2)(s - s_3)(s - s_4). \qquad (12.17)$$

The roots of the denominator of (12.17) are complex; if $(1 + a)k\omega_o^2$ is very small, a frequency response similar to a stagger-tuned amplifier is obtained. If the two tuned circuits are loosely coupled, $k \ll 1$, and $(1 + a)k\omega_o^2$ has the necessary small value to yield the response of Fig. 12.11.

12.6 Pole-Zero Representation of Tuned Amplifiers

An alternate and widely used representation of a transfer function is given by a plot of the roots of its numerator and denominator in the complex plane, referred to as the *pole-zero diagram*. Let us apply this method to (12.7). We first write the equation in terms of s and separate the roots.

$$A_v = \frac{-g_m s/C}{s^2 + 2\alpha s + \omega_o^2}$$

$$= \frac{-g_m s/C}{(s + \alpha - j\sqrt{\omega_o^2 - \alpha^2})(s + \alpha + j\sqrt{\omega_o^2 - \alpha^2})}. \qquad (12.18)$$

The pole-zero plot of (12.18) is given in Fig. 12.13. A pole is represented by X and a zero by 0. The information gained from a pole-zero diagram is different from the plots of amplitude and phase angle as a function of frequency. From Fig. 12.13 it is seen that the real part of the conjugate poles is $-\alpha$ and the imaginary part is $(\omega_o^2 - \alpha^2)^{1/2}$. One condition for a good tuned amplifier is to make α negligible with respect to ω_o. By showing the location of poles, verification and modification of values are easily accomplished.

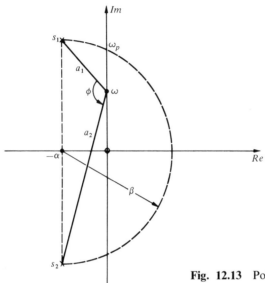

Fig. 12.13 Pole-zero diagram of a tuned amplifier.

The amplitude of V_2/V_1 may be calculated at a given frequency by replacing s by $j\omega$ in (12.13) and letting $a_1 = |s_1 - j\omega|$ and $a_2 = |s_2 - j\omega|$; therefore,

$$|A_v| = |V_2/V_1| = g_m\omega/Ca_1a_2. \tag{12.19}$$

The gain may also be calculated in terms of ϕ, the angle between a_1 and a_2, rather than in terms of a_1 and a_2. This has the advantage of making the gain dependent on a single variable ϕ. The area of the triangle bounded by $s_1, j\omega$, and s_2 is

$$(1/2)a_1a_2 \sin \phi = \alpha\beta$$

or

$$a_1a_2 = 2\alpha\beta/\sin \phi;$$

then

$$|A_v| = |V_2/V_1| = (g_m\omega/2\alpha\beta C) \sin \phi. \tag{12.20}$$

This shows that the maximum value of $|A_v|$ will be obtained for $\sin \phi = 1$:

$$|A_v|_{max} \approx g_m/(2\alpha C), \tag{12.21}$$

which is the same as expression (12.8), after $\alpha = 1/(2RC)$ has been substituted.

The frequency at the resonant peak in the amplitude characteristic is given by the intersection of the circle with radius β and centered on the real axis at a distance $-\alpha$ from the imaginary axis. It follows from Fig. 12.13 that the frequency at the peak ω_p is $\omega_p^2 = \beta^2 - \alpha^2 = \omega_o^2 - 2\alpha^2$ and if $\alpha \ll \omega_o$, then $\omega_p \approx \omega_o$.

Useful information may also be obtained from the expression given for the stagger-tuned or double-tuned amplifier. The general expression is of the form:

$$V_2/V_1 = Ks^2/(s - s_1)(s - s_2)(s - s_3)(s - s_4). \tag{12.22}$$

Replacing s by $j\omega$, we obtain

$$V_2/V_1 = -K\omega^2/(j\omega - s_1)(j\omega - s_2)(j\omega - s_3)(j\omega - s_4), \tag{12.23}$$

where $s_1 = -\alpha - j\beta_1$; $s_2 = -\alpha + j\beta_1$; $s_3 = -\alpha - j\beta_2$; $s_4 = -\alpha + j\beta_2$. The pole zero plot is given in Fig. 12.14. Near resonance one may write $j\omega - s_2 \approx 2j\omega$ and $j\omega - s_4 \approx 2j\omega$; therefore,

$$V_2/V_1 = K/4(j\omega - s_1)(j\omega - s_3). \tag{12.24}$$

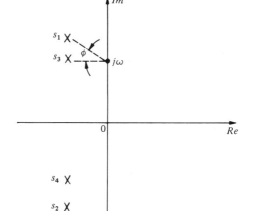

Fig. 12.14 Pole-zero plot for a stagger- or double-tuned amplifier.

In Fig. 12.15 the area around s_1 and s_3 of Fig. 12.14 is shown in greater scale. Based on this figure and the previous discussion of single-tuned amplifiers, we obtain

$$|A_v| = |V_2/V_1| = K \sin \phi/4\Delta\alpha, \tag{12.25}$$

where Δ is the diameter of the semicircle. Again the peak voltage gain A_{vp} occurs for $\sin \phi = 1$. This peak will exist for two frequencies that are obtained by the intersection of a circle with diameter Δ, centered at a distance $-\alpha$ from ω_c. Frequency ω_c is

$$\omega_c = (\omega_o + \omega'_o)/2,$$

where ω_o is the resonant frequency of one stage and ω'_o the resonant frequency of the other stage. Then,

$$|A_{vp}| = K/4\Delta\alpha.$$

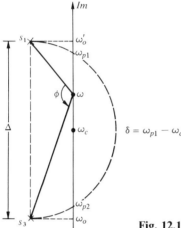

Fig. 12.15 Area around points s_1 and s_3 of Fig. 12.14.

For stagger-tuned amplifiers using the same active device in both stages, the peak value of gain is

$$|A_{vp}| = |V_2/V_1| = g_m^2/4C_1C_2\Delta\alpha \tag{12.26}$$

and

$$A_v = A_{vp}\sin\phi. \tag{12.27}$$

If α is less than $\Delta/2$, the circle cuts the imaginary axis at two points; two peaks therefore occur as shown in Fig. 12.16. If $\alpha > \Delta/2$, then only one peak will result. The frequencies at which the double peaks occur are

$$\omega_p = \omega_c \pm \delta, \tag{12.28}$$

where δ is the difference between ω_p and ω_c. Because the radius of the circle is $\Delta/2$,

$$\delta^2 = (\Delta/2)^2 - \alpha^2. \tag{12.29}$$

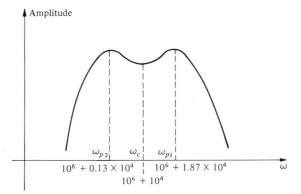

Fig. 12.16 Plot of amplitude response for Example 12.3.

Example 12.3

A stagger-tuned amplifier with the following parameters is to be analyzed:

$$\alpha = 0.5 \times 10^4 \text{ rad/s} \qquad \omega_o = 10^6 \text{ rad/s}$$

$$\Delta = 2 \times 10^4 \text{ rad/s} \qquad g_m = 5 \times 10^{-3} \text{ mhos}$$

$$C_1 = 600 \text{ pF} \qquad C_2 = 3000 \text{ pF}$$

Calculate the peak voltage gain, the corresponding frequencies ω_{p1} and ω_{p2} and the center frequency ω_c.

Solution

The center frequency is given by

$$\omega_c = 10^6 + (2 \times 10^4)/2 = 10^6 + 10^4 \text{ rad/s}.$$

The peak value of gain is calculated from (12.26)

$$|A_{vp}| = (5 \times 10^{-3})^2/(4 \times 6 \times 3 \times 10^{-19} \times 10^8) = 3.47 \times 10^4.$$

The frequencies at which the peak value of gain occur are, from (12.29),

$$\delta^2 = (10^4)^2 - (0.5 \times 10^4)^2 = 0.75 \times 10^8,$$

$$\delta = 0.87 \times 10^4,$$

$$\omega_{p1} = 10^6 + 10^4 + 0.87 \times 10^4 = 10^6 + 1.87 \times 10^4,$$

$$\omega_{p2} = 10^6 + 10^4 - 0.87 \times 10^4 = 10^6 + 0.13 \times 10^4.$$

The plot of the amplitude response is given in Fig. 12.16.

12.7 Class C Tuned Amplifier

The tuned amplifiers described in the previous sections of the chapter operate as class A. There is a type of high-power amplifier used in transmitters where output power and efficiency are important. The output power of these amplifiers may be of the order of kilowatts, and special vacuum tubes are used in their circuits. As yet, solid-state devices are not available that operate at these large power ratings. These amplifiers are operated as class C, where the conversion efficiency can approach 100%. The tuned circuit used in a class C amplifier may be viewed as a pendulum operating at a fixed frequency and absorbing enough energy from the power element to maintain movement; in this case the power element is the vacuum tube and its associated power supply.

Figure 12.17A shows the circuit of a class C amplifier and in Fig. 12.17B the plots of plate voltage v_b, plate current, i_b, grid voltage v_c, grid current i_c, and conduction angle θ_1 are given. Reference angle θ coincides with the peak values of i_b and v_c. The tube voltage v_b is obtained by writing the loop equation for the output circuit. Figure 12.17B shows that plate current flows for the period of time when v_c is above the voltage required to cut off the tube and the grid conducts for positive values of v_c. From Fig. 12.17A,

$$v_c = V_{cc} + V_s \cos \omega t,$$

where $V_s \cos \omega t$ is the input voltage. To simplify the calculation, let $\omega t = \theta$; therefore,

$$v_c = V_{cc} + V_s \cos \theta. \tag{12.30}$$

The plate voltage is

$$v_b = V_{bb} - I_1 R_L \cos \theta; \tag{12.31}$$

where R_L is the resonant impedance of the tuned circuit, and I_1 is the peak value of the fundamental component of plate current. The following discussion explains the meaning of resonant impedance R_L.

Consider the parallel resonant circuit of Fig. 12.2 and let $L' = L$, $R' = R$, and $C' = C$. The total admittance of the circuit is the sum of the admittances of the capacitor C and the R-L branch; then,

$$Y_c = j\omega C$$

$$Y_L = R/(R^2 + \omega^2 L^2) - j\omega L/(R^2 + \omega^2 L^2).$$

The total admittance Y is

$$Y = \frac{R}{R^2 + \omega^2 L^2} - j\left(\frac{\omega L}{R^2 + \omega^2 L^2} - \omega C\right). \tag{12.32}$$

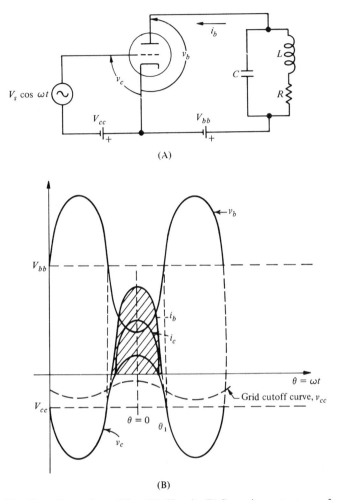

Fig. 12.17 Class C tuned amplifier. (A) Circuit. (B) Some important waveforms.

The definition for the condition of parallel resonance requires that the circuit be resistive. For this to be true, the imaginary term must equal zero, that is,

$$\omega L/(R^2 + \omega^2 L^2) = \omega C.$$

Therefore,

$$Y = Y_o = R/(R^2 + \omega^2 L^2),$$

and the resonant impedance R_L is defined as

$$R_L = 1/Y_o = (R^2 + \omega^2 L^2)/R. \qquad (12.33)$$

The cutoff point of the tube occurs at

$$v_{cc} = -v_b/\mu. \tag{12.34}$$

As v_b varies with the input signal, indicated by (12.31), relationship (12.34) shows that the cutoff voltage also varies as θ changes. Equations (12.30), (12.31), and (12.34) permit the computation of bias voltage V_{cc} as a function of the conduction angle θ_1 :

$$V_{cc} = -V_{bb}/\mu - (V_s - I_1 R_L/\mu) \cos \theta_1. \tag{12.35}$$

Term $I_1 R_L = V_o$ is the amplitude of the fundamental voltage across the resonant circuit. Equation (12.35) shows that the conduction angle can be controlled.

If $\cos \theta$ is eliminated from (12.30) and (12.31), solving for v_b, one obtains

$$v_b = V_{bb} + V_{cc}V_o/V_s - V_o v_c/V_s. \tag{12.36}$$

In (12.36) V_{bb} and V_{cc} are constant values and V_s and V_o represent the peak values of the input signal and the fundamental of the Fourier series of the output voltage, respectively. Expression (12.36) is therefore an equation of a straight line with v_b the dependent variable and v_c the independent variable. This line may be drawn in the v_c-v_b plane and is called the *operating line*. Because of the location of the quiescent point, that is, the device is biased beyond cutoff, the load line in the $v_b - i_b$ plane is not linear and does not help in this analysis.

The tube characteristics of Fig. 12.18, called the *constant current character-istics*, are useful for the analysis of class C operation. Two points of operation determine the operating line. The quiescent point is determined by the value of V_{bb} and the choice of V_{cc}. In practice V_{cc} is chosen such that the tube is biased beyond twice the value of cutoff. A second point is selected at maximum grid voltage ($v_{c(max)}$) corresponding to minimum plate voltage ($v_{b(min)}$). As shown in Fig. 12.17B, the maximum grid voltage occurs at a time the plate voltage is at its minimum. In the next section it will be shown that the maximum efficiency will be obtained if $v_{b(min)} = v_{c(max)}$. With the value of bias voltage known from the Q-point, a choice of signal amplitude and the condition $v_{b(min)} = v_{c(max)}$, the second point of the operating line is found (point A).

The current i_b as a function of time is a series of pulses (see Fig. 12.17B). To calculate the output power a plot of i_b must be obtained. With the help of the constant current characteristics, the operating line, and expression (12.31), i_b can be plotted as a function of θ. From (12.31), the value of $\cos \theta$ as a function of v_b is

$$V_o \cos \theta = V_{bb} - v_b. \tag{12.37}$$

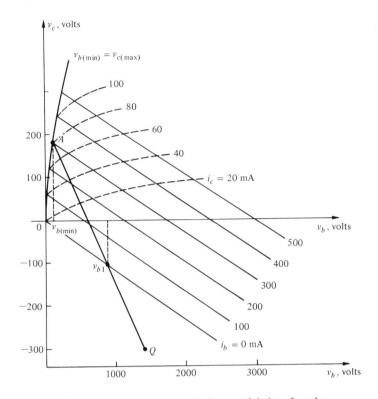

Fig. 12.18 Constant current charactericistics of a tube.

The value of v_b, corresponding to the start of conduction, may be found from Fig. 12.18 ; then,

$$\cos \theta_1 = (V_{bb} - v_{b1})/V_o, \qquad (12.38)$$

where $V_o = V_{bb} - v_{b(min)}$.

The values of i_b as a function of θ may be plotted as shown in Fig. 12.19. The average value of i_b is

$$I_b = \frac{1}{2\pi} \int_{-\pi}^{\pi} i_b \, d\theta. \qquad (12.39)$$

The above value may be calculated graphically by the trapezoidal rule. The trapezoidal rule used for graphical integration consists of dividing the curve into equal segments $\Delta\theta$, as shown in Fig. 12.19. Recognizing the existence of even-axis symmetry, one obtains

$$I_b = 2 \times (1/2\pi)\Delta\theta(i_o/2 + i_1 + i_2 + \cdots + i_{n-1}). \qquad (12.40)$$

The instantaneous and average values of grid current are calculated in the same manner as i_b.

It is also possible to use the Fourier expansion to find the peak value of the fundamental ac component:

$$I_1 = \frac{2}{\pi} \int_0^\theta i_b \cos\theta \, d\theta. \tag{12.41}$$

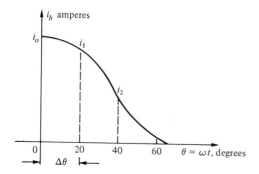

Fig. 12.19 Value of plate current as a function of angle, θ.

We plot $i_b \cos\theta$ and use the trapezoidal rule to calculate I_1:

$$I_1 = (2/\pi)\Delta\theta(i_0'/2 + i_1' + i_2' + \cdots + i_{n-1}'), \tag{12.42}$$

where $i' = i\cos\theta$.

Example 12.4

The constant-current characteristics of the triode used in a class C amplifier are shown in Fig. 12.20. Plate supply voltage $V_{bb} = 2000$ V, $V_{cc} = -300$ V, and the signal input $v_s = 500\cos\omega t$. (a) Assuming $v_{b(min)} = v_{c(max)}$, draw the operating line; (b) draw i_b as a function of θ; and (c) calculate I_b.

Solution

(a) $v_{c(max)} = 500 - 300 = 200$ V. The Q-point is therefore located at $V_b = 2000$ V and $V_c = -300$ V. The second point (A) is located at $v_{c(min)} = v_{b(max)}$. Since $v_{c(min)} = 200$ V, $v_{b(min)} = 200$ V. The operating line is drawn in Fig. 12.20.

(b) $V_o = 2000 - 200 = 1800$ V. From the characteristics, $v_{b1} = 1200$ V.

$$\cos\theta_1 = (2000 - 1200)/1800 = 0.445.$$

For other values of θ the following table can be constructed.

i_b, A	v_b, V	$\cos \theta$	θ, deg
0	1200	0.445	64
0.2	1050	0.526	58
0.5	950	0.585	54
1	900	0.61	53
2	750	0.695	46
3	600	0.78	39
4	500	0.835	33
6	200	1	0

The plot of i_b as a function of θ is shown in Fig. 12.21.
(c) To calculate I_b we take $\Delta\theta = 21.3$ deg. From (12.40)

$$I_b = (1/\pi) \times [\pi(21.3)/180](6/2 + 5 + 2.9) \approx 1.6 \text{ A.}$$

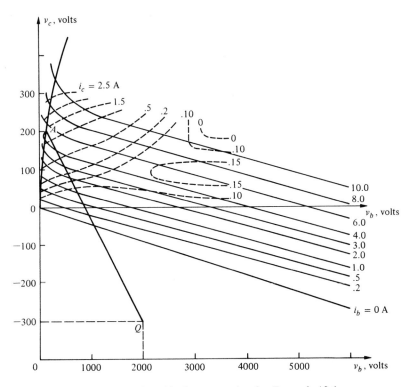

Fig. 12.20 Graphical construction for Example 12.4.

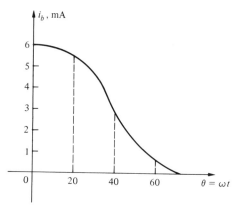

Fig. 12.21 Plot of i_b as a function of θ for Example 12.4.

Power and Efficiency Consideration in Class C Tuned Amplifiers

The class C amplifier is a power amplifier; hence efficiency and output power are important factors to consider in its design. On an instantaneous basis, power lost, or dissipated, at the anode is $i_b v_b$. The losses will be reduced if the value of v_b is reduced during the time of current flow. If, however, $v_{b(min)} < v_{c(max)}$ the secondary emission flow of electrons pass through the grid and the plate current is reduced sharply. This causes the output power and efficiency to fall; the best operation is then for $v_{b(min)} = v_{c(max)}$.

The plate input power P_{dc} is given by

$$P_{dc} = V_{bb}I_b.$$

The output power P_o of the fundamental frequency with the resonant impedance R_L is

$$P_o = I_1^2 R_L/2.$$

The plate efficiency η_p is therefore given by

$$\eta_p = (I_1^2 R_L/2V_{bb}I_b) \times 100\%. \tag{12.43}$$

The fundamental value of plate current I_1 may be calculated by using (12.42).

Example 12.5

In Example 12.4, calculate (a) The resonant impedance R_L of the tuned circuit, and (b) the plate conversion efficiency.

Solution

(a) From (12.36) and the operating line shown in Fig. 12.20, one obtains

$$V_o = 2000 - 200 = 1800 \text{ V}.$$

To find $R_L = V_o/I_1$ we calculate I_1. Current I_1 may be calculated by plotting the curve $i_b \cos \theta$ and using (12.42). The following table gives $i_b \cos \theta$ as a function of θ:

i_b, A	θ, deg	$\cos \theta$	$i_b \cos \theta$
0	64	0.445	0
0.2	58	0.526	0.105
0.5	54	0.585	0.3
1	53	0.61	0.61
2	46	0.695	1.39
3	39	0.78	2.34
4	33	0.835	3.34
6	0	1	6

The plot of $i_b \cos \theta$ versus θ is shown in Fig. 12.22. To calculate I_1, we take $\Delta\theta = 21.3$ deg and use (12.42):

$$I_1 = (2/\pi) \times [(\pi \times 21.3)/180](6/2 + 4 + 2) \approx 2.13 \text{ A}$$

and $R_L = V_o/I_1 = 1800/2.13 \approx 900$ ohms.
(b) From (12.43),

$$\eta_p = \frac{(213)^2 \times 900}{2 \times 2000 \times 1.6} \times 100\% \approx 71\%.$$

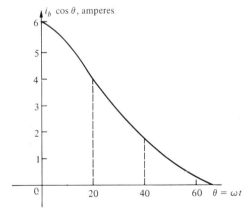

Fig. 12.22 Plot of $i_b \cos \theta$ as a function of θ for Example 12.5.

12.8   Summary

Tuned amplifiers are used to amplify narrowband signals. Besides providing gain, they are required to reject signals outside the useful passband.

To perform this function, a well-designed tuned amplifier must have a frequency response symmetrical with respect to the center frequency of the passband; in addition, the gain must be flat and the phase shift be as linear as possible within the passband. To have good rejection the gain must fall very rapidly outside the passband. Well-designed synchronous- and staggered-tuning amplifiers generally satisfy the above requirements.

Class C tuned amplifiers are high-power circuits used typically in transmitters. Output power and efficiency are of prime interest. The output power of class C amplifiers is often in the order of kilowatts, and special tubes are used in their circuits. As yet, solid-state designs are not available that operate at these large power ratings.

References

ANGELO, JR., E. J., *Electronic Circuits*, McGraw-Hill, New York, 2nd ed., 1964.

———, *BJT's FET's, and Microcircuits*, McGraw-Hill, New York, 1969.

RYDER, J. D., *Electronic Fundamentals and Applications*, Prentice-Hall, Englewood Cliffs, New Jersey, 3rd ed., 1964.

Problems

12.1 The parameters of a parallel RLC resonant circuit are $R = 10$ K, $L = 0.1$ H, and $C = 0.01\ \mu$F. Plot its frequency response, and calculate the maximum amplitude. At what frequency does the maximum occur? Is the response of the circuit suitable for a tuned amplifier? Why?

12.2 Repeat Prob. 12.1 for $R = 1$ K. Is this design suitable for a tuned amplifier? Why?

12.3 Transform the parallel circuit of Prob. 12.1 to that of Fig. 12.2.

12.4 For the FET amplifier of Fig. 12.5A, assume that $r_p = 100$ K, $\mu = 50$, $R_L = 10$ K, $R_s = 10$ ohms, $C = 1000$ pF, and $L = 10^{-4}$ H. Calculate (a) the resonant frequency; (b) the bandwidth; and (c) the maximum voltage gain.

12.5 Repeat Prob. 12.4 for a vacuum tube whose $r_p = 10$ K. All other values remain the same. Compare results.

12.6 In the tuned amplifier of Fig. P12.6, assume that the coupling and bypass capacitors act as shorts and the RFC as an open circuit to ac. The transistor parameters are $r_{b'e} = 1$ K, $r_{bb'} = 0$, $h_{fe} = 50$, $f_T = 400$ MHz, and $C_{b'c} = 4$ pF. Calculate (a) the value of L for the circuit to resonate at 10 MHz; (b) the bandwidth; and (c) the current gain i_L/i_s as a function of frequency.

12.7 In Prob. 12.6 it is desired to reduce the bandwidth to 10 kHz and maintain the other characteristics. A transformer introduced across

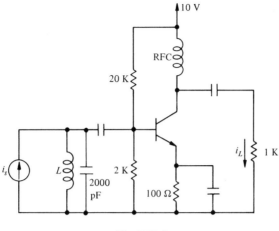

Fig. P12.6

the input side of the amplifier will be used for this purpose. At the primary side of the transformer the total capacitance can be as high as 100 pF. Calculate (a) the value of inductance to be connected across the primary side and (b) the primary to secondary turns ratio.

12.8   Assume that two identical stages of Fig. P12.6 are cascaded. (a) Calculate the bandwidth and peak value of gain. (b) Write an expression for the current gain as a function of frequency. (c) Is this a good method for reducing bandwidth. What are some disadvantages?

12.9   The FET amplifier of Fig. P12.9 is tuned at 1 MHz. Assume that the coupling and bypass capacitors act as shorts and the RFC as an open circuit to ac. The total input capacitance to the FET is 200 pF;

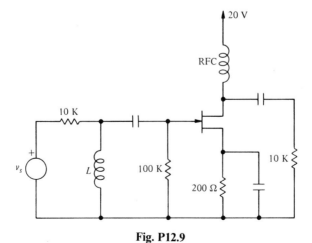

Fig. P12.9

$r_p = 100\,\text{K}$; and $\mu = 50$. Calculate (a) the value of L and (b) the bandwidth. (c) Write an expression for voltage gain as a function of frequency.

12.10   Repeat Prob. 12.9 if the amplifier is tuned at 100 kHz.

12.11   An incremental model of a tuned amplifier is given in Fig. P12.11. (a) Derive an expression for V_o/V_s. (b) As L varies, draw the locus of poles of V_o/V_s.

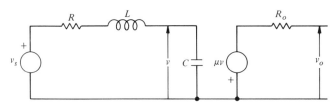

Fig. P 12.11

12.12   In Fig. P12.11, $\mu = 20$, $R = 1\,\text{K}$, $R_o = 2\,\text{K}$, $L = 100\,\text{mH}$, and $C = 100\,\text{pF}$. (a) Examine the frequency response with the aid of the Bode plot. (b) Determine the poles of V_o/V_s. (c) Using a graphical construction similar to that of Fig. 12.13, determine the value of ω_p.

12.13   In the double-tuned amplifier of Fig. 12.12A, assume that $a = 1$ at $\omega_o = 10^7\,\text{rad/s}$, $R = 100\,\text{K}$, $C = 500\,\text{pF}$, and $g_m = 5\,\text{mmhos}$. (a) Calculate the value of L. (b) Choose a suitable value for L_m and write an expression for the voltage gain.

12.14   Repeat Prob. 12.13 for $a = 0.5$.

12.15   In Prob. 12.6, (a) plot the poles and zeros; (b) identify the value of ω_p; and (c) determine the maximum voltage gain.

12.16   Design a stagger-tuned amplifier with the same resonant frequency and bandwidth as used for Example 12.3. Modify the values of the passive components to obtain a response such that the valley just vanishes. For this case, how is the pole-zero plot of Fig. 12.15 altered?

12.17   In the parallel resonant circuit of Fig. 12.2, it is desired to obtain a resonant frequency of $10^7\,\text{rad/s}$; $C' = 100\,\text{pF}$ and $R' = 100\,\text{ohms}$. Calculate the value of (a) resonant impedance and (b) the impedance at $10^6\,\text{rad/s}$.

12.18   The triode characteristics of a 3CW5000A3 used in a class C amplifier is given in the Appendix. Assume that $v_{b(\min)} = 400\,\text{V}$. If $V_{bb} = 2500\,\text{V}$, $V_{cc} = -300\,\text{V}$, and the input signal is $v_s = 500\cos\omega t$, (a) Draw the operating load line. (b) Draw the curve of i_b as a function of θ. (c) Calculate I_b and I_1. (d) Is this amplifier operating at maximum efficiency? Why?

12.19 In Prob. 12.18 assume that $v_{b(min)} = v_{c(max)}$ and all other values, except v_s, remain the same. Calculate (a) the plate efficiency and (b) the value of v_s.

12.20 In example 12.4, (a) write an expression for the operating line, and (b) calculate the resonant impedance.

Sinusoidal Oscillators

In the previous chapters our concern was amplifiers; in this chapter we embark on a study of sinusoidal oscillators. An electronic oscillator is defined here as a circuit that generates a sinusoidal voltage or current waveform. Sinusoidal oscillators are used for testing and to generate the carrier frequency in a communications system. Contrary to the amplifier, where an input signal is required, no input signal is needed for the operation of an oscillator. A source of dc power is sufficient for its operation.

Two-terminal devices, such as tunnel diodes, or three-terminal devices, such as transistors, may be used for active elements in conjunction with resistors, inductors, and capacitors. The sinusoidal oscillator may be divided into two categories: negative-resistance oscillators and external feedback oscillators.

13.1 Negative-Resistance Oscillators

A negative resistance behaves like a source of energy. It can supply power to a resonant circuit containing resistance. Sustained oscillation with constant amplitude will occur if the amount of energy given up by the negative resistance equals the energy absorbed by the resonant circuit. An example of a negative-resistance oscillator is the tunnel diode oscillator.

The electrical characteristics of a tunnel diode are shown in Fig. 13.1A. If operated in region AB, which has a negative slope, the diode acts as a negative resistance. A simplified high-frequency model of the tunnel diode is shown in Fig. 13.2; capacitance C_d is the shunt capacity of the device.

A tunnel diode oscillator circuit is given in Fig. 13.3A, and the model of the circuit is shown in Fig. 13.3B. If $G = 1/R = g$, a lossless tuned circuit is obtained. Because the tunnel diode exhibits a nonlinear characteristic, the slope of the curve in the negative region is such that if the magnitude of g becomes larger than G, the output voltage increases and causes g to decrease to a value to satisfy the relation $G = g$.

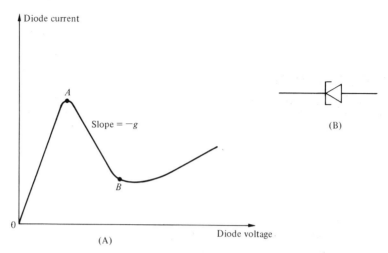

Fig. 13.1 The tunnel diode. (A) Electrical characteristics. (B) Symbol.

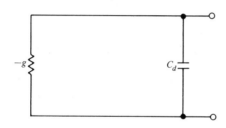

Fig. 13.2 Simplified high-frequency model of a tunnel diode.

Example 3.1

The characteristic curve of a tunnel diode used in the oscillator of Fig. 13.4B is shown in Fig. 13.4A. The diode has a shunt capacitance of 10 pF. Values of the circuit components are given in Fig. 13.4B. Find the frequency of oscillation and the voltage across the tuned circuit.

Solution

The frequency of oscillation is given by the resonant frequency of the LC circuit. In this problem $C = 10 + 90 = 100\,\text{pF}$; therefore,

$$\omega = \frac{1}{(10 \times 10^{-3} \times 100 \times 10^{-12})^{1/2}} = 10^6 \text{ rad/s.}$$

To obtain the amplitude of the voltage across the tuned circuit, the quiescent point is located at 0.1 V, shown in Fig. 13.4A. A tangent drawn to the curve at this point indicates that the slope $di/dv = -g = -0.01$ mho. If a large ac output voltage is assumed, a line such as CD with

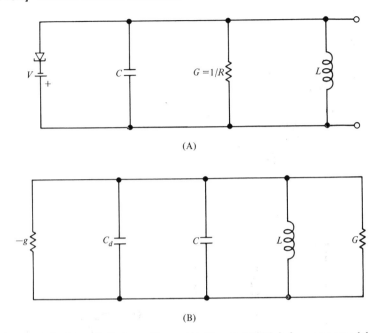

Fig. 13.3   Tunnel-diode oscillator. (A) Circuit. (B) High-frequency model.

a slope of -0.002 mho (Fig. 13.4A) is drawn through the Q-point. The slope of CD is the average admittance of the diode for an ac signal greater than $0.13 - 0.1 = 0.03$ V indicated by line QB. This value of g, however, is insufficient to maintain the output and automatically the amplitude reduces to a value corresponding to a slope of $-g = -0.01$ mho. From Fig. 13.4A, the peak voltage amplitude across the tuned circuit is $0.13 - 0.1 = 0.03$ V.

13.2   External Feedback Oscillators

In Chapter 11 it was seen that amplifiers with feedback can become unstable. If the roots of the corresponding characteristic equation are located on the $j\omega$-axis, the output becomes a sinewave with constant amplitude; this is the requirement for oscillation. In practice, the design of an oscillator is such that the circuit is made capable of becoming unstable, that is, the roots of the appropriate characteristic equation are located on the right-hand side of the $j\omega$-axis (right-hand plane).

The nonlinear characteristics of the active device cause its parameters to vary in such a manner that the roots initially in the right-half plane become located on the $j\omega$-axis. Most oscillators use positive feedback, but as we have seen in Chapter 11, negative feedback may also result in unstable operation.

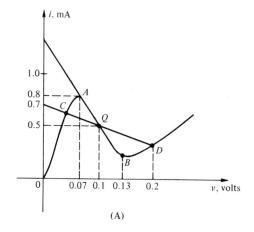

(A)

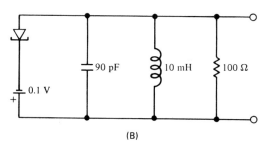

(B)

Fig. 13.4 Example 13.1. (A) Tunnel diode characteristics. (B) Circuit.

Consider the typical external feedback circuit shown in Fig. 11.3; the transfer function found in Chapter 11 is

$$O/I = G/(I + GH).$$

If the feedback is positive, we obtain

$$O/I = G/(1 - GH). \tag{13.1}$$

Because it is possible to obtain oscillation with positive or negative feedback, we write the following general expression for the feedback loop:

$$O/I = G/(1 \pm GH). \tag{13.2}$$

To find the conditions for oscillation one approach is to say that in (13.2) a sinusoidal output O must be obtained in the absence of any input, that is, when the input I is zero. This requires that

$$1 \pm G(j\omega)H(j\omega) = 0. \tag{13.3}$$

Another approach is that the roots of the characteristic equation $1 \pm GH$ must be located on the $j\omega$-axis; we should then look for the values of the parameters that make (13.3) equal to zero. Of course, either approach yields the same result. The starting condition for oscillation requires that the roots of the characteristic equation be initially located in the right-half plane.

If the circuit does not oscillate, there is no value of ω that satisfies (13.3). When (13.3) is equated to zero, the real and imaginary parts must be equated to zero independently, as illustrated in the following discussion.

RC Oscillators

A circuit of an RC oscillator using a field-effect transistor is shown in Fig. 13.5. If we assume that none of the RC sections loads the previous ones nor does the first section load the amplifier output, and class-A operation exists, the gain G in the range of frequencies where bypass capacitor C_S acts as a short circuit will be

$$G = v_1/v_f = -g_m R_T,$$

where

$$R_T = R_D r_p/(R_D + r_p).$$

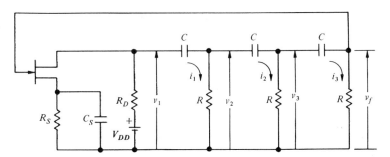

Fig. 13.5 An RC oscillator using a field-effect transistor.

The transfer function of the feedback element $H(s)$ is

$$H(s) = (sCR)^n/(1 + sCR)^n,$$

where n is the number of RC elements; then

$$1 - GH = 1 + [(sCR)^n/(1 + sCR)^n]g_m R_T = 0$$

and

$$1 - G(j\omega)H(j\omega) = 1 + [(j\omega CR)^n/(1 + j\omega CR)^n]g_m R_T = 0,$$

or

$$(1 + j\omega CR)^n + (j\omega CR)^n g_m R_T = 0. \tag{13.4}$$

In order to satisfy (13.4), the real and imaginary parts of the equation must be independently set equal to zero. Equation (13.4) does not provide a solution for $n = 1$ and $n = 2$; for these two values we obtain $1 = 0$ and $2j\omega CR = 0$, respectively, which is not possible. For $n = 3$, we get

$$1 - 3\omega^2 C^2 R^2 + 3j\omega CR - j\omega^3 C^3 R^3 - j\omega^3 C^3 R^3 g_m R_T = 0.$$

The real part gives $1 - 3\omega^2 C^2 R^2 = 0$ from which

$$\omega^2 = 1/(3C^2 R^2). \tag{13.5}$$

Equating the imaginary part to zero yields

$$3\omega CR - \omega^3 C^3 R^3 - \omega^3 C^3 R^3 g_m R_T = 0. \tag{13.6}$$

Replacing (13.5) in (13.6) results in

$$g_m R_T = 8. \tag{13.7}$$

Expression (13.5) gives the frequency of oscillation and (13.7) the condition for the roots of the characteristic equation to be located on the $j\omega$-axis. The condition for starting the oscillation is $g_m R_T > 8$. If this inequality is satisfied after oscillation begins, the nonlinear parameters of the active device vary to locate the roots on the $j\omega$-axis such that $g_m R_T = 8$.

The effect of loading on each branch of the feedback elements cannot be neglected in practical operation. Let us consider a practical case where only the loading of the feedback network as a whole is neglected with respect to the load current of the amplifier. Since the current of each feedback branch is not negligible with respect to the current flowing in other branches, the transfer function $H(s)$ is calculated. Considering only the three RC stages of Fig. 13.5 and writing loop equations, we obtain

$$V_1 = (R + 1/sC)I_1 - RI_2,$$

$$0 = -RI_1 + (2R + 1/sC)I_2 - RI_3,$$

$$0 = -RI_2 + (2R + 1/sC)I_3.$$

Solving the preceding equations for I_3 and noting that $V_f = I_3 R$, we obtain

$$H(s) = \frac{V_f(s)}{V_1(s)} = \frac{R}{\left[\left(\dfrac{1/sC + 2R}{R}\right)^2 - 1\right](1/sC + R) - (1/sC + 2R)}. \tag{13.8}$$

To find the conditions for oscillation, one writes

$$1 - GH = 0$$

or $$[(1/sC + 2R)^2 - 1](1/sC + R) - (1/sC + 2R) + g_m R_T R = 0.$$

Replacing $s = j\omega$ and separating the real and imaginary parts gives

$$\text{Imaginary part} = -1/\omega^3 C^3 R^2 + 6/\omega C = 0$$

or $$\omega^2 = 1/6C^2 R^2: \tag{13.9}$$

$$\text{Real part} = -5/\omega^2 C^2 R^2 + 1 + g_m R_T = 0$$

or $$\omega^2 = 5/C^2 R^2(1 + g_m R_T). \tag{13.10}$$

Replacing ω^2 from (13.9) in (13.10) yields

$$g_m R_T = 29. \tag{13.11}$$

The frequency of oscillation is

$$\omega = 1/(\sqrt{6}RC), \tag{13.12}$$

and the starting condition is

$$g_m R_T \geqslant 29. \tag{13.13}$$

These expressions are different from those obtained where no loading was assumed.

Colpitts Oscillator

The preceding methods are valid for all feedback oscillators. For example, consider the circuit of Fig. 13.6, the Colpitts oscillator. The inductance labeled RFC stands for "radio-frequency choke." Its purpose is to prevent the ac signal from the oscillator getting into the power supply V_{CC}. At the same time, it does not hinder the flow of dc.

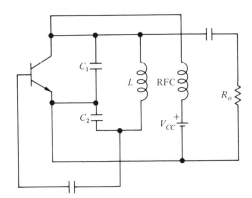

Fig. 13.6 The Colpitts oscillator.

A simplified high-frequency model for the circuit is shown in Fig. 13.7 where $r_{ce} = \infty$ and $C_2' = C_2 + C_i$. Then, from Fig. 13.7, we find

$$H(s) = \frac{r_{b'e}}{r_{b'e} + sL(1 + sC_2' r_{b'e})}.$$

If we assume that

$$R_o \gg \left| \frac{1}{j\omega C_1} \middle/\middle/ \frac{r_{b'e}}{1 + j\omega C_2' r_{b'e}} + j\omega L \right|,$$

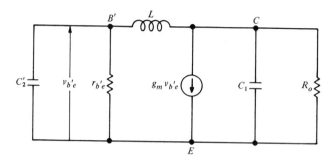

Fig. 13.7 High-frequency model of the Colpitts oscillator.

the load impedance Z_L is

$$Z_L = \frac{[(r_{b'e} + sL(1 + sC_2'r_{b'e})]/sC_1}{(1 + sC_2'r_{b'e})/sC_1 + r_{b'e} + sL(1 + sC_2'r_{b'e})}$$

and

$$G(s) = -Z_L g_m.$$

Equating $1 - GH$ to zero yields

$$1 + sC_2'r_{b'e} + [r_{b'e} + sL(1 + sC_2'r_{b'e})]sC_1 + g_m r_{b'e} = 0. \qquad (13.14)$$

Substituting $s = j\omega$ in (13.14) and equating the imaginary part to zero, we obtain the frequency of oscillation:

$$\omega^2 = (C_1 + C_2')/LC_2'C_1. \qquad (13.15)$$

Equating the real part to zero gives

$$1 - \omega^2 LC_1 + g_m r_{b'e} = 0. \qquad (13.16)$$

Substitution of (13.15) in (13.16) yields

$$C_1/C_2' = g_m r_{b'e}$$

or

$$C_1/C_2' = h_{fe}. \qquad (13.17)$$

Equation (13.17) shows the limit of h_{fe} for which oscillation can be maintained.

The resonant circuit may be put at the input or output of the active device. The circuit of Fig. 13.8 is a Colpitts oscillator with the resonant circuit located at its input. The circuit of Fig. 13.9 is another feedback circuit, called the Hartley oscillator, using a FET. There are many other possible networks for producing sinusoidal oscillation. The reader must be able to separate G and H in each circuit to find the frequency of oscillation and the starting condition as was done in the previous examples.

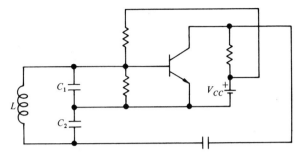

Fig. 13.8 Colpitts oscillator with resonant circuit at the input.

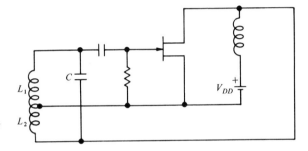

Fig. 13.9 A Hartley oscillator.

13.3 Frequency Stability of Oscillators

From the preceding analysis we have seen that the frequency of oscillation depends on the passive parameters in the circuits. In some cases it may also depend on the parameters of the active device. A very important factor is the effect of temperature variation on the frequency of oscillation.

Temperature variation in an LC circuit can be compensated for to a great extent by use of special negative-temperature coefficient capacitors which vary inversely with temperature and tend to cancel the temperature variations in the inductance which has a positive temperature coefficient. A constant LC over a reasonable temperature range can therefore be maintained. The resonant circuit used in oscillators must also have a high Q. A high-Q circuit is required to maintain the resonant frequency independent of the resonant impedance and its variation with temperature. A high Q also reduces the energy dissipated in the resonant circuit.

In order to make the frequency of oscillation less dependent on loading effects induced by stages following the oscillator, it is customary to follow an oscillator with a class A operated amplifier called a *buffer* amplifier. The buffer amplifier provides isolation and does not load down the oscillator, which would affect the frequency and stability of oscillation.

13.4 Crystal-Controlled Oscillators

A class of oscillators which achieves very good frequency stability is the crystal-controlled oscillator. In the crystal oscillator the conventional LC network is replaced by a quartz crystal. The crystal has the property of producing a potential difference between its parallel faces when the crystal is mechanically strained, or deformed. Inversely, when a potential difference is applied across its faces, it will deform, or change, its shape. This property, known as the *piezo-electric effect*, after its discoverer, makes the crystal behave like a very high-Q RLC resonant circuit.

The crystal is cut into very thin slices and then carefully ground to the desired resonant frequency. The orientation of the crystal slice with respect to the crystal axis determines the properties of the crystal. The electrical symbol and equivalent electrical model of a crystal are shown in Fig. 13.10. The crystal itself behaves like a series RLC circuit; however, electrical connections must be made to the crystal holder. This introduces a parallel capacitance C_h shown in Fig. 13.10B.

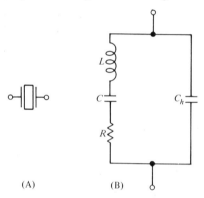

(A)   (B)

Fig. 13.10 The quartz crystal. (A) The electrical symbol. (B) Electrical model.

Crystals can be made to resonate at fundamental frequencies ranging from about 4 kHz to 50 MHz. The low-frequency crystals are large and heavy; for frequencies above 1 MHz the quartz crystal becomes very thin and fragile. The resonant frequency of a given crystal is a function of temperature. It may have either a positive or negative temperature coefficient, depending on the crystal cut. By proper orientation of the axis at which the crystal cut is made, a zero-temperature coefficient crystal is possible.

Figures 13.11A and B show oscillator circuits using a crystal as the resonant element. The variation in input capacitance owing to wiring and the active device has negligible effect on the frequency of oscillation. The model of the input circuit of Fig. 13.11B is shown in Fig. 13.12. The equivalent capacitance C_e used to calculate the resonant frequency is

$$C_e = C(C_h + C_{in})/(C + C_h + C_{in}), \tag{13.18}$$

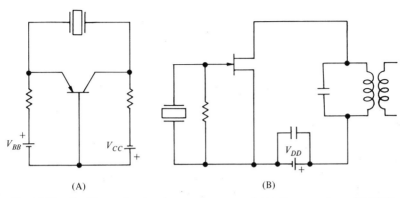

(A)   (B)

Fig. 13.11 Oscillator circuit using a quartz crystal. (A) Common base. (B) FET.

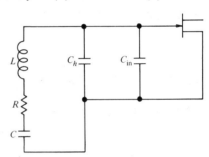

Fig. 13.12 Model of the input circuit of Fig. 13.11B.

where C_{in} is the input capacitance of the active device. The resonant frequency of the crystal oscillator is given by

$$\omega = \sqrt{\frac{1}{LC}\left(1 + \frac{C}{C_h + C_{in}}\right)}. \qquad (13.19)$$

Because C is very small with respect to C_h and C_{in}, the variation of C_{in} will have very little influence on ω.

Example 13.2

A crystal has the following electrical characteristics: $L = 3H$; $C = 0.03$ pF; $R = 5000$ ohms; $C_h = 10$ pF. Assuming $C_{in} = 10$ pF, calculate the variation of frequency for a 10% change in C_{in}.

Solution

$$\omega_1 = \sqrt{\frac{1}{LC}\left(1 + \frac{C}{C_h + C_{in}}\right)} = \sqrt{\frac{1}{LC}\left(1 + \frac{0.03}{10 + 10}\right)}$$

$$= \sqrt{\frac{1}{LC}\left(1 + \frac{3}{2000}\right)}.$$

With a 10% increase in C_{in},

$$\omega_2 = \sqrt{\frac{1}{LC}\left(1 + \frac{3}{2100}\right)},$$

then

$$\omega_1/\omega_2 = 1.00015/1.00014.$$

13.5   Summary

There are two classes of sinusoidal oscillators: the negative-resistance and the external feedback oscillator. The negative-resistance oscillator uses a device that exhibits a negative resistance, such as a tunnel diode. Sustained sinusoidal oscillations with constant amplitude occur when the amount of energy supplied by the negative resistance equals the energy absorbed by the dissipating resistance in the resonant circuit.

The analysis of the starting conditions of external feedback oscillators was approached by the application of the general theory of feedback systems. A feedback system behaves like a sinusoidal oscillator when the roots of the appropriate characteristic equation are located on the $j\omega$-axis. Because physical systems are composed of nonlinear elements an initially unstable system eventually finds itself operating as an oscillator if the nonlinear parameters are made to vary. The operating point adjusts itself so that the roots of the characteristic equation are on the $j\omega$-axis.

Since the mathematical condition for oscillation requires that the roots of the characteristic equation be located on the $j\omega$-axis, one can find the conditions for oscillation as follows: Variable s is replaced by $j\omega$ in the characteristic equation. Then the real and imaginary parts of the resulting expressions are equated to zero and solved for the frequency of oscillation and required gain.

References

ALLEY, C. L., and K. W. ATWOOD, *Electronic Engineering*, Wiley, New York, 2nd ed., 1966.

DE PIAN, L., *Linear Active Network Theory*, Prentice-Hall, Englewood Cliffs, New Jersey, 1962.

RYDER, J. D., *Electronic Fundamentals and Applications*, Prentice-Hall, Englewood Cliffs, New Jersey, 3rd ed., 1964.

Problems

13.1   In Example 13.1 the value of resistance in Fig. 13.4B is reduced from 100 to 30 ohms. How does this affect the frequency of oscillation and the voltage across the tuned circuit?

13.2 Given a single-loop feedback system with

$$G = -1/(s^2 + 2s).$$

Determine an expression for H required to make the system perform as an oscillator.

13.3 In a feedback system

$$G = 10/s(1 + s)(2 + s)$$

and $H = k$, where $0 < k \leqslant 1$. Could the system oscillate if negative feedback is employed? Why?

13.4 If, in Prob. 13.3, positive feedback is used, will the system oscillate? Why?

13.5 In Fig. 13.5, $r_p = 100$ K, $g_m = 3$ mmhos, $R_D = 12$ K, $R = 100$ K, and $C = 100$ pF. (a) Can the circuit oscillate? Why? (b) If your answer to (a) is yes, calculate the frequency of oscillation.

13.6 In the oscillator of Fig. 13.5 assume that the number of RC sections is increased to four; $r_p = 100$ K, $g_m = 2$ mmhos, and $R_D = 10$ K. (a) Can the circuit oscillate? Why? (b) If your answer to (a) is affirmative, determine the conditions for oscillation.

13.7 An integrated-circuit version of a Wien bridge oscillator is given in Fig. P13.7A and the simplified model of the circuit is shown in Fig. P13.7B.

$$G \approx -h_{fe}R_C/(2h_{ie}) \approx v_L/(v_{b1} - v_{b2}).$$

(a) Based on the model, draw a block diagram of the oscillator. (b) Write the conditions for oscillation.

13.8 In the Colpitt's oscillator of Fig. 13.6, replace the BJT by a FET and calculate the conditions for oscillation.

13.9 In Fig. 13.6, the transistor has the following parameters: $g_m = 0.02$ mho, $r_{b'e} = 1$ K, $r_{bb'} = 0$, $C_{b'e} = 50$ pF, and $C_{b'c} = 1$ pF. $R_o = 50$ K and $L = 10 \, \mu$H. Calculate the values of C_1 and C_2 for a frequency of oscillation of 1 MHz.

13.10 If, in Prob. 13.9, $C_2 = 10^4$ pF, determine the values of C_1 and the frequency of oscillation.

13.11 Derive the conditions for oscillation for the oscillator of Fig. 13.8.

13.12 Write the conditions for oscillation for the Hartley oscillator of Fig. 13.9.

13.13 A quartz crystal is characterized by the following electrical parameters: $L = 100$ H, $C = 0.02$ pF, $R = 1500$ ohms, and $C_h = 5$ pF. A transistor having the same characteristics as that used in Prob. 13.9 is used as the active element in a crystal oscillator where $R_o = 50$ K.

Calculate (a) the frequency of oscillation and (b) the variation in frequency if the transistor capacitance varies by $\pm 20\%$.

13.14 Repeat Prob. 13.13 for $L = 50$ H. All other values remain the same.

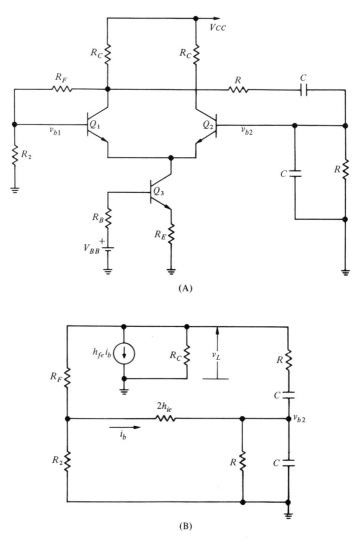

(A)

(B)

Fig. P13.7.

Modulation

14

To this point we have analyzed amplifier circuits where it is usually desirable that the output, or response, have the same form as the input signal, or excitation. We have also studied sinewave oscillators where a sinewave output is available without the need of signal excitation. In this chapter we consider networks in which the form of a sinusoidal input is changed intentionally. Examples of these networks are *modulators* and the process is called *modulation*. In modulation the amplitude, frequency, or phase of a sinewave may be altered. Modulation is used to convey information, such as speech, music, and visual scenes, where some features of the sinewave, such as amplitude, frequency, or phase, is varied in accordance with the information to be transmitted.

A block diagram of a radio transmitter, where the amplitude of a sinewave is varied according to the information to be transmitted, called *amplitude modulation* (AM), is shown in Fig. 14.1. The desired sinewave frequency, referred to as the *carrier signal*, is generated at a low power level by a stable oscillator, ordinarily a crystal oscillator. This is followed by class C amplifiers that increase the power level and isolate the oscillator from the modulator circuit. If the frequency to be radiated is higher than can be obtained from a crystal oscillator, harmonic generators are also included. The information, or *modulating signal*, is amplified and fed into the modulator. The resulting waveform emanating from the antenna is an amplitude-modulated signal.

14.1 Amplitude Modulation (AM)

An unmodulated sinewave voltage of amplitude A may be expressed as

$$v = A \sin(\omega_c t + \theta), \qquad (14.1)$$

where ω_c is the angular frequency, and θ is the phase angle of the carrier frequency. Assume the modulating signal v_m is a sinewave of amplitude V_m and angular frequency ω_m:

$$v_m = V_m \cos \omega_m t. \qquad (14.2)$$

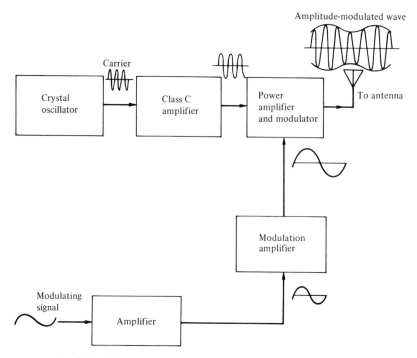

Fig. 14.1 Simplified block diagram of an AM radio transmitter.

The amplitude A of (14.1) is made to vary as

$$A = V_c + V_m \cos \omega_m t$$
$$= V_c[1 + (V_m/V_c) \cos \omega_m t], \tag{14.3}$$

where V_c is the amplitude of the carrier. Substitution of (14.3) in (14.1) yields

$$v = V_c(1 + m \cos \omega_m t) \sin(\omega_c t + \theta), \tag{14.4}$$

where $m = V_m/V_c$ is the *modulation factor*, or *index*. If the value of m is multiplied by 100%, it is expressed as a *modulation percentage*. As seen from (14.3), m is proportional to the modulating signal voltage. The value of m should not exceed 1 (or 100%); it will be between 0 and 1:

$$0 \leqslant m \leqslant 1.$$

To simplify the analysis, assume the phase angle $\theta = 0$. Expanding (14.4) and using appropriate trigonometric identities, we obtain

$$v = V_c \sin \omega_c t + \frac{mV_c}{2} \sin(\omega_c - \omega_m)t + \frac{mV_c}{2} \sin(\omega_c + \omega_m)t. \tag{14.5}$$

From (14.5) we see that a single-frequency modulated wave contains three separate component frequencies: the carrier frequency ω_c, the sum of the carrier and modulating frequencies $\omega_c + \omega_m$, and the difference between the carrier and modulating frequencies $\omega_c - \omega_m$. It is clear that an amplitude-modulated signal is not just the sum of the carrier and modulating frequencies.

Term $\omega_c + \omega_m$ is referred to as the *upper sideband* frequency and term $\omega_c - \omega_m$ the *lower sideband* frequency. The modulating signal frequency ω_m (or f_m) is always much less than the carrier frequency ω_c (or f_c). For example, f_c may be 1 MHz, while the greatest value for f_m is 10 kHz for a typical amplitude-modulated signal. A single-frequency AM signal waveform is shown in Fig. 14.2A.

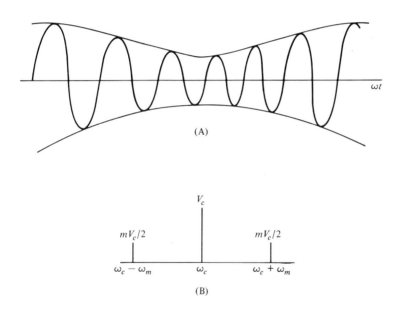

(A)

(B)

Fig. 14.2 Amplitude modulation. (A) A single-frequency AM wave. (B) Frequency spectrum of an AM wave having a single modulating frequency.

If the modulated signal contains more than one modulating frequency, the expression for the resulting wave contains additional sideband terms. Consider two modulating frequencies ω_1 and ω_2 with their respective modulation factors m_1 and m_2; then,

$$v = V_c(1 + m_1 \cos \omega_1 t + m_2 \cos \omega_2 t) \sin \omega_c t. \qquad (14.6)$$

By the use of trigonometric identities, (14.6) may be reduced to

$$v = V_c \sin \omega_c t + \frac{m_1 V_c}{2} \sin(\omega_c - \omega_1)t + \frac{m_1 V_c}{2} \sin(\omega_c + \omega_1)t$$

$$+ \frac{m_2 V_c}{2} \sin(\omega_c - \omega_2)t + \frac{m_2 V_c}{2} \sin(\omega_c + \omega_2)t. \tag{14.7}$$

Besides the carrier there are two lower-sideband and two upper-sideband frequencies. One manner of representing the frequencies, and their corresponding amplitudes, of a modulated wave is illustrated in Fig. 14.2B. This representation is called a *frequency spectrum plot*.

The power of a modulated wave dissipated in a resistance R will be considered. From (14.5),

$$\text{Carrier power} = V_c^2/(2R)$$

$$\text{Sideband power} = V_c^2 m^2/(8R)$$

$$\text{Total sideband power} = V_c^2 m^2/(4R),$$

which equals $(m^2/2)$(carrier power).

Modulation is said to be linear if the envelope of the modulated waveform has the same form as the modulating signal. This requires an active device with linear characteristics, although the modulation process itself is non-linear.

The following analysis demonstrates how a device exhibiting nonlinear characteristics can be used for modulation. A power series relating input voltage and output current will be used to approximate the nonlinear characteristics. Let

$$i = a_0 + a_1 v + a_2 v^2 \tag{14.8}$$

and

$$v = V_1 \sin \omega_c t + V_2 \cos \omega_m t. \tag{14.9}$$

Substitution of (14.9) in (14.8) and the use of appropriate trigonometric identities yields

$$i = a_0 + a_1(V_1 \sin \omega_c t + V_2 \cos \omega_m t) + (a_2 V_1^2/2)(1 - \cos 2\omega_c t)$$

$$+ (a_2 V_2^2/2)(1 + \cos 2\omega_m t) + (a_2 V_1 V_2)(\sin(\omega_c + \omega_m)t + \sin(\omega_c - \omega_m)t). \tag{14.10}$$

Examination of (14.10) shows that the frequencies ω_c, $\omega_c - \omega_m$, $\omega_c + \omega_m$, $2\omega_c$, $2\omega_m$, and ω_m are present in the expression for current i. By means of a bandpass filter centered at carrier frequency ω_c, the desired frequencies ω_c, $\omega_c + \omega_m$, and $\omega_c - \omega_m$ will be permitted to pass while the other frequencies will be attenuated.

From our analysis we observe that the multiplication of two sinewaves results in an amplitude-modulated wave. For instance, if the value of an impedance is varied sinusoidally and a sinewave current of a different frequency flows through it, the voltage across the impedance is a special kind of an amplitude-modulated wave. If $i = I \sin \omega_c t$ and $z = Z \sin \omega_m t$, then

$$v = IZ \sin \omega_c t \sin \omega_m t$$

$$= (IZ/2)(\cos(\omega_c - \omega_m)t - \cos(\omega_c + \omega_m)t). \tag{14.11}$$

Expression (14.11) shows that only the sum and difference frequencies are present in the resultant waveform. This type of amplitude-modulated wave is called a *suppressed-carrier* wave, or double-sideband signal.

Example 14.1

An amplitude-modulated wave is given by the following expression:

$$v = 10(1 + 0.1 \cos 2\pi 10^3 t) \cos(2\pi 10^6 t).$$

(a) Calculate the frequencies present, their amplitude, and modulation index. (b) Calculate the carrier and sideband power developed across a 10-ohm resistance.

Solution

(a) By the application of suitable trigonometric identities, the given expression may be rewritten as

$$v = 10 \cos 2\pi 10^6 t + 0.5 \cos 2\pi (10^6 + 10^3)t$$

$$+ 0.5 \cos 2\pi (10^6 - 10^3)t,$$

where $f_c = 10^6$ Hz, $(f_c + f_m) = (10^6 + 10^3)$ Hz, $(f_c - f_m) = (10^6 - 10^3)$ Hz, $V(f_c) = 10$ V, and $V(f_c + f_m) = V(f_c - f_m) = 0.5$ V. The modulation index $m = 0.1$.

(b)   Carrier power $= V_c^2/(2R) = 10^2/(2 \times 10) = 5$ W,

Total sideband power $= V_c^2 m^2/(4R) = 10^2 \times 0.1^2/(4 \times 10)$

$$= 25 \text{ mW}.$$

14.2 Modulator Circuits

A variety of circuits are used for amplitude modulation, of which a few will be analyzed. An example of a nonlinear modulator is the van der Bijl modulator developed originally for the vacuum tube. A transistor version is shown in Fig. 14.3.

The transistor is biased for class A operation. Let the nonlinear relationship between collector current i_c and the base-emitter voltage v_{be} be approximated by the following power series:

$$i_c = a_0 + a_1 v_{be} + a_2 v_{be}^2. \tag{14.12}$$

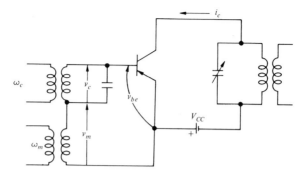

Fig. 14.3 Transistor version of the van der Bijl modulator.

From Fig. 14.3 it is seen that input voltage v_{be} is equal to the sum of the carrier and modulating signal voltages $v_c + v_m$; therefore,

$$v_{be} = V_c \cos \omega_c t + V_m \cos \omega_m t. \tag{14.13}$$

Substituting (14.13) in (14.12) and simplifying, we obtain

$$i_c = a_0 + a_1(V_c \cos \omega_c t + V_m \cos \omega_m t) + (a_2 V_c^2/2)(1 + \cos 2\omega_c t)$$
$$+ (a_2 V_m^2/2)(1 + \cos 2\omega_m t) \tag{14.14}$$
$$+ a_2 V_c V_m(\cos(\omega_c + \omega_m)t + \cos(\omega_c - \omega_m)t).$$

The tuned circuit at the output behaves as a filter and eliminates all frequencies except ω_c, $\omega_c + \omega_m$, and $\omega_c - \omega_m$. Figure 14.4 shows the input voltage and output current waveforms.

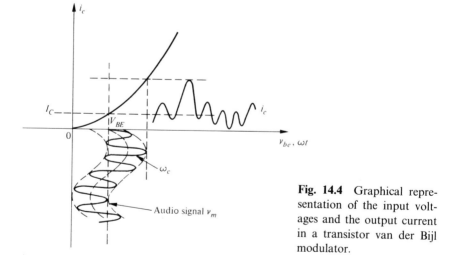

Fig. 14.4 Graphical representation of the input voltages and the output current in a transistor van der Bijl modulator.

The difference between class C operation, to be considered here, and class A operation discussed in the previous section, is that the output characteristic in class C operation is considered linear. The quiescent operating point in class C is located below cutoff. When the carrier and modulating signals are applied to the class C modulator, the operating point moves from the cutoff region into the conducting region. Figure 14.5 shows a class C amplifier operating as a grid-biased modulator. Although the circuit is similar to that of Fig. 14.4, its operation is different. It must be remembered that the circuit of Fig. 14.4 is class A, and the continuous nonlinearity of the device characteristics is responsible for amplitude modulation.

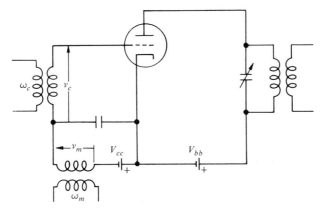

Fig. 14.5 Class C modulator using a triode.

Figure 14.6 illustrates graphically the operation of the grid-biased modulator. Comparison of the output waveform of Fig. 14.6 with that of Fig. 14.4 shows that the output current in the circuit of Fig. 14.5 consists of discontinuous pulses; in class A the output is continuous. A class C operated base-modulated transistor amplifier is given in Fig. 14.7A. The operation of the circuit is similar to that of the vacuum tube modulator. As shown in Fig. 14.7B, the piecewise-linear characteristic of the transistor is used. The amplifier is biased beyond cutoff and, as in the case of the vacuum tube, the output current is a series of pulses.

Balanced Modulator

In an amplitude-modulated wave the intelligence is contained in each of the sidebands. If a modulator produces only sidebands the power owing to the carrier is saved and the efficiency of transmission thereby increased. A modulated wave without the carrier, which was derived as (14.11), is a suppressed-carrier modulated wave. An example of a circuit producing

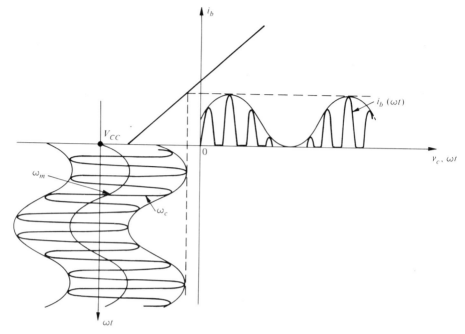

Fig. 14.6 The input voltages and the output current of a class C modulator.

suppressed-carrier modulation is the *balanced modulator* of Fig. 14.8. In this circuit the characteristics of each transistor is nonlinear. The relation between output current and input voltage for each transistor may be approximated by the following power series:

$$i_1 = a_0 + a_1 v_{b1} + a_2 v_{b1}^2 \tag{14.15a}$$

$$i_2 = a_0 + a_1 v_{b2} + a_2 v_{b2}^2. \tag{14.15b}$$

Reference to Fig. 14.8 shows that the carrier is applied to both transistors; the modulating signals, however, are 180° out of phase at the transistor bases. The input voltages are, therefore,

$$v_{b1} = V_c \cos \omega_c t + V_m \cos \omega_m t \tag{14.16a}$$

$$v_{b2} = V_c \cos \omega_c t - V_m \cos \omega_m t. \tag{14.16b}$$

Substituting (14.16a, b) in (14.15a, b) yields

$$i_1 = a_0 + a_1(V_c \cos \omega_c t + V_m \cos \omega_m t) + a_2(V_c \cos \omega_c t + V_m \cos \omega_m t)^2$$

and
$$i_2 = a_0 + a_1(V_c \cos \omega_c t - V_m \cos \omega_m t) + a_2(V_c \cos \omega_c t - V_m \cos \omega_m t)^2.$$

Because the transistors are connected in push pull the output current $i =$ $i_1 - i_2$; therefore,
$$i = 2a_1 V_m \cos \omega_m t + 4a_2 V_c V_m \cos \omega_c t \cos \omega_m t.$$

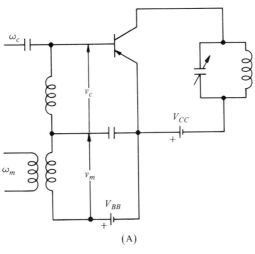

(A)

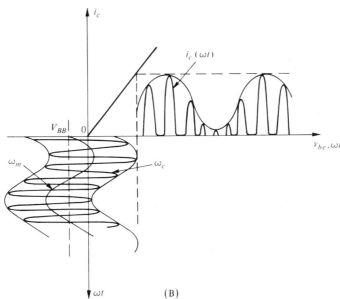

(B)

Fig. 14.7 Class C base-modulated transistor amplifier. (A) Circuit. (B) Waveforms.

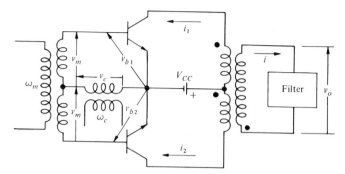

Fig. 14.8 Balanced modulator.

The resonant output circuit filters the unwanted frequencies and the output voltage v_o obtained is

$$v_o = 2a_2 V_c V_m[\cos(\omega_c + \omega_m)t + \cos(\omega_c - \omega_m)t]. \qquad (14.17)$$

Equation (14.17) shows that the output contains only sideband frequencies.

Single Sideband (SSB)

Because the modulating information is contained in each of the sidebands of (14.17), one sideband is sufficient for the transmission of signals. There are two basic techniques used for generating a single-sideband (SSB) signal: the *phase-shift* and *filter* methods. In this section we shall consider the phase-shift method.

A block diagram of a phase-shift SSB modulator is shown in Fig. 14.9A. Two balanced modulators are used in the system. The carrier and modulating signals are fed directly into balanced modulator 1, while the carrier and modulating signals to modulator 2 are each shifted by 90°. The output voltage of modulator 1 has the same expression as (14.17). For modulator 2,

$$v_{b1}' = V_c \sin \omega_c t + V_m \sin \omega_m t$$

$$v_{b2}' = V_c \sin \omega_c t - V_m \sin \omega_m t$$

and

$$i_1' = a_0 + a_1(V_c \sin \omega_c t + V_m \sin \omega_m t) + a_2(V_c \sin \omega_c t + V_m \sin \omega_m t)^2$$

$$i_2' = a_0 + a_1(V_c \sin \omega_c t - V_m \sin \omega_m t) + a_2(V_c \sin \omega_c t - V_m \sin \omega_m t)^2.$$

Since $i' = i_1' - i_2'$, one obtains

$$i' = 2V_m \sin \omega_m t + 4a_2 V_c V_m \sin \omega_m t \sin \omega_c t.$$

After filtering, we have

$$v_o' = 2a_2 V_c V_m[\cos(\omega_c + \omega_m)t - \cos(\omega_c - \omega_m)t].$$

The output is

$$v_o - v_o' = 4a_2 V_c V_m \cos(\omega_c - \omega_m)t. \tag{14.18}$$

The lower sideband is preserved.

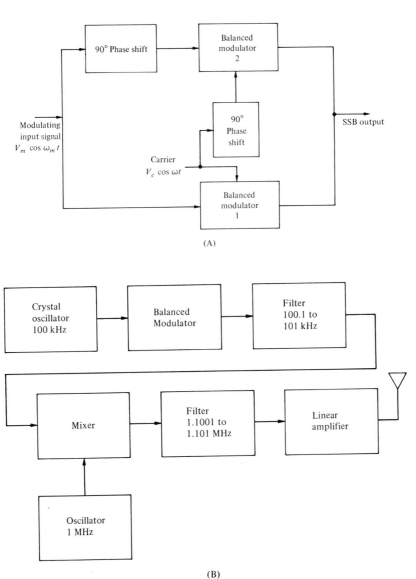

(A)

(B)

Fig. 14.9 Single-sideband generation. (A) Block diagram of an SSB phase shift generator. (B) Block diagram of a transmitter using the filter method for SSB generation.

Example 4.2

Calculate the ratio of power in a single-sideband signal to that of an amplitude-modulated signal. For $m = 1$, what is the value of the power ratio?

Solution

$$\text{Let } P_1 = \text{sideband power} = V_c^2 m^2/(8R),$$

$$P_2 = \text{power in both sidebands and carrier,}$$

$$= \frac{V_c^2 m^2(2 + 4/m^2)}{8R}.$$

Therefore, $P_1/P_2 = 1/2(1 + 2/m^2)$.

For $m = 1$, $P_1/P_2 = 1/6$.

Example 4.3

Assume the nonlinear characteristic of a transistor used in the balanced modulator of Fig. 14.8 is given by

$$i_1 = 0.01 + 0.02v_b + 0.005v_b^2.$$

The carrier and modulating voltages are, respectively,

$$v_c = 2 \cos 10^6 t,$$

$$v_m = \cos 10^3 t.$$

Calculate (a) the modulation index and the expression for the output voltage of a single-sideband signal and (b) the ratio of power required in SSB to that of AM for the given values.

Solution

(a) From (14.18),

$$\text{Output voltage} = v_o - v_o' = 4a_2 V_c V_m \cos (\omega_c - \omega_m)t$$

$$= 4 \times 0.005 \times 2 \cos(10^6 - 10^3)t$$

$$= 0.04 \cos(10^6 - 10^3)t.$$

Modulation index $m = V_m/V_c = 1/2$.

(b) Using the result of Example 14.2, we obtain

$$P_1/P_2 = 1/2(1 + 2/0.5^2) = 1/18.$$

A second means of obtaining a single-sideband signal, the *filter method*, eliminates the unwanted sideband by a filter that is sufficiently selective to transmit one sideband while suppressing the other. Filter requirements are, however, very severe. For example, if the carrier frequency is 1 MHz and the lowest modulating frequency is 100 Hz, the filter must transmit $(10^6 + 100)$ Hz without attenuation, while rejecting completely $(10^6 - 100)$ Hz, or vice versa. This kind of response is too demanding on practical filters.

The filter method is suitable for obtaining single-sideband signals corresponding to low, or moderate, carrier frequencies. If a high carrier frequency is required, the circuit of Fig. 14.9B is used. In this configuration the signal is first modulated at a low carrier frequency and after filtering the frequency is increased by a second oscillator. For our illustration, assume the first oscillator produces a carrier frequency of 100 kHz. The modulating frequencies, between 100 Hz and 1 kHz, are introduced in the balanced modulator. Because the smallest signal frequency is 100 Hz, the first filter transmits $(10^5 + 100)$ Hz while rejecting $(10^5 - 100)$ Hz. The second oscillator generates a 1-MHz carrier. The function of the *mixer* is to modulate (that is, produce sum and difference frequencies) the output of the second oscillator with the output of the first filter. This operation is also referred to as *heterdyning*. We obtain here $(10^6 + 1.001 \times 10^5)$ Hz and $(10^6 - 1.001 \times 10^5)$ Hz. The second filter transmits $(10^6 + 1.001 \times 10^5)$ Hz and rejects $(10^6 - 1.001 \times 10^5)$ Hz. By this method, filters having reasonable specifications can be employed.

Since it is difficult to design a 90° phase-shift network that provides a constant 90° for a range of frequencies, the filter method enjoys an important advantage over the phase-shifting method for generating SSB signals. The filter method does not depend on phase-shifting networks. With the use of mechanical or crystal filters, excellent rejection of the unwanted sideband is attained.

14.3 Frequency Modulation (FM)

In frequency modulation, the amplitude of the radio frequency wave is held constant, while its instantaneous frequency is varied in accordance with the modulating signal. This is illustrated in Fig. 14.10. The number of times per second that the instantaneous frequency is varied about the average frequency (the carrier) is the modulating frequency. The amount of frequency variation, often called *frequency deviation*, is proportional to the amplitude of the modulating signal. For instance, if a 1000-Hz sound wave is to be transmitted by frequency modulation of a 2,000,000-Hz carrier, this may be accomplished by varying 1000 times per second the instantaneous frequency between 2,000,050 and 1,999,950 Hz.

If the pitch of the sound is reduced to 500 Hz, the instantaneous frequency would vary between the same two limits but at a rate of 500 times per second. The change in the intensity of the modulating signal affects the change in instantaneous frequency. For example, a modulating wave with half the

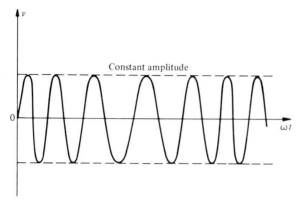

Fig. 14.10 A frequency-modulated wave.

intensity of the preceding signal would be transmitted with an instantaneous frequency variation between 2,000,025 and 1,999,975 Hz.

In order to represent the frequency-modulated wave by a mathematical expression, one should remember that the instantaneous frequency is variable; hence, the alternating voltages may be defined by

$$v = V_c \sin\left(\int \omega dt + \theta_o\right), \tag{14.19}$$

where ω = instantaneous angular frequency, and θ_o = phase angle. Note that (14.19) reduces to a sinewave if the instantaneous frequency has a constant value.

By definition, a frequency-modulated wave with sinusoidal modulation is a wave in which the instantaneous angular frequency varies as

$$\omega = \omega_c + 2\pi\Delta f \cos \omega_m t, \tag{14.20}$$

where ω_c = angular frequency of carrier, ω_m = angular modulating frequency, and Δf = maximum deviation of the instantaneous frequency. Substituting (14.20) in (14.19) for ω and assuming $\theta_o = 0$ gives

$$v = V_c \sin(\omega_c t + (2\pi\Delta f/\omega_m) \sin \omega_m t).$$

The modulation index m_f, also called the *deviation ratio*, is defined as

$$m_f = \Delta f/f_m,$$

where $f_m = \omega_m/2\pi$. Then,

$$v = V_c \sin(\omega_c t + m_f \sin \omega_m t). \tag{14.21}$$

The trigonometric expansion of (14.21) results in the following expression:

$$v = V_c(\sin \omega_c t \cos(m_f \sin \omega_m t) + \cos \omega_c t \sin(m_f \sin \omega_m t)). \tag{14.22}$$

In (14.22) we have terms of the form $\cos(m_f \sin \omega_m t)$ and $\sin(m_f \sin \omega_m t)$. These terms are nonlinear and their values may be obtained with the help of the Bessel function. Using this function we obtain

$$\cos(m_f \sin \omega_m t) = J_0(m_f) + 2J_2(m_f)\cos \omega_m t + 2J_4(m_f)\cos 4\omega_m t + \cdots$$
$$(14.23a)$$

$$\sin(m_f \sin \omega_m t) = 2J_1(m_f)\sin \omega_m t + 2J_3(m_f)\sin 3\omega_m t + \cdots . \qquad (14.23b)$$

The J_n's are Bessel functions of the first kind and order n. They are defined by an infinite series and may be evaluated from the table given in the Appendix.

Substituting (14.23a,b) in (14.22) and using appropriate trigonometric identities yields

$$\begin{aligned}
v = V_c\{ &J_0(m_f)\sin \omega_c t + J_2(m_f)[\sin(\omega_c + 2\omega_m)t + \sin(\omega_c - 2\omega_m)t] \\
&+ J_4(m_f)[\sin(\omega_c + 4w_m)t + \sin(\omega_c - 4w_m)t] \\
&+ J_1(m_f)[\sin(\omega_c + \omega_m)t - \sin(\omega_c - \omega_m)t] \\
&+ J_3(m_f)[\sin(\omega_c + 3\omega_m)t - \sin(\omega_c - 3\omega_m)t] + \cdots \}. \qquad (14.24)
\end{aligned}$$

Equation (14.24) shows that a frequency-modulated wave is composed of a center frequency $\omega_c/2\pi$ and an infinite number of sideband frequencies. The amplitude of each sideband is given by the corresponding Bessel coefficient. Expression (14.24) also shows that the sideband frequencies are symmetrical with respect to the carrier frequency ω_c and are spaced by an amount equal to the modulating frequency.

It is thus seen that a frequency-modulated signal has a frequency spectrum of infinite bandwidth. Fortunately, the J_n coefficients decrease rapidly and the series converges. The bandwidth required for good transmission is, therefore, finite and depends on the amplitude and frequency of the modulating signal. Figure 14.11 illustrates examples of frequency spectra of frequency-modulated waveforms with different modulation indices.

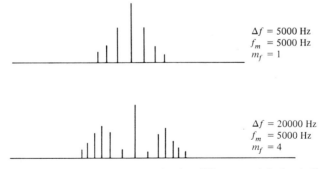

$\Delta f = 5000$ Hz
$f_m = 5000$ Hz
$m_f = 1$

$\Delta f = 20000$ Hz
$f_m = 5000$ Hz
$m_f = 4$

Fig. 14.11   Spectra of FM waves having different modulation indices.

Frequency modulation has the advantage over AM with regard to noise. Atmospheric or man-made electrical noise creates reception problems. Noise signals amplitude modulate the carrier and can therefore be heard on the receiver. Because in FM the useful information is frequency modulated, any amplitude variations due to noise is greatly minimized in the receiver without distorting the modulating signal. This will be discussed further in Chapter 15 covering demodulation.

Narrowband FM(NBFM)

A special case of frequency modulation, where the modulation index $m_f \ll \pi/2$, is called *narrowband FM* (*NBFM*). This is in contrast with wideband FM, where $m_f \geqslant \pi/2$. Narrowband FM may be studied without the help of the Bessel function. In (14.22) for $m_f \ll \pi/2$, $\cos(m_f \sin \omega_m t) \approx 1$ and $\sin(m_f \sin \omega_m t) \approx m_f \sin \omega_m t$. The NBFM waveform then may be expressed by

$$v = V_c(\sin \omega_c t + m_f \cos \omega_c t \sin \omega_m t). \qquad (14.25)$$

Equation (14.25) has a form similar to that found for the amplitude-modulated wave: It contains the carrier signal plus the upper and lower sideband frequencies $\omega_c + \omega_m$ and $\omega_c - \omega_m$, respectively. Narrowband FM for a single modulating frequency therefore has only two sideband frequencies; there is, however, the same basic differences between narrowband FM and AM as between wideband FM and AM. In the following we shall prove this point by comparing (14.25) with (14.5) derived for AM.

Expanding (14.25) and using appropriate trigonometric identities, we obtain

$$v = V_c \sin \omega_c t + m_f V_c/2[\sin(\omega_c + \omega_m)t - \sin(\omega_c - \omega_m)t]. \qquad (14.26)$$

Expression (14.26) may be also written as

$$v = Im\{V_c \exp(j\omega_c t)[1 + (m_f/2) \exp(j\omega_m t) - (m_f/2) \exp(-j\omega_m t)]\} \qquad (14.27)$$

where Im is the imaginary part of the expression between brackets. By the same format, (14.5) becomes

$$v = Im\{V_c \exp(j\omega_c t)[1 + (m/2) \exp(-j\omega_m t) + (m/2) \exp(j\omega_m t)]\} \qquad (14.28)$$

In each case the imaginary part of the resultant phasor, from (14.27) and (14.28), represents voltage v. Figure 14.12A, the narrowband FM signal described by (14.27), shows that for $m_f \ll \pi/2$, the sidebands change the amplitude of the resultant phasor by a negligible amount, and the phase angle θ varies with time. The variation in θ is a property of frequency modulated waves.

Figure 14.12B illustrates an AM waveform and shows that the sidebands change the amplitude of v, while the phase angle remains constant.

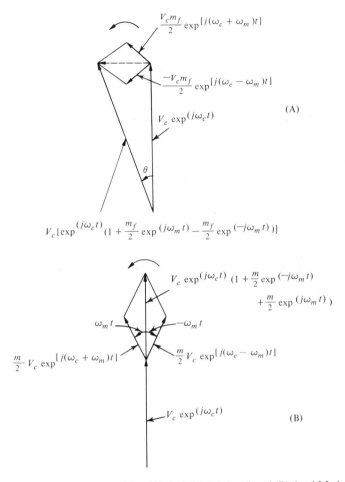

$$\frac{V_c m_f}{2} \exp [j(\omega_c + \omega_m)t]$$

$$\frac{-V_c m_f}{2} \exp [j(\omega_c - \omega_m)t]$$

$$V_c \exp (j\omega_c t)$$

(A)

$$V_c [\exp^{(j\omega_c t)}(1 + \frac{m_f}{2} \exp^{(j\omega_m t)} - \frac{m_f}{2} \exp^{(-j\omega_m t)})]$$

$$V_c \exp^{(j\omega_c t)}(1 + \frac{m}{2} \exp^{(-j\omega_m t)}$$
$$+ \frac{m}{2} \exp^{(j\omega_m t)})$$

$$\omega_m t \qquad -\omega_m t$$

$$\frac{m}{2} V_c \exp^{[j(\omega_c + \omega_m)t]} \qquad \frac{m}{2} V_c \exp^{[j(\omega_c - \omega_m)t]}$$

$$-V_c \exp^{(j\omega_c t)} \qquad \text{(B)}$$

Fig. 14.12 Phasor diagrams for (A) An NBFM signal and (B) An AM signal.

14.4 Frequency Modulators

The simplest manner of obtaining frequency modulation is to connect a capacitor microphone across the tuned circuit of an LC oscillator. The capacitor microphone has a thin diaphragm in front of a fixed metal plate. If someone talks into the mike, the changes in air pressure produce vibration of the diaphragm and induce corresponding changes in capacitance.

This method, however, is not very practical because the oscillator frequency would also depend on the stray capacitance, the length of the cable, and so on. A better method is to use an active device, such as a pentode or a FET. A schematic diagram of a pentode circuit, called a *reactance modulator*, and the corresponding model are shown in Figs. 14.13A and B. From Fig. 14.13B, one obtains

$$I = \frac{V}{R + 1/j\omega C} + g_m V_g + V/r_p. \tag{14.29}$$

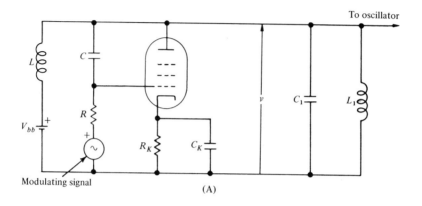

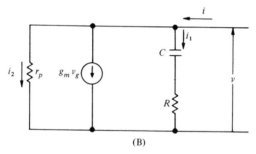

Fig. 14.13 A reactance tube modulator. (A) Circuit. (B) Incremental model.

The value of r_p for a pentode or FET is of the order of 100 K or higher; therefore V/r_p may be neglected in (14.29). This is the reason why a pentode or FET is generally used in the circuit. Equation (14.29) reduces to

$$I = \frac{V}{R + 1/j\omega C} + g_m V_g.$$

But

$$V_g = \frac{VR}{R + 1/j\omega C},$$

then

$$I = \frac{V(1 + g_m R)}{R + 1/j\omega C}. \tag{14.30}$$

Expression (14.30) shows that the output impedance, Z_o of the reactance modulator is

$$Z_o = R/(1 + g_m R) - j/\omega C(1 + g_m R)$$

If we require that $1/\omega C \gg R$, then impedance Z_o becomes

$$Z_o = -j/\omega C(1 + g_m R). \tag{14.31}$$

Equation (14.31) indicates that the output impedance is equivalent to a capacitor C_e with the value of

$$C_e = C(1 + g_m R) \approx g_m RC. \tag{14.32}$$

The g_m of the pentode (or FET) is now made to vary according to a sine-wave signal. If the signal is small, of the order of a few volts, then the effective value of g_m may be written as

$$g_m = g_a(1 + kV_m \cos \omega_m t),$$

where g_a = quiescent value of g_m without signal.

If the output of a reactance modulator is connected to the LC circuit of an oscillator, a frequency modulator is obtained. Figure 14.14 shows a frequency modulator using a FET as the variable reactance element and a junction transistor oscillator. It must be mentioned, however, that as the drain-to-gate capacitance is not negligible in a field-effect transistor, the use of a pentode is more practical at higher frequencies. From (14.32) and Fig. 14.14, one may write

$$\omega = \frac{1}{\sqrt{L_1[C_1 + RCg_a(1 + kV_m \cos \omega_m t)]}}$$

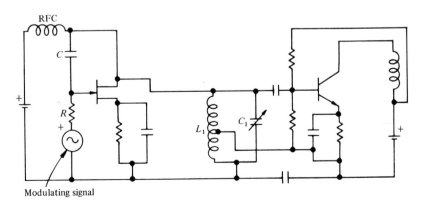

Fig. 14.14 A frequency modulator using a field-effect transistor.

The center frequency is

$$\omega_c = \sqrt{\frac{1}{L_1(C_1 + RCg_a)}}.$$

Therefore,

$$\omega = \omega_c \sqrt{\frac{1}{1 + (kV_m \cos \omega_m t)/(1 + C_1/RCg_a)}}$$

Expansion of the above expression, by the binomial theorem, yields approximately

$$\omega = \omega_c \left[1 - \frac{kV_m \cos \omega_m t}{2(1 + C_1/RCg_a)} \right].$$

With the assumption that $kV_m \cos \omega_m t/[2(1 + C_1/RCg_a)] \ll 1$, then

$$\Delta f = \frac{kV_m \omega_c}{4\pi(1 + C_1/RCg_a)}. \tag{14.33}$$

The capacitance of a diode may be also used for frequency modulation; a basic circuit of such a modulator is shown in Fig. 14.15. The diode is reverse biased. Capacitor C prevents dc from being applied across the inductance; the value of C should be large with respect to the diode capacitance C_d. Further, in order to prevent the application of the modulating voltage directly across inductance L, the reactance of C should be large in comparison with resistance R. We also assume that the values of winding and stray capacitances are negligible with respect to the diode capacitance. The resonant frequency will therefore be

$$\omega = 1/\sqrt{LC_d}. \tag{14.34}$$

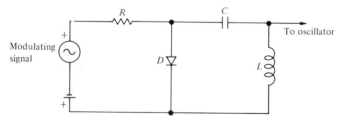

Fig. 14.15 A frequency modulator employing a diode (D) as a variable capacitor.

But the diode capacitance varies as a function of the applied voltage. It may be approximated by

$$C_d = Kv_d^{-1/2}, \tag{14.35}$$

where v_d = voltage across the diode, and K = constant depending on junction area and impurity concentration of diode. Substituting (14.35) in (14.34) gives

$$\omega = (LKv_d^{-1/2})^{-1/2}. \tag{14.36}$$

Relation (14.36) is nonlinear. It may be linearized by the use of the Taylor series:

$$\frac{v_d^{1/4}}{(LK)^{1/2}} = \frac{v_{do}^{1/4}}{(LK)^{1/2}} + \frac{1}{4(LKv_{do}^{3/2})^{1/2}}(v_d - v_{do})$$

$$- \frac{3}{16(LKv_{do}^{7/2})^{1/2}}(v_d - v_{do})^2 \pm \cdots, \tag{14.37}$$

where v_{do} = the bias voltage across the diode. The first term of (14.37) is a constant, the second term is linear. If the remaining terms are forced to become negligible, (14.37) reduces to a linear expression. This may be realized by operating the diode in the incremental region as was done for small-signal amplifiers.

With sinusoidal signals we have

$$v_d - v_{do} = V_m \sin \omega_m t.$$

Term $(v_d - v_{do})^2$ gives rise to second harmonics.

Example 14.4

In the reactance-tube modulator of Fig. 14.13A the parameters of significance are g_a = 1 milimho (and it may be made to vary by $\pm 10\%$), f_c = 500 kHz, f_m = 5 kHz, C = 1 pF, C_1 = 25 pF, and R = 50 K. Calculate the maximum frequency deviation Δf and the modulation index m_f.

Solution

The expression for the mutual conductance of the tube g_m is

$$g_m = g_a(1 + kV_m \cos \omega_m t).$$

Because g_a can change by $\pm 10\%$, kV_m = 0.1. Therefore,

$$\Delta f = \frac{0.1 \times 500 \times 10^3}{2\left[1 + \dfrac{25}{1 \times 10^{-3} \times 50 \times 10^3}\right]} = 13.3 \text{ kHz},$$

and $m_f = (13.3 \times 10^3)/(5 \times 10^3) = 2.22$, which is low and of limited application.

Example 14.5

In the diode modulator of Fig. 14.15 the bias voltage is 20 V, and the modulating voltage is $5 \cos(2\pi 1000 t)$. Calculate the percentage of second-harmonic distortion present.

Solution

From expressions (14.36) and (14.37) and the fact that

$$v_d - v_{do} = V_m \cos \omega_m t \quad \text{and} \quad (v_d - v_{do})^2 = (V_m^2/2)(1 + \cos 2\omega_m t),$$

we may write

$$\omega = \frac{v_{do}^{1/4}}{(LK)^{1/2}} - \frac{3V_m^2}{32(LKv_{do}^{7/2})^{1/2}} + \frac{V_m \cos \omega_m t}{4(LKv_{do}^{3/2})^{1/2}}$$

$$- \frac{3V_m^2 \cos 2\omega_m t}{32(LKv_{do}^{7/2})^{1/2}}. \tag{14.38}$$

From (14.38), the ratio of the second harmonic to the fundamental term is

$$\frac{\text{Second harmonic}}{\text{fundamental}} = \frac{3V_m}{8v_{do}} = \frac{3 \times 5}{8 \times 20} \approx 10\%.$$

14.5 Phase Modulation

In (14.19), if ω remains constant and θ_o varies as a function of the modulating frequency, *phase modulation* is obtained. Phase and frequency modulation are both examples of *angle* modulation; the results of phase modulation is therefore similar to frequency modulation. In fact, an FM receiver cannot detect any difference between the two signals.

With ω constant and equal to ω_c, the carrier frequency, (14.19) becomes

$$v = V_c \sin(\omega_c t + \theta_o). \tag{14.39}$$

With $\theta_o = KV_m \cos \omega_m t$, then

$$v = V_c \sin(\omega_c t + KV_m \cos \omega_m t). \tag{14.40}$$

Equation (14.40) is of the same form as (14.21) derived for frequency modulation. Calculations made for this case also hold for phase modulation.

14.6 Summary

In this chapter the subject of modulators was introduced. It was shown that an amplitude-modulated (AM) waveform contains a carrier and sidebands. Each of the sidebands contains the modulating signal, or information.

In single-sideband (SSB) transmission, only one sideband is transmitted. The sidebands of a frequency-modulated (FM) wave are represented by a frequency spectrum of infinite bandwidth. The amplitudes of the higher sidebands, however, decrease rapidly. A few representative sinusoidal modulator circuits that use junction and field-effect transistors, vacuum tubes, and diodes were analyzed.

References

ALLEY, C. L., and K. W. ATWOOD, *Electronics Engineering*, Wiley, New York, 2nd ed., 1968.

CARLSON, A. B., *Communication Systems*, McGraw-Hill, New York, 1968.

RYDER, J. C., *Electronic Fundamentals and Applications*, Prentice-Hall, Englewood Cliffs, New Jersey, 3rd ed., 1964.

SCHWARTZ, M., *Information Transmission, Modulation, and Noise*, McGraw-Hill, New York, 1959.

TERMAN, F. E., *Electronic and Radio Engineering*, McGraw-Hill, New York, 4th ed., 1955.

Problems

14.1 In an amplitude-modulated wave the modulation signal is given by $v_m = 10(\cos 377t + \cos 754t)$ and the carrier by $v_c = 25 \cos(6.28 \times 10^4)t$. (a) Write an expression for the modulated waveform and calculate the modulation indices. (b) Calculate the power absorbed by a 1-ohm resistance due to the modulated wave.

14.2 A power series relating input voltage v and output current i is expressed by

$$i = a_0 + a_1v + a_2v^2 + a_3v^3.$$

For $v = V_1 \cos \omega_c t + V_2 \cos \omega_m t$ calculate the frequencies and the amplitudes of the sinewaves contained in current i.

14.3 A suppressed-carrier amplitude-modulated wave ($m = 1$) contains a carrier $v_c = 10 \sin 10^4 t$; the modulating frequency is 10^3 rad/s. Draw and dimension the modulated waveform as a function of ωt.

14.4 A current $i = (1 + 0.1 \sin 10^3 t)\sin 10^4 t$ flows in the resonant circuit of Fig. P14.4. Calculate the value of (a) C and (b) all frequencies and their voltage amplitudes across the circuit.

14.5 In the van der Bijl modulator of Fig. 14.3, $i_c = 1 + 0.1v_{be} + 0.05v_{be}^2$ and $v_{be} = 10 \sin(6.28 \times 10^6)t + 3 \sin(6.28 \times 10^3)t$. (a) Write an expression for i_c. (b) Design a parallel resonant circuit to be connected across the output of the modulator. Is a Q of 5 and an inductance of 0.2 mH reasonable? Why?

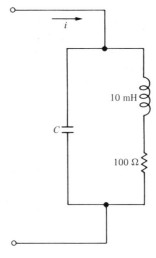

Fig. P14.4

14.6 Assume that the same $i_c - v_{be}$ relationship given in Prob. 14.5 is applicable to the balanced modulator of Fig. 14.8. If $v_{be1} = 10 \sin(6.28 \times 10^6)t + 3 \sin(6.28 \times 10^3)t$ and $v_{be2} = 10 \sin(6.28 \times 10^6)t - 3 \sin(6.28 \times 10^3)t$, (a) Calculate the output voltage. (b) Is the resonant circuit of Prob. 14.5(b) usable here? Why?

14.7 The balanced modulator of Prob. 14.6 is used in the generation of SSB signals. (a) Calculate the modulation index and derive an expression for the output voltage. (b) Determine the ratio of power required in an SSB signal to that of a signal with both sidebands (double-sideband (DSB) signal) and to that of an AM signal.

14.8 The block diagram of Fig. 14.9B illustrates the filter method of SSB generation. Assume that the modulating frequencies range between 200 Hz and 2 kHz, and the frequencies of the first and second local oscillators are 50 kHz and 1 MHz, respectively. Calculate the frequencies at the output of each block corresponding to the modulating frequencies of 200 Hz and 2 kHz.

14.9 Compare the following frequency-modulated waves in terms of their modulating signal and intensity: (a) frequency variation from 100,050 to 99,950 Hz at the rate of 1000 times per second; (b) the same frequency variation as in (a) but at the rate of 400 times per second; (c) frequency variation from 100,100 to 99,900 Hz at 1000 times per second.

14.10 In an FM wave the instantaneous angular frequency, in radians per second, is $\omega = \omega_c + 2\pi\Delta f \cos \omega_m t$. For each case of Prob. 14.9, determine the values of ω_c, ω_m, and Δf.

14.11 A carrier having a peak amplitude of 10 V and a frequency of 10 MHz is frequency modulated at 10 kHz and frequency deviation of 70 kHz. (a) Plot the frequency spectrum. (b) Determine the amplitudes of the center and the four closest sideband frequencies of the spectrum.

14.12 Repeat Prob. 14.11 for a frequency deviation of 50 kHz. Compare results.

14.13 Identify the following modulated waveforms: (a) $\cos \omega_c t - m \cos \omega_m t \sin \omega_c t$; (b) $\cos \omega_c t + m \cos \omega_c t \cos \omega_m t$; (c) $\sin \omega_c t + m \cos \omega_c t \sin \omega_m t$; and (d) $\sin \omega_c t + m \cos \omega_m t \sin \omega_c t$.

14.14 For $m = 0.25$, draw and dimension phasor diagrams for each waveform of Prob. 14.13.

14.15 In the reactance modulator of Fig. 14.13A assume that $g_a = 1$ mmho and may be varied by $\pm 10\%$, $L_1 = 1$ mH, $C_1 = 50$ pF, $R = 50$ K, $C = 1$ pF, and $f_m = 5$ kHz. Calculate the (a) center frequency f_c; (b) maximum frequency deviation Δf; and (c) modulation index m_f. (d) Is the value of m_f obtained reasonable? Why?

14.16 Repeat Prob. 14.15 for $f_m = 1$ kHz. Compare results.

14.17 In the diode modulator of Fig. 14.15 the diode is biased at 10 V and the corresponding diode capacitance for that voltage is 10 pF. If $L = 1$ mH and the modulating signal is $5 \cos(6.28 \times 10^3)t$, (a) calculate the percentage of second-harmonic distortion and (b) derive an expression for the frequency.

14.18 Repeat Prob. 14.17 for a modulating signal of $8 \cos(6.28 \times 5000)t$. Compare results.

14.19 Repeat Prob. 14.17 if the diode is biased at 20 V. Compare results.

Demodulation

The process of recovering the signal from a modulated waveform is called *demodulation*, or *detection*. Recovery is necessary if one is to use the signal for such purposes as the reproduction of sound. It was noted in the previous chapter that a modulated wave may contain both the carrier and sideband frequencies. In radio communications the modulating signals, or frequencies, are reproduced in the receiver.

For example, in the broadcasting of entertainment the carrier may be modulated by the sounds emanating from an orchestra. The carrier and its sidebands are received from the transmitting antenna in the form of electromagnetic waves. These waves, in turn, produce a small voltage in the receiving antenna that is amplified within the receiver. Tuned amplifiers are used to amplify the total signal, that is, the carrier and its sidebands. If the output of the tuned amplifiers were fed directly into a loudspeaker, no sounds would be heard. Because of the loudspeaker's inertia, it is insensitive to the high-frequency carrier and sidebands. It is therefore necessary that the receiver have a demodulator circuit to recover the modulating signal.

15.1 Amplitude Demodulation

Because the demodulation process is the reverse of modulation, the same devices may be used. Nonlinear devices exhibiting the so-called square-law characteristic, like a transistor, may be used in the square-law detector of Fig. 15.1A. The nonlinear relationship between the output current i_o and the input voltage v_i may be represented by a power series:

$$i_o = a_0 + a_1 v_i + a_2 v_i^2. \qquad (15.1)$$

Expression (15.1) is of the same form as (14.12) used for the transistor modulator. Input voltage v_i, which represents the modulated signal, is

$$v_i = V_c \cos \omega_c t + (mV_c/2)\cos(\omega_c + \omega_m)t + (mV_c/2)\cos(\omega_c - \omega_m)t. \qquad (15.2)$$

Substituting (15.2) in (15.1) yields

$$i_o = a_0 + a_1[V_c \cos \omega_c t + (mV_c/2) \cos(\omega_c + \omega_m)t + (mV_c/2) \cos(\omega_c - \omega_m)t]$$

$$+ a_2 \left[V_c^2 \left(\frac{1 + \cos 2\omega_c t}{2} \right) + \left(\frac{mV_c}{2} \right)^2 \left(\frac{1 + \cos 2(\omega_c + \omega_m)t}{2} \right. \right.$$

$$+ \left. \frac{1 + \cos 2(\omega_c - \omega_m)t}{2} \right) \bigg] + \frac{V_c^2 m a_2}{2}[\cos(2\omega_c + \omega_m)t + 2 \cos \omega_m t$$

$$+ \cos(2\omega_c - \omega_m)t] + \frac{V_c^2 m^2 a_2}{4}(\cos 2\omega_m t + \cos 2\omega_c t). \tag{15.3}$$

Among the terms found in (15.3) is one containing the modulating frequency ω_m. The dc and higher frequency terms, ω_c, $2\omega_c$, $\omega_c + \omega_m$, and so on, can be easily filtered out. After filtering, the resulting expression is

$$i_o' = (a_2 m V_c^2/2)(2 \cos \omega_m t + (m/2) \cos 2\omega_m t). \tag{15.4}$$

The output voltage will be of the form of (15.4) which contains a second-harmonic term $2\omega_m t$. The distortion owing to the second harmonic is a result of using square-law detection.

Example 15.1

Prove that for the square-law detector the output will be distortionless when a single-sideband signal plus the carrier are applied to the input.

Solution

The input voltage v_i is

$$v_i = K_1 \cos(\omega_c + \omega_m)t + K_2 \cos \omega_c t,$$

where $K_1 \cos(\omega_c + \omega_m)t$ is the upper sideband signal and $K_2 \cos \omega_c t$ is the carrier added to, or *injected* into, the detector circuit. This is a common method for demodulating single-sideband signals; the circuit used for this purpose is called a *product detector*.
From (15.1),

$$i_o = a_0 + a_1 K_1 \cos(\omega_c + \omega_m)t + K_2 a_1 \cos \omega_c t + a_2 K_1^2 \cos^2(\omega_c + \omega_m)t$$

$$+ a_2 K_2^2 \cos^2 \omega_c t + 2a_2 K_1 K_2 \cos(\omega_c + \omega_m)t \cos \omega_c t$$

or

$$i_o = a_0 + a_1 K_1 \cos(\omega_c + \omega_m)t + a_1 K_2 \cos \omega_c t$$

$$+ (a_2 K_1^2/2)[1 + \cos 2(\omega_c + \omega_m)t] + (a_2 K_2^2/2)(1 + \cos 2\omega_c t)$$

$$+ a_2 K_1 K_2[\cos(2\omega_c + \omega_m)t + \cos \omega_m t].$$

After filtering the high frequency and dc terms, we obtain

$$i_o'' = a_2 K_1 K_2 \cos \omega_m t.$$

The resulting expression shows that only the modulating signal ω_m is derived at the output.

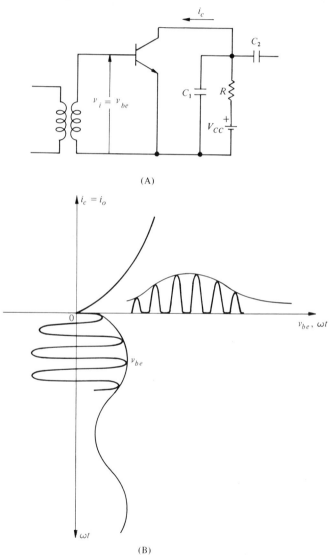

(A)

(B)

Fig. 15.1 A transistor square-law demodulator. (A) Circuit. (B) Input and output waveforms.

Nonlinear (Square-Law) Detection Circuits

Either transistors or vacuum tubes may be used in nonlinear detector circuits. Figure 15.1A illustrates a demodulator using a transistor that is biased for class B operation, and Fig. 15.1B shows the input and output waveforms. The value of capacitor C_1 is such that it acts as a short circuit to frequencies ω_c and higher and as an open circuit to the modulating frequency ω_m.

The vacuum tube version of a square-law detector is given in Fig. 15.2A.

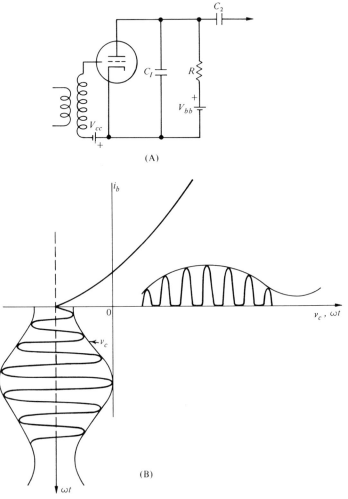

Fig. 15.2 A vacuum tube square-law demodulator. (A) Circuit. (B) Input and output waveforms.

The tube is also biased for class B; for vacuum tubes an external dc source V_{cc} is required for class B. Figure 15.2B shows the input and output waveforms for the vacuum tube circuit.

Linear Detection

Distortionless detection may be realized with the use of a diode in series with a resistance R to linearize the total characteristic. The input voltage and output current waveforms for such a detector are shown in Fig. 15.3. It may be demonstrated that the envelope of current i has no distortion terms. The input voltage v_i is an amplitude-modulated waveform expressed by

$$v_i = V_c(1 + m \cos \omega_m t) \cos \omega_c t.$$

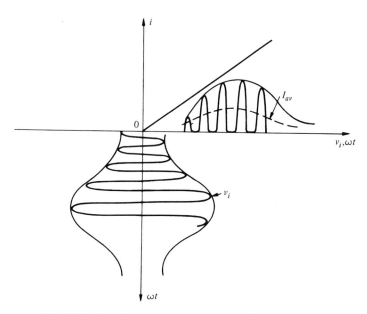

Fig. 15.3 Waveform characteristics of a diode detector.

The average current calculated over one cycle of the carrier frequency is

$$I_{av} = \frac{1}{2\pi} \int_{-\pi/2}^{\pi/2} \frac{V_c}{r_d + R} (1 + m \cos \omega_m t) \cos \omega_c t \, d(\omega_c t)$$

$$= \frac{V_c}{\pi(r_d + R)} + \frac{m V_c \cos \omega_m t}{\pi(r_d + R)},$$

(15.5)

where r_d is the diode resistance. From (15.5) the average output voltage V_{av} will be

$$V_{av} = V_c R(1 + m \cos \omega_m t)/\pi(r_d + R). \qquad (15.6)$$

Because of linear operation, (15.6) shows that the second-harmonic frequency term $2\omega_m$, which was found in the square-law detector output, does not appear.

The basic diode detector is not, however, practical. The output voltage is only a small fraction of the input, giving low efficiency. Detector efficiency η_d may be defined as the ratio of the output voltage V_{av} given by (15.6) to the amplitude of the input signal $V_c(1 + m \cos \omega_m t)$:

$$\eta_d = R/\pi(r_d + R). \qquad (15.7)$$

If $R/r_d \to \infty$, the maximum value of efficiency obtained is

$$\eta_{d(max)} = 1/\pi.$$

The output current (or voltage) waveform, shown in Fig. 15.3, has a carrier frequency component in the load as well as harmonics of the carrier frequency. A reasonable solution for the removal of these terms is the addition of a capacitor C in parallel with resistor R, much the same as used for smoothing the rectified output of a rectifier. Certain requirements are, however, different for this case. A wide range of frequencies are present here, and it is necessary to reduce the ripple owing to the carrier frequency ω_c. At the same time, the capacitor should not affect the modulating frequency ω_m.

Figure 15.4A is a practical circuit of a linear demodulator. From Fig. 15.4B one sees how capacitor C charges and discharges during one cycle of the carrier frequency. This operation is similar to the capacitor filter analyzed in Chapter 4. The modulated input voltage may be expressed as $v_i = V_p \cos \omega_c t$ where $V_p = V_c(1 + m \cos \omega_m t)$. In a well-designed demodulator, $RC \gg 1/f_c$ so that during one cycle of the carrier frequency the output voltage V_{av} remains nearly constant. In Fig. 15.4B V_{av} is the average value of the output voltage over one cycle of the carrier frequency f_c (or ω_c). During the conduction time, current i_d, from Fig. 15.4B, is

$$i_d = (v - V_{av})/r_d = (V_p \cos \omega_c t - V_{av})/r_d. \qquad (15.8)$$

The average value of i_d (I_d) over one cycle of the carrier frequency is

$$I_d = \frac{1}{2\pi r_d} \int_{-\theta_1}^{\theta_1} (V_p \cos \theta - V_{av}) \, d\theta$$

$$= \frac{V_p \sin \theta_1 - V_{av}\theta_1}{\pi r_d}, \qquad (15.9)$$

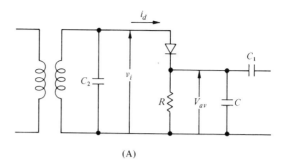

(A)

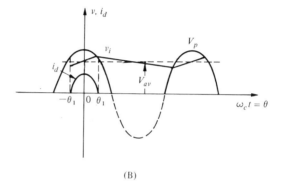

Fig. 15.4 An example of a practical diode detector. (A) Circuit. (B) Waveforms of the output voltage and current over one cycle of the carrier frequency.

(B)

where $\theta = \omega_o t$ and θ_1 is the conduction angle of the diode. From Fig. 15.4B, because $RC \gg 1/f_c$,

$$V_{av} \approx V_p \cos \theta_1. \tag{15.10}$$

Substituting the value of $V_p = V_c(1 + m \cos \omega_m t)$ and calculating $V_{av} = RI_d$ results in

$$V_{av} = \frac{V_c R}{\pi r_d}[(\sin \theta_1 - \theta_1 \cos \theta_1) + m(\sin \theta_1 - \theta_1 \cos \theta_1) \cos \omega_m t]. \tag{15.11}$$

The detector efficiency is

$$\eta_d = (R/\pi r_d)(\sin \theta_1 - \theta_1 \cos \theta_1). \tag{15.12}$$

A simpler expression for the efficiency may be obtained. Returning to Fig. 15.4B and to the definition of detector efficiency given earlier, we obtain

$$\eta_d = V_{av}/V_p = \cos \theta_1. \tag{15.13}$$

The value of efficiency depends on θ_1 which, in turn, depends on R/r_d. For $R/r_d \to \infty$, $\theta_1 = 0$, and the efficiency is maximum, $\eta_d = 1$.

Possible Causes of Distortion

In Fig. 15.4A the time constant RC should be such that during the discharge of the capacitor through resistor R the slope of the discharge curve is greater than, or equal to, the slope of the envelope of the carrier. This must occur during the descending period of the envelope. Figure 15.5 shows how distortion appears if this requirement is not satisfied. To find the conditions for eliminating this type of distortion, we shall specify that the slope of the discharge curve be greater than or equal to the slope of the envelope of the carrier. The envelope of the carrier is $V_c(1 + m \cos \omega_m t)$. Differentiating with respect to time, we obtain

$$\frac{d}{dt}[V_c(1 + m \cos \omega_m t)] = -V_c m \omega_m \sin \omega_m t. \tag{15.14}$$

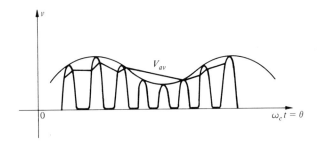

Fig. 15.5 Illustration of output distortion in a linear detector.

From the discharge curve,

$$v_c = V_{av} \exp(-t/RC)$$

or $$dv_c/dt = -v_c/RC. \tag{15.15}$$

The discharge voltage is approximately equal to the modulation envelope; then

$$v_c = V_p = V_c(1 + m \cos \omega_m t). \tag{15.16}$$

By combining (15.14), (15.15), and (15.16) the condition for minimum distortion is obtained:

$$V_c(1 + m \cos \omega_m t)/RC \geqslant V_c m \omega_m \sin \omega_m t$$

or $$RC \leqslant (1 + m \cos \omega_m t)/(\omega_m m \sin \omega_m t). \tag{15.17}$$

It should be noted that the maximum value of the load time constant, RC, which will still permit the envelope of the carrier to be followed, must be found. We therefore should maximize (15.17) with respect to time, t. Taking the derivative of the right-hand side of (15.17) with respect to time and setting the result equal to zero gives

$$m^2 \omega_m + m \omega_m \cos \omega_m t = 0$$

or $$\cos \omega_m t = -m;$$

then $$\sin \omega_m t = (1 - m^2)^{1/2}.$$

Substituting these expressions in (15.17) yields

$$RC \leqslant (1 - m^2)^{1/2}/(m\omega_m). \tag{15.18}$$

In a well-designed detector circuit the condition of (15.18) must be satisfied for minimum distortion.

A second source of amplitude distortion occurs when the diode detector circuit is connected to a load resistance R_1, as shown in Fig. 15.6. Current in the diode can flow only in the forward direction, thereby limiting the ac component of diode current. The amplitude of the ac current should not exceed the average value for a distortionless output; otherwise, *peak clipping* occurs. With the aid of (15.11), one may write

$$\text{Amplitude of } V_{ac}/V_{dc} = m,$$

where the amplitude of $V_{ac} = mV_cR(\sin \theta_1 - \theta_1 \cos \theta_1)/(\pi r_d)$, $V_{dc} = V_cR(\sin \theta_1 - \theta_1 \cos \theta_1)/(\pi r_d)$, and m is the modulation index. But in the present case, one should write

$$\text{Amplitude of } V_{ac}/V_{dc} = \text{Amplitude of } I_{ac}R_2/I_{dc}R = m, \tag{15.19}$$

where $R_2 = R//R_1$. For no distortion, the amplitude of $I_{ac} \leqslant I_{dc}$; therefore, (15.19) becomes

$$m \leqslant R_1/(R_1 + R). \tag{15.20}$$

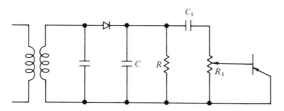

Fig. 15.6 A complete diode detector circuit including its load.

Example 15.2

Assume the values for a given linear-diode detector are $r_d = 10$ K and $R = 200$ K. (a) Calculate the efficiency if no capacitor is present at the output. (b) With a modulation frequency of 1000 Hz and $C = 200$ pF, calculate the maximum modulation index m so no distortion occurs. (c) Is a resistor $R_1 = 20$ K acceptable for the condition of (b)?

Solution

(a) From (15.7), $\eta_d = 200/(210\pi) \approx 1/\pi$.

(b) From (15.18), one obtains

$$4 \times 10^{-5} \leqslant (1/2{,}000\pi) \times (1 - m^2)^{1/2}/m.$$

In the limit, $m \leqslant 0.97$.

(c) $R_1/(R_1 + R) = 20/(20 + 200) \approx 0.1$.

The value of $R_1 = 20$ K is only acceptable if $m \leqslant 0.1$.

15.2   Frequency Demodulation

The detection of FM signals is more involved than the detection of AM waveforms. First the frequency variations of the FM signal have to be transformed to corresponding amplitude variations, and then a circuit similar to an AM detector is used to derive the modulation signal. The detection process, however, must not distort the signal or compromise the principal advantage of FM over AM, namely the minimization of noise, or interference. This characteristic of FM was mentioned in Chapter 14 and will be discussed further in this section.

A simple method for detecting an FM signal is to use a tuned circuit discussed in Chapter 12 and described by (12.2) for a parallel resonant circuit, and (12.5) for another resonant circuit. The gain versus frequency plot for a tuned circuit is shown in Fig. 15.7. Assume the parallel resonant circuit is chosen and the FM input is a current source. The carrier frequency of the FM signal is located on the sloping portion, or skirt, of the response curve and to the left of the resonant frequency of the parallel circuit (Fig. 15.7).

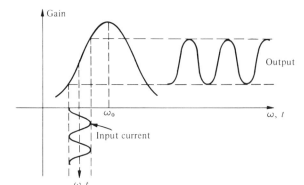

Fig. 15.7 Illustration of a single-tuned circuit used as an FM detector.

Output voltage variations will therefore depend on signal frequency variations. If, however, the amplitude of the input signal varies, the output voltage will also change. Besides the circuit being sensitive to amplitude variations, owing to the nonlinear skirt of the response curve, distortion is also produced. These shortcomings make the simple detector unsatisfactory as an FM demodulator.

Foster–Seeley Discriminator

An improved version of this circuit, called the Foster–Seeley, or phase-shift discriminator, is illustrated in Fig. 15.8. A double-tuned circuit is used where the center tap of the secondary winding of inductance L_s is loosely coupled to the primary winding of inductance L_p with a large value of capacitance C which acts as a short to ac. The inductance labeled RFC (radio frequency choke) has a large reactance, and the full primary voltage V_p can be assumed to be across it. From Fig. 15.8, we obtain

$$V_{a1} = V_p + V_s/2 \qquad (15.21)$$

$$V_{a2} = V_p - V_s/2, \qquad (15.22)$$

where V_p = the primary voltage, and V_s = the total secondary voltage phasors.

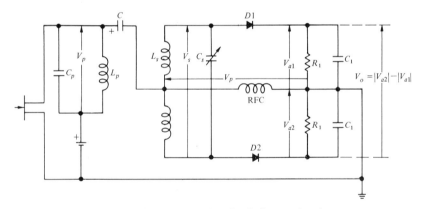

Fig. 15.8 Foster-Seeley discriminator circuit.

Considering the mutual coupling M between the primary and secondary inductances, one can also write

$$V_s = V_1 + V'_1, \qquad (15.23)$$

where V_1 is the induced voltage, and V'_1 is the voltage across the secondary inductance. These are expressed by

$$V_1 = j\omega M I_p \qquad (15.24)$$

$$V'_1 = j\omega I_s L_s, \qquad (15.25)$$

where I_p and I_s are the primary and secondary currents, respectively. Expression (15.24) shows that voltage V_1 is in phase with V_p and, because of loose coupling, is much less than V'_1; consequently V_1 may be neglected in (15.23) and $V_s \approx V'_1$. At the carrier frequency the circuit is in resonance and, as seen in Fig. 15.9, the secondary current I_s will be in phase with induced voltage V_1. Then, from (15.25), V'_1 is 90° out of phase with V_1, or V_p.

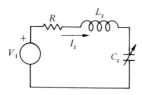

Fig. 15.9 A model for the secondary side of transformer used in Fig. 15.8.

Phasor diagrams for (15.21) and (15.22) are drawn in Fig. 15.10. At resonance, $V_s/2 \approx V'_1/2$ is ±90° out of phase with respect to the primary voltage V_p (Fig. 15.10A). At other frequencies the phase angle of $V_s/2$ is different from 90° as shown in Figs. 15.10 B and C. If diodes $D1$ and $D2$ in Fig. 15.8 are assumed ideal, the output voltage V_o is expressed by $V_o = |V_{a2}| - |V_{a1}|$. At resonance the output will be zero (Fig. 15.10A). For frequencies above and below resonances an output voltage will exist.

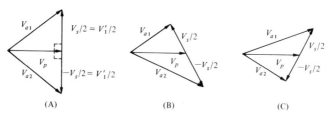

(A)   (B)   (C)

Fig. 15.10 Phasors representing voltages of the circuit of Fig. 15.8. (A) At resonance. (B) Above resonance. (C) Below resonance.

Plots of V_{a1} and V_{a2} described by (15.21) and (15.22) are shown in Fig. 15.11, where the voltages are plotted as a function of frequency. Figure 15.12 is the discriminator response, or "S" curve, obtained by taking the difference of the magnitudes of V_{a2} and V_{a1} of Fig. 15.11. The output voltage is essentially proportional to the frequency deviation as long as the deviations remain in the linear portion of the S curve. As the frequency approaches ω_1 or ω_2, the output becomes flattened and distortion appears.

Although the operation is distortionless within the linear region of the S curve, the output voltage V_o is directly proportional to the primary input voltage V_p. This may be seen from Fig. 15.13, where the frequency does not change its deviation but the input voltage V_p is increased by ΔV_p to $V_p + \Delta V_p$.

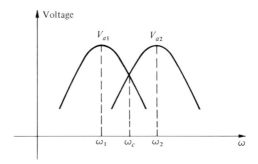

Fig. 15.11 Representing voltages V_{a1} and V_{a2} of Fig. 15.8.

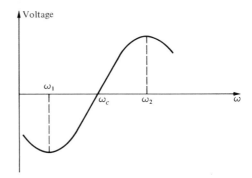

Fig. 15.12 Discriminator "S" curve, $|V_{a2}| - |V_{a1}|$, as a function of frequency.

Because there is no change in frequency deviation, phase angle θ remains constant. From Fig. 15.13, we can write the following expressions:

$$\frac{|V_{a1} + \Delta V_{a1}|}{|V_{a1}|} = \frac{|V_{a2} + \Delta V_{a2}|}{|V_{a2}|} = \frac{|V_p + \Delta V_p|}{|V_p|}, \tag{15.26}$$

or

$$\frac{|V_{a1} + \Delta V_{a1}| - |V_{a2} + \Delta V_{a2}|}{|V_{a1}| - |V_{a2}|} = \frac{|V_o + \Delta V_o|}{|V_o|} = \frac{|V_p + \Delta V_p|}{|V_p|}. \tag{15.27}$$

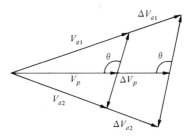

Fig. 15.13 Illustrating the effect of the variation in the input voltage on the output voltage in the Foster-Seeley discriminator.

Expression (15.27) shows that, indeed, the output voltage is proportional to the primary, or input, voltage. One may conclude that although the Foster–Seeley circuit provides good linearity it is sensitive to amplitude variations. To minimize the amplitude variations, an amplitude *limiter* must precede the circuit if the noise-rejecting capabilities of FM are to be realized. An amplitude limiter is an amplifier in which the input signal exceeds the voltage needed to drive the active device between saturation and cutoff, thereby producing a constant output for all signals beyond the limiting levels.

The Ratio Detector

In the ratio detector, a modification of the Foster–Seeley circuit, the output voltage is made independent of the amplitude variations of the input signal without the need of a limiter stage. A basic ratio detector is shown in Fig. 15.14A. From (15.26) one may write

$$\frac{|V_{a1} + \Delta V_{a1}|}{|V_{a2} + \Delta V_{a2}|} = \frac{|V_{a1}|}{|V_{a2}|}. \tag{15.28}$$

If the output voltage V_o is in the ratio of $|V_{a1}|/|V_{a2}|$, it will be independent of the input voltage V_p. Reference to Fig. 15.14A shows that the main difference between the ratio detector and the Foster–Seeley discriminator is that diode $D2$ is reversed in the ratio detector. This is done to obtain $V = |V_{a1}| + |V_{a2}|$, which is plotted in Fig. 15.14B. Voltage V is approximately independent of the frequency in the frequency range of ω_1 to ω_2. If the time constant of the $R_o C_o$ circuit is long, of the order of 0.1 s, voltage V will be independent of any amplitude variations in the input signal.

Output voltage V_o is taken between points A and B. Point B always remains at a fixed potential because V is independent of frequency and amplitude. The potential of point A, however, depends on the ratio of $|V_{a1}|/|V_{a2}|$, which is only a function of frequency as may be seen from Fig. 15.10. Although the output voltage theoretically depends only on the frequency deviation of the input signal, in practice, the ratio detector does not perform as well as the limiter and Foster–Seeley discriminator combination.

15.3 FM Versus AM

It has already been mentioned that the chief advantage of FM over AM is that FM is rather insensitive to noise interference. Interference tends to amplitude modulate the waveform, thereby distorting the modulation envelope. In FM, the modulation is in terms of frequency variations, and any amplitude modulation due to noise is removed by the limiter or in the ratio detector without affecting the modulating signal.

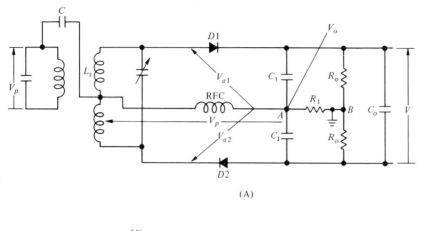

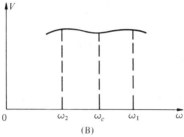

Fig. 15.14 The ratio detector. (A) Circuit. (B) The sum $|V_{a1}| + |V_{a2}| = V$ as a function of frequency.

To demonstrate this, an amplitude-modulated waveform with interference may be expressed as

$$v = Im V_c \exp(j\omega_c t) + Im\{V_c \exp(j\omega_c t)[(m/2)\exp(j\omega_m t) + (m/2)\exp(-j\omega_m t)]$$

$$+ V_c \exp(j\omega_c t)[(m_i/2)\exp(j\omega_i t) + (m_i/2)\exp(-j\omega_i t)]\}, \qquad (15.29)$$

where ω_i is the interference frequency, and m_i is the modulation index for the interfering signal. The phasor diagram for (15.29) is given in Fig. 15.15. It is seen that the interference has an appreciable effect on the total result. In the case of FM, however, the angle is modulated. Also, any amplitude variations are suppressed by a limiter or in the ratio detector.

The effect of the interference on the modulation angle depends on the modulation index m_f; for $m_f \geqslant 5$, it is negligible. For example, if $m_f = 10$, the angle variation is $2\pi \times 10 = 20\pi$ rad. Now, owing to interference, assume the angle is modulated by an additional $\frac{1}{2}$ rad, which is actually quite large. It is negligible, with regard to 20π rad; narrowband FM is, however, sensitive to interfering signals.

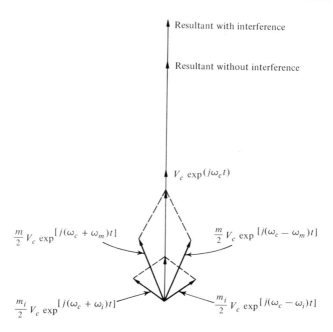

Resultant with interference

Resultant without interference

$V_c \exp(j\omega_c t)$

$\frac{m}{2} V_c \exp^{[j(\omega_c + \omega_m)t]}$

$\frac{m}{2} V_c \exp^{[j(\omega_c - \omega_m)t]}$

$\frac{m_i}{2} V_c \exp^{[j(\omega_c + \omega_i)t]}$

$\frac{m_i}{2} V_c \exp^{[j(\omega_c - \omega_i)t]}$

Fig. 15.15 Phasor diagram of an AM wave with, and without, interference.

15.4   Frequency Conversion

It was shown in Chapter 14 that frequency conversion was required for the filter method of generating single-sideband signals. This was achieved by the mixing of two signals of different frequencies as illustrated in Fig. 14.9B. In the case of the *superheterodyne receiver*, which is used practically for the reception of all signals, frequency conversion is also required. A mixer is used which converts the incoming rf signal and a sinusoidal signal generated within the receiver to obtain a desired difference frequency.

The Superheterodyne Receiver

A block diagram of a superheterodyne (also referred to as the *superhet*) receiver for the reception of AM signals is given in Fig. 15.16. The amplitude-modulated signal picked up by the receiving antenna is amplified by an RF amplifier, which is tuned to the signal's carrier frequency. The mixer stage accepts, in addition to the amplified rf signal, an unmodulated sinewave signal from the circuit referred to as the *local oscillator*. The frequency f_o of the local oscillator is different from the carrier frequency f_c by a fixed amount called the *intermediate frequency* (IF) which shall be designated f_i. The dashed line connecting the RF amplifier and oscillator circuits in Fig. 15.16 is used to indicate that both circuits are tuned together. As the RF amplifier is tuned to a new carrier frequency, the oscillator frequency changes such that the difference between them, $f_o - f_c$, is equal to the intermediate frequency f_i.

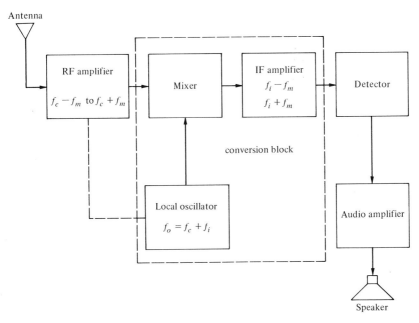

Fig. 15.16 Block diagram of a superheterodyne receiver for AM.

Because mixing is nonlinear, at the output of the mixer there exist a number of frequencies including $f_o - f_c$, $f_o + f_c$, and various harmonics. The IF amplifier is tuned to the difference, or intermediate frequency, $f_o - f_c = f_i$, and then amplified. An AM demodulator of a type considered earlier in the chapter, demodulates the signal which is then amplified by voltage and power amplifier stages. The output of the power amplifier is fed into a coupling transformer or directly into the voice coil of a loudspeaker which converts the amplified modulating signals to sound waves.

The advantages of frequency conversion are higher gain and better stability. Requirements for the detector are less stringent and the detector circuit is optimized for one frequency, the intermediate frequency, regardless of the signal carrier frequency. For commercial AM, the range of carrier frequencies is from 540 to 1600 Hz. A commonly used intermediate frequency is 455 kHZ, which requires the frequency of the local oscillator to change between $540 + 455 = 995$ kHz to $1600 + 455 = 2055$ kHz.

Oscillator-Mixer Circuit

A possible circuit of a local oscillator and mixer employing field-effect transistors is shown in Fig. 15.17. The output current of the mixer, i_d, is

$$i_d = g_m v_g, \tag{15.30}$$

where g_m is the transconductance of the FET, and v_g is the gate voltage.

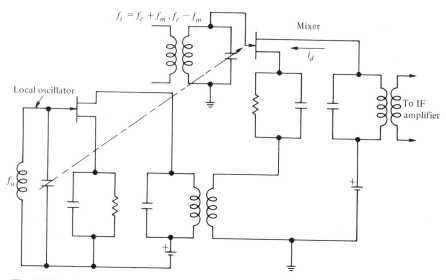

Fig. 15.17   An example of a local oscillator and mixer used for frequency conversion.

For an amplitude-modulated signal, with the gain of the RF amplifier neglected, v_g may be expressed by

$$v_g = V_c[\sin \omega_c t + (m/2) \cos(\omega_c - \omega_m)t + (m/2) \cos(\omega_c + \omega_m)t]. \tag{15.31}$$

If g_m is made to vary according to the local oscillator frequency, like in the reactance modulator considered in Chapter 14, we obtain

$$g_m = g_a(1 + kV_m \cos \omega_o t), \tag{15.32}$$

where g_a is the average value of the transconductance, $\omega_o = 2\pi f_o$, and k is a factor of proportionality. Combining (15.30), (15.31), and (15.32) yields the output current in the mixer i_d:

$$i_d = V_c g_a(1 + kV_m \cos \omega_o t)[\sin \omega_c t + (m/2) \cos(\omega_c - \omega_m)t$$
$$+ (m/2) \cos(\omega_c + \omega_m)t]. \tag{15.33}$$

The output of the mixer is fed to the IF amplifier which is tuned to the intermediate frequency $\omega_o - \omega_c$; the resulting current from the IF amplifier

i_{if} becomes

$$i_{if} = V_c g_a [(-kV_m/2) \sin(\omega_o - \omega_c)t + (kV_m m/2) \cos(\omega_o - \omega_c + \omega_m)t$$
$$+ (kV_m m/2) \cos(\omega_o - \omega_c - \omega_m)t]. \tag{15.34}$$

Equation (15.34) shows that the carrier frequency has been translated to $\omega_o - \omega_c = \omega_i$, the intermediate frequency in radians per second.

Image Frequencies

The superhet, invented in the 1920s by Armstrong, exhibits good *selectivity*, that is, the ability to discriminate between carrier frequencies close to each other. An inherent deficiency, however, is the reception of *image frequencies*, which is the simultaneous reception of two different signals at a desired frequency setting of the receiver. For example, assume that the IF is 300 kHz, and the carrier frequency is 700 kHz. For these frequency values, the local oscillator is tuned to $300 + 700 = 1000$ kHz. But the same IF is also obtained for a carrier frequency of 1300 kHz, since $1300 - 1000 = 300$ kHz. The image frequency in this case would be 1300 kHz. Image frequencies may be minimized by using a higher IF frequency, additional RF amplifier stages, or more than one frequency conversion. Where more than one frequency conversion is used, the first conversion normally occurs at a higher intermediate frequency than the second conversion. Up to three frequency conversions are practical, and receivers with more than one conversion are referred to as double- and triple-conversion receivers.

Although we have talked about the reception of AM signals (sidebands plus carrier), the superhet of Fig. 15.16 may be also used for the reception of SSB signals. In this case, the simple AM demodulator is replaced by a product detector.

Example 15.3

In the mixer of Fig. 15.17 the modulation percentage of the incoming RF signal is 50%. The average transconductance of the FET is $g_a = 10^{-3}$ mho and cannot vary by more than $\pm 10\%$. The IF = 455 kHz and $V_c = 10$ V. The mixer is used in the commercial AM broadcast band. (a) Find the lower and upper values of ω_c, ω_o, and determine the expression for i_{if}. (b) Is it possible to receive image frequencies? What must the limits be on the carrier frequency to prevent image frequencies?

Solution

(a) For the commercial AM band $\omega_{c(min)} = 2\pi \times 540$ krad/s and $\omega_{c(max)} = 2\pi \times 1600$ krad/s. Then $\omega_{o(min)} = 2\pi \times 995$ krad/s and $\omega_{o(max)} = 2\pi \times 2055$ krad/s.

Because g_a cannot vary by more than 10%, from (15.32) $kV_m = 0.1$ and

$$i_{if} = 0.01[-0.05\sin(2\pi \times 455 \times 10^3)t + 0.025\cos(2\pi \times 455 \times 10^3$$
$$+ \omega_m)t + 0.025\cos(2\pi \times 455 \times 10^3 - \omega_m)t].$$

(b) For $f_{c(max)} = 1600\,\text{kHz}$ and $f_i = 455\,\text{kHz}$, it is required that the local oscillator frequency $f_o = 2055\,\text{kHz}$. In order to satisfy the relation $f_c - f_o = f_i$, the carrier frequency f_c must be greater than $2055\,\text{kHz}$. This is out of the range of the commercial broadcast band.

For $f_{c(min)} = 540\,\text{kHz}$, $f_o = 995\,\text{kHz}$. Then $f_c - f_o = 455$ gives $f_c = 1450\,\text{kHz}$ which is an image frequency in the broadcast band. Image frequencies will exist for values of carrier frequency up to $f_c = 540 + (1600 - 1450) = 690\,\text{kHz}$.

15.5   Automatic Gain Control (AGC)

Because radio broadcast stations are located at different distances and generally transmit signals of different powers, the amplitude of the received signal can vary a great deal from one station to another. In addition, the signal strength of a received signal from a distant station depends on the conditions of the ionosphere. For these reasons the gain of the receiver is controlled automatically by an *automatic gain control* (AGC), also referred to as the automatic volume control (AVC) circuit. Such a circuit is shown in Fig. 15.18.

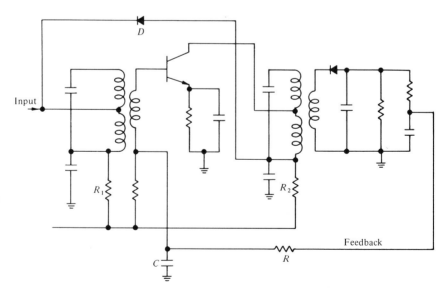

Fig. 15.18   An example of an automatic-gain control (AGC) circuit.

Automatic gain control action is realized by letting a voltage, which is proportional to the carrier amplitude and derived from the detector circuit, affect the gain of the RF or IF amplifier stages. This application is an example of negative feedback considered in Chapter 11.

The derived voltage is integrated by an RC network to obtain a negative dc bias proportional to the signal amplitude. The negative bias reduces the emitter current of the transistors, which results in changes in transistor parameters and a reduction in power gain.

Diode D in Fig. 15.18 is included to provide additional feedback for very strong signals. At the usual signal levels, the diode is back biased by the bias voltage developed by resistors R_1 and R_2.

15.6   FM Receiver

A block diagram of a typical FM receiver is the same as for an AM receiver except for the detector circuit where a limiter and Foster–Seeley discriminator are used. If a ratio detector were employed no limiter would be necessary.

Commercial FM is broadcast over a frequency range of 88 to 108 MHz. An intermediate frequency of 10.7 MHz is used for minimum image frequency response. It is interesting to note that in commercial television the video information is amplitude modulated and the sound frequency modulated. This provides a good compromise for the utilization of bandwidth in the radio frequency spectrum.

15.7   Summary

Because demodulation is the inverse of modulation, the same devices may be used. Nonlinear devices exhibiting the so-called square-law characteristics may be used for amplitude demodulation. Distortionless detection may be realized with the use of a diode-capacitance circuit which is similar to a half-wave power rectifier with a capacitor filter. The requirements of the detection of FM signals are more demanding than for AM detection. Frequency variations must be transformed into corresponding amplitude variations. Although many circuits exist, two commonly used configurations are the Foster–Seeley discriminator and the ratio detector. Because the discriminator is amplitude sensitive, a limiter stage is required; theoretically, this is not necessary for the ratio detector. In both the AM and FM superhet receiver, frequency conversion is used. Although the superhet has excellent selectivity, image frequencies can be a source of trouble. AGC is required for the uniform reception of signals of different amplitudes.

References

ALLEY, C. L., and K. W. ATWOOD, *Electronic Engineering*, Wiley, New York, 2nd ed., 1966.

GE Transistor Manual, 7th ed., 1964.

RYDER, J. D., *Electronic Fundamentals and Applications*, Prentice-Hall, Englewood Cliffs, New Jersey, 3rd ed., 1964.

SCHWARTZ, M., *Information Transmission, Modulation, and Noise*, McGraw-Hill, New York, 1959.

TERMAN, F., *Electronic and Radio Engineering*, McGraw-Hill, New York, 3rd ed., 1955.

Problems

15.1   For the transistor demodulator of Fig. 15.1A, current i_o and voltage v_i are related by: $i_o = 10^{-4}v_i + 10^{-5}v_i^2$ mA. If $v_i = 2\cos 10^5 t + 0.5 \cos(10^5 + 10^3)t + 0.5\cos(10^5 - 10^3)t$, (a) Find all the frequency components and their amplitudes in i_o. (b) What is the percentage of second-harmonic distortion?

15.2   Repeat Prob. 15.1 for $v_i = 2\cos 10^5 t + 0.5\cos(10^5 - 10^3)t$. Compare and discuss your results.

15.3   In a basic diode detector, diode resistance $r_d = 5$ K, load resistance $R = 50$ K, and $v_i = [1 + 0.5\cos(6.28 \times 1000)t]\cos(6.28 \times 10^5)t$. (a) Draw and dimension $i(t)$. (b) Calculate the average value of the current over one cycle of the carrier frequency. (c) What is the detector efficiency?

15.4   Repeat Prob. 15.3 for $R = 100$ K. Compare results.

15.5   In Fig. 15.4A assume that $r_d = 1$ K, $R = 100$ K, and $v_i = [1 + 0.5\cos(6.28 \times 1000)t]\cos(6.28 \times 10^5)t$. (a) What is the approximate value of C for a detection efficiency of 90%? (b) Verify the condition for minimum distortion.

15.6   Repeat Prob. 15.5 for $R = 200$ K. Compare results.

15.7   The detector considered in Prob. 15.5 is used in the circuit of Fig. 15.6. Calculate the minimum value of R_1 required to avoid distortion (peak clipping) due to the load.

15.8   In Fig. 15.6 let $r_d = 5$ K, $R = 100$ K, $R_1 = 200$ K, $C = 100$ pF, and $C_1 = 0.1\,\mu$F. If $f_c = 1$ MHz and $f_m = 100$ Hz, calculate (a) the minimum value of m for no peak clipping and (b) R_1 for $m \approx 1$ to avoid peak clipping.

15.9   A parallel resonant circuit ($Q = 50$) with $C = 500$ pF is resonant at 1 MHz. The circuit is used as a demodulator at a center frequency of 0.5 MHz and a current of 100 μA. Calculate the voltage across the circuit if the frequency deviation is ± 10 kHz.

15.10 Repeat Prob. 15.9 for a center frequency of 0.8 MHz. Compare and discuss your results.

15.11 Explain what happens if, in Fig. 15.8, the coupling between the primary and secondary windings is tight instead of loose.

15.12 (a) Draw the phaser diagrams of a Foster–Seeley discriminator for: $f_c = 1$ MHz, $V_p = 1\underline{/0°}$ V, $V_s/2 = 0.5\underline{/90°}$ V; $f = 1.1$ MHz, $V_p = 1\underline{/0°}$ V, $V_s/2 = 0.5\underline{/120°}$ V; and $f = 0.9$ MHz, $V_p = 1\underline{/0°}$ V, $V_s/2 = 0.5\underline{/60°}$ V. (b) Plot the discriminator response curve.

15.13 Assume that $V_p = 1.2\underline{/0°}$ V in Prob. 15.12. For this value, plot the discriminator response curve. Compare and discuss your results.

15.14 Using the values of V_{a1} and V_{a2} obtained in Probs. 15.12 and 15.13, show graphically that the output remains essentially constant if the same values were obtained for a ratio detector.

15.15 If, in an FM wave, the maximum modulation frequency is 1500 Hz and $\Delta f = 20$ kHz, show that a one-third radian change in angle owing to noise modulation results in negligible interference.

15.16 Draw a block diagram of an AM superhet receiver that operates in the commercial band of frequencies. If the IF $= 800$ kHz, calculate the tuning range of the local oscillator.

15.17 In Prob. 15.16, the receiver is tuned to 800 kHz. What is the image frequency? Does it fall within the band of commercial frequencies?

15.18 For the mixer of Fig. 15.17, the incoming signal is 30% amplitude modulated. The average transconductance of the FET is $g_a = 10^{-3}$ mho and can vary by no more than $\pm 15\%$. The mixer operates over a band of frequencies from 200 kHz to 1 MHz; the IF $= 400$ kHz. (a) Determine the lower and upper values of ω_c, ω_o, and determine the expression for i_{if}. (b) Calculate the image frequencies corresponding to 200 kHz and 1 MHz. Assume $V_c = 10$ V.

Linear Integrated Circuits

Since the invention of the transistor in 1948, there has been an accelerated and burgeoning development of new semiconductor devices and applications. The transistor of 1948, a point-contact device, was characterized by an inherent instability that hampered the amplifier designer. In the early 1950s, the bipolar junction transistor (BJT) became available. Its superior characteristics and performance soon made the point-contact transistor a relic of the past. The structure of the BJT underwent various process changes, which led to improvements in frequency response and power-handling capabilities. These technological advances culminated in the epitaxial-diffused device of the 1960s. At the same time the field-effect transistor (FET) began to be produced in reasonable quantities and to take its place in the family of semiconductor devices.

The development of the transistor, especially the diffused devices, was a necessary step in the development of the integrated circuit (IC). In the *monolithic* (derived from a Greek word meaning "single stone") integrated circuit, all components, such as transistors, diodes, resistors, and capacitors, are formed in a very tiny chip of silicon. The first available monolithics were digital integrated circuits (DIC), such as the flip-flop stages used in computers. These were followed by linear integrated circuits (LIC), such as amplifiers. Our concern will be with linear integrated circuits.

Besides the obvious advantages of small size and low cost per component, the integrated circuit tends to be more reliable than its discrete counterpart. One major source of failure in discrete electronic circuits is the interconnections between components. In the monolithic integrated circuit all connections between components are made on a single chip. A typical chip containing perhaps 20 or more components is of the order of 0.05 by 0.05 in. Furthermore, because the transistors in a chip are formed simultaneously and are physically close to each other, their electrical and thermal properties can be closely matched.

Our objective in this chapter is to provide the reader with an introduction to integrated circuit technology and to the basic circuits used in LIC's. To understand why particular circuits, such as the differential amplifier, are used in such profusion in IC designs, it is essential that we have at least an acquaintance with the processes used in fabricating the integrated circuit and an awareness of their limitations. We shall see that for the monolithic structure it may be difficult to obtain resistances with tolerances better than $\pm 25\%$; resistance and capacitance values are limited; parasitic elements are present; and it is virtually impossible to fabricate a practical monolithic inductor. Once these inherent limitations are known, the analysis and design of linear integrated circuits can then proceed efficiently. Toward the end of the chapter, we shall examine some current examples of LIC designs to learn their circuit configurations and characteristics.

16.1   IC Technology

Besides the monolithic IC there are other forms of integrated circuits. One process yields the *thin-film* circuit. In thin-film technology, passive components, such as resistors, capacitors, and inductors of very small values, as well as their interconnections, are deposited on a substrate. A commonly used substrate is ceramic, and deposition methods include vacuum evaporation, sputtering, and silk screening (which yields the *thick-film* circuit). The advantages of thin- and thick-film over monolithic resistors and capacitors are better component tolerances and a larger range of attainable resistor and capacitor values. Success in fabricating thin-film active devices, however, has been limited.

When discrete transistors, diodes, or monolithic chips are connected to a thin- or thick-film passive network, the *hybrid* integrated circuit is obtained. This approach is ideal for small-quantity production, prototypes, and for those cases where no monolithic IC that meets circuit requirements is available. Artwork and photo masks needed for the manufacture of monolithics are very expensive and are therefore economical only for large-production runs. The preparation for the hybrid circuit is considerably less costly.

Another variation in IC technology is the *compatible* IC. In this process both monolithic and thin-film techniques are employed. Where some special value resistor or capacitor of good tolerance is required, the component is deposited on top of the silicon chip by thin-film techniques.

The Planar-Diffusion Process

Since the monolithic IC may be viewed as an extension of the planar-diffused structure, we consider this device first. This permits us to concentrate on the basic process steps that are also used in making the monolithic

IC. An *n-p-n* planar-diffused transistor, whose cross-sectional view is illustrated in Fig. 16.1, will be the basis of our discussion. The process steps are summarized as follows:

1. An *n*-type silicon wafer of suitable conductivity is covered with a thin layer of silicon dioxide (SiO_2). The layer is formed by placing the silicon wafer in a furnace set at a temperature of approximately 1100°C and introducing an oxidizing agent such as oxygen, or water vapor. The layer of SiO_2 plays a most important role in photo masking and etching operations. It also acts to *passivate* the silicon, that is, to make it less vulnerable to contamination which is always a problem in the manufacture of semiconductor devices.

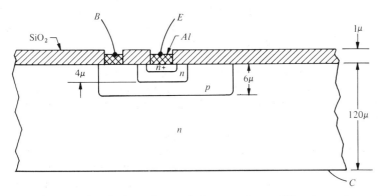

Fig. 16.1 Cross-sectional view of a typical *n-p-n* planar-diffused transistor. (One micron $\mu = 10^{-4}$ cm.).

2. A small section of the oxide is removed by etching in hydrofluoric acid to form a "window" of suitable dimensions for the base region. This is accomplished by first making the SiO_2 layer sensitive to ultraviolet light. For this purpose an organic compound, referred to as the *photoresist*, is applied to the oxide layer. A photo mask containing the base window pattern, which is opaque to light, is placed in contact with the photoresist and exposed. The exposed photoresist becomes *polymerized*, or hardened, and thus invulnerable to the acid etch. The unexposed SiO_2, however, is affected by the etch. Because the hardened photoresist can contaminate the silicon, it is removed before diffusion. Boron, a commonly used *p*-type impurity, is then diffused through the etched window into the wafer to a proper depth to form the collector-base junction.

3. Upon completion of the base diffusion, the top of the wafer is reoxidized, as described in step 1.

4. Photoresist is applied again to the oxide and exposed through a photo mask containing an opaque emitter window. The SiO_2 under the emitter

window is etched and an *n*-type impurity, typically phosphorus, is diffused into the *p*-region to form an emitter-base junction. A sufficient quantity of *n*-type impurity is diffused into the wafer to overcompensate for the *p*-type impurity already present.

5. The top of the wafer is reoxidized.

6. Connections now have to be made to the two diffused regions for bringing out the emitter and base leads and to the collector region. The connection to the collector is generally made directly to the bottom side of the *n*-region. Because aluminum may be used for the base and emitter leads (in integrated circuits, aluminum is generally used for interconnections), it is essential that an *ohmic*, or *nonrectifying*, contact be made to the *n*-type emitter region. Since aluminum is a *p*-type material, if it is in contact with an *n*-type material, a *p-n* junction is formed. To prevent this from happening, additional *n*-type material is diffused into the top of the emitter region, making it highly conductive; this region is denoted by n^+ in Fig. 16.1.

7. Although we have described the process steps for a single transistor, actually some 3000 transistors can be made simultaneously on a wafer $1\frac{1}{2}$ to 2 in. in diameter. Upon completion of the previously described processing steps, the wafer is scribed and diced, that is, cut along its *x*- and *y*-axes to yield individual transistors.

8. Each transistor is tested and packaged.

Obviously, those transistors located on the periphery of the wafer are not usable. Because of random defects and imperfections in the wafer itself, there is a further reduction in potentially good devices. During processing and packaging, additional losses will be incurred. The actual number of good devices to the maximum number of attainable devices may be defined as the *yield factor*. If, for example, out of 3000 possible transistors only 1500 good units are realized, the yield factor is 50 percent.

The questions one may ask are: Why can't two or more transistors, or diodes, or perhaps passive components such as resistors be diffused simultaneously in silicon? Since these different components would share the same wafer, or substrate, how can they be isolated electrically? These questions are not difficult to answer, since we now have an idea of how a planar-diffused transistor is fabricated. The diffusion process used in making transistors permits the simultaneous fabrication of all components in a single chip of silicon with approximately the same number of process steps and photo masks required for making diffused transistors.

Electrical Isolation and Parasitics

Assume that two discrete transistors are to be integrated and each transistor collector is connected to a different potential. These conditions require that the transistors be electrically isolated. Electrical isolation is commonly provided for components contained in a monolithic chip by employing reverse-biased *p-n* junctions. These junctions are, in a sense, "built into" the chip.

To achieve isolation one may begin with a *p*-doped silicon wafer, or substrate. Two *n*-regions, referred to as *islands*, which serve as the collectors for transistors *Q*1 and *Q*2, are formed as illustrated in Fig. 16.2A. The successive diffusion of *p*- and *n*-type impurities, as described in the making of the planar-diffused transistor, yield the base and emitter regions. The resultant structure in reality is a four-layer, *p-n-p-n*, three-junction device. If the *p*-substrate is returned to the most negative potential of the circuit in which the chip is used, the junction between the *p*-substrate and each collector becomes reverse biased, and electrical isolation is obtained.

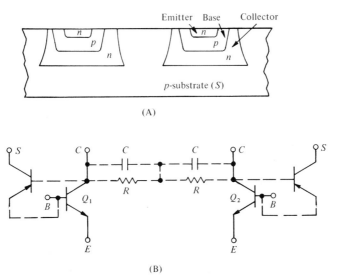

(A)

(B)

Fig. 16.2 Electrical isolation of IC components in a wafer. Two transistors, *Q*1 and 2, are to be integrated. (A) Cross-sectional view of wafer containing the two transistors. (B) Model of the integrated transistors and their associated parasitic elements.

The model of a reverse-biased diode, considered in Chapter 2, may be represented by a resistance of several megohms shunted by a capacitance of a few picofarads, as illustrated in Fig. 16.2B. In addition there are unwanted *p-n-p* transistors, where the substrate acts as the *p*-collector, the *n*-region as the base, and the *p*-base region as the emitter, that shunt each of the desired transistors. The reverse-biased diodes and the *p-n-p* transistors are examples of *parasitic* components that limit the frequency response of a monolithic circuit.

Another method of isolation to ensure electrical separation of diffused components in a silicon chip makes use of *dielectric barriers*. The dielectric used for this purpose is generally silicon dioxide. A cross-sectional view of such a structure is shown in Fig. 16.3. Although this method provides excellent isolation with a minimum of parasitics, the device is more costly because additional photo masks and processing steps are necessary.

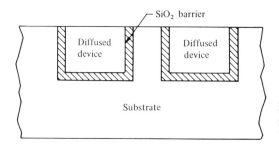

Fig. 16.3 Obtaining electrical isolation with a SiO$_2$ dielectric barrier.

In summary, all collector regions that have different voltages must be isolated. To ensure isolation, the *n*-region is reverse biased with respect to the *p*-substrate. This requires that the substrate be connected to the most negative voltage point available in the circuit. Resistors, to be described later, may be diffused in a common *n*-type isolation region (island), provided the region is connected to the most positive potential in the circuit.

Monolithic IC Process

The process generally used in the manufacture of monolithic integrated circuits is the *epitaxial-diffused* process, which is a variation of the planar-diffused process considered earlier. The epitaxial-diffused process will be the basis for our discussion. To illustrate the various steps, assume that we are required to integrate the circuit of Fig. 16.4 containing one transistor $Q1$,

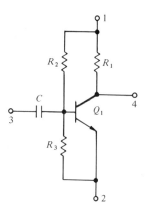

Fig. 16.4 Transistor amplifier to be integrated.

three resistors R_1, R_2, and R_3, and capacitor C. The process steps in our description will refer to Figs. 16.5A through F.

A. An n-type silicon epitaxial layer, typical of 0.5 ohm-cm resistivity and 25 microns (μ; $1\mu = 10^{-4}$ cm) thick, is grown on a p-type silicon substrate with a typical bulk resistivity of 10 ohm-cm. *Epitaxial* means that the n-type layer has the same crystalline structure as does the p-type substrate.

A thin passivating film (approximately 1μ thick) of SiO_2 is formed upon the epitaxial layer.

B. Photoresist is applied to the SiO_2 film and exposed through a suitable mask to form the n-type isolation islands for the various active and passive components to be diffused. Sufficient p-type impurity is introduced to over-compensate for the n-type material. Because there is some lateral, in addition to vertical, diffusion of the p-type impurity, the walls of the islands are curved. Three islands are required: one each for the transistor and capacitor and a third for the three resistors.

A new layer of SiO_2 is grown over the structure which adds to the existing oxide layer of step A. In order to keep the diagram simple, this is not shown.

C. Photoresist is applied again and the wafer is exposed through a second photo mask containing, in the general case, the pattern for the transistor bases, resistors, capacitors, and the p-side of diodes. These elements require the diffusion of a p-type impurity, such as boron. For the specific circuit of Fig. 16.4 that we are attempting to integrate, the mask will have windows for the base region of the transistor, for the p-region for a diode that will be reverse biased and serve as a capacitor, and for the three resistors. Upon the completion of exposure, etching, and diffusion, the three required regions are obtained.

A layer of SiO_2 is formed.

D. Again photoresist is applied to the wafer and a third mask, containing the emitter and n^+ contact patterns for the collector and other n-type regions to which contact will be made, is exposed. Sufficient n-type impurity is diffused into the wafer.

A layer of SiO_2 is formed.

E. A fourth mask containing windows for the remaining contacts is exposed.

A layer of SiO_2 is formed.

F. Aluminum is vacuum-deposited on the surface. Photoresist is applied and exposed through a fifth mask containing the interconnection pattern. The unexposed aluminum is etched and the integrated circuit is completed.

The completed wafer is scribed, diced, tested, and packaged.

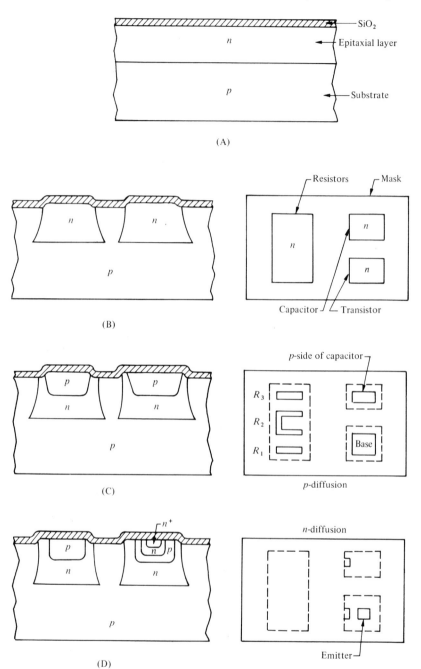

Fig. 16.5 Steps in integrating the transistor amplifier of Fig. 16.4. (See text for details.)

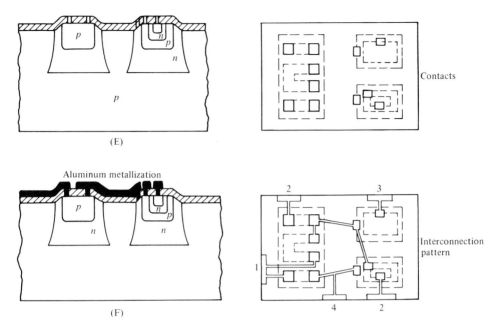

Fig. 16.5 (continued)

16.2 Electrical Characteristics of IC Components

Our attention is directed now to a study of the electrical characteristics and limitations of diffused transistors, diodes, resistors, and capacitors in a monolithic integrated circuit. Having knowledge of the impurity profile and the geometry of a monolithic component, one can use a number of proven equations of solid-state physics to estimate its electrical characteristics. Because this is outside the province of the text, we shall be content with a summary of typical device parameters and their limitations.

Transistors

The layout and dimensions of a typical integrated transistor are illustrated in Fig. 16.6. The configuration exhibits a double-base stripe geometry, that is, there are two metalized base stripes surrounding the emitter. In contrast with a single-stripe base, the double-stripe base increases the current rating of a transistor and reduces the base-spreading resistance.

Typical unit capacitances, in pF/cm², associated with the IC transistor layout of Fig. 16.6 are

$$C_E \ (V_{BE} = 0.5 \text{ V}): 12 \times 10^4 \text{ pF/cm}^2$$
$$C_C \ (V_{CB} = -5 \text{ V}): 10^4 \text{ pF/cm}^2$$

$C_{S(\text{bottom})} (V_{CS} = -5 \text{ V}): 0.5 \times 10^4 \text{ pF/cm}^2$
$C_{S(\text{sidewall})} (V_{CS} = -5 \text{ V}): 0.7 \times 10^4 \text{ pF/cm}^2$

Capacitance C_E is the unit forward-bias base-emitter transition capacity; C_C the unit reverse-bias collector-base transition (depletion) capacity; and C_S the unit reverse-bias collector-substrate capacity. Two values of capacitance are included for the parasitic component, because the bottom component is primarily due to a step junction, and the sidewall component is due to a graded junction. In the calculation of transistor capacitances the sidewall dimensions have to be included.

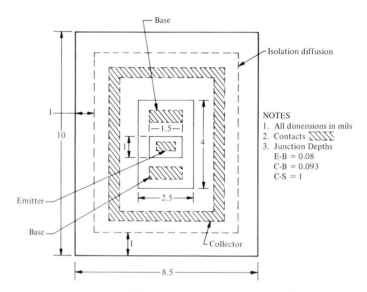

Fig. 16.6   Layout of an IC transistor with double-stripe base geometry.

Example 16.1

For the transistor dimensions given in Fig. 16.6, calculate the base-emitter diffusion capacitance $C_{b'e}$, the collector-base transition capacitance $C_{b'c}$, and the parasitic capacitance C_p. Use the unit capacitance values given above. It is customary to use the units of microns and mils in characterizing the dimensions of integrated circuits. One mil equals $25.4 \, \mu$ and one μ equals 10^{-4} cm.

Solution

Base-emitter capacitance $C_{b'e}$: Total area, including sidewalls, is
$1 \times 1.5 + (1 + 1 + 1.5 + 1.5) \times 0.08 = 1.9 \text{ mils}^2 \times 6.45 \times 10^{-6}$

$cm^2/mil^2 = 12.3 \times 10^{-6} cm^2$. $C_{b'e} = 12.3 \times 10^{-6} cm^2 \times 12 \times 10^4 pF/cm^2 = 1.5 pF$. Based on physical theory, the actual value is $4 \times 1.5 = 6 pF$.

Collector-base capacitance $C_{b'c}$: Total area is $2.5 \times 4 + (2.5 + 2.5 + 4 + 4) \times 0.093 = 11.2 mil^2 \times 6.45 \times 10^{-6} cm^2/mil^2 = 72.3 \times 10^{-6} cm^2$. $C_{b'c} = 72.3 cm^2 \times 10^4 pF/cm^2 = 0.72 pF$.

Parasitic capacitance C_p: Bottom component C_{pb} is equal to $(6.5 \times 8) mil^2 \times 6.45 \times 10^{-6} cm^2/mil^2 \times 0.5 \times 10^4 pF/cm^2 = 1.68 pF$. Sidewall component $C_{ps} = (6.5 + 6.5 + 8 + 8) \times 1 \times 6.45 \times 10^{-6} \times 0.7 \times 10^4 = 1.31 pF$. $C_p = C_{pb} + C_{ps} = 3 pF$.

Gain-bandwidth products (f_T) of 3 GHz and greater may be realized with integrated transistors. Current gains of the order of 100 at mid frequencies and BV_{CEO} values of 20 to 30 V are typical. A lumped high-frequency model for the integrated transistor is shown in Fig. 16.7. It is very similar to the hybrid-pi model of the discrete transistor described in Chapter 8. Resistance R_p is the collector-substrate bulk resistance, with a value ranging from a few to a hundred ohms depending on the resistivity and geometry of the structure. Capacitance C_p is the parasitic capacitance across the substrate and collector.

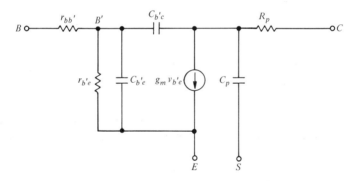

Fig. 16.7 Lumped-high frequency model of an IC transistor.

Diodes

A transistor can be converted to a diode in a number of ways. A few possible connections are illustrated in Fig. 16.8. The maximum breakdown voltage is limited by the emitter-base junction for configurations A and B and the collector-base junction for C. For A and B the breakdown voltage is of the order of 7 to 8 V, whereas for C it is 50 to 60 V. The forward voltage drop is least for A and greatest for C; at a forward current of 10 mA, the range is from 0.85 to 0.95 V. The reverse leakage current ranges from 0.1 to 100 nA.

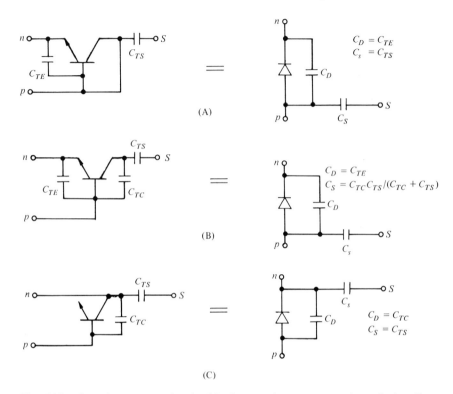

(A)

(B)

(C)

Fig. 16.8 Capacitances associated with the transistors connected as diodes. Connection B exhibits the least parasitic capacity.

The smaller values of leakage current will be observed in those diode configurations where the collector is connected to the base ($V_{CB} = 0$) or the collector is open ($I_C = 0$).

Capacitances associated with the diffused diodes are also shown in Fig. 16.8. The parasitic capacitance is minimum for configuration *B*.

Junction Capacitors

The depletion region of a *p-n* junction is characterized by immobile uncovered charges: positive ions in the *n*-region and negative ions in the *p*-region. Applying a reverse bias across the junction results in an increase in thickness, or width, of the depletion region. Since there are very few free electrons and holes in this region, we can neglect them. The depletion region may therefore be compared to the dielectric and its boundaries to the plates of a capacitor. As the reverse bias is increased, the width of the depletion region increases, thereby reducing the value of capacity. The width of the depletion region is a function of the reverse bias voltage V. The junction capacitance C may be expressed by

$$C = kA/(V + V_B)^n, \tag{16.1}$$

where k depends on the dielectric constant and doping density; $A =$ junction area; $V_B =$ barrier voltage of junction at zero bias (V_B is subtracted if p is positive); and $n = \frac{1}{3}$ or $\frac{1}{2}$, depending on whether the junction is graded or step, respectively.

In monolithic integrated circuits the capacitor is formed simultaneously with the collector-base junction of a transistor. A simplified view of such a capacitor is illustrated in Fig. 16.9, where the capacitor junction is designated

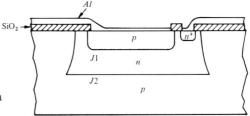

Fig. 16.9 Cross-sectional view of a diffused capacitor.

$J1$. Because of the p-substrate, a second junction $J2$ is formed with the n-region. Two possible models for a junction capacitor are shown in Fig. 16.10. Capacitance C is desired, and C_p is the parasitic component of capacity.

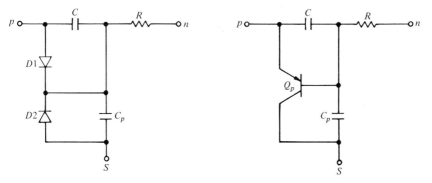

Fig. 16.10 Two models of a diffused capacitor. (A) Parasitic diodes $D1$ and 2 are included. (B) Parasitic transistor Q_p replaces the parasitic diodes.

Resistance R is the bulk resistance of the n-region, with a typical value of 50 ohms. Diodes $D1$ and $D2$ are parasitic diodes owing to junctions $J1$ and $J2$, respectively. In Fig. 16.10B junctions $J1$ and $J2$ are included in the parasitic transistor Q_p. From either Fig. 16.10A or B it is seen that it is essential that both junctions be reverse biased to minimize the effects of the parasitic elements.

In addition to using the collector-base junction as a capacitor, the substrate-collector (S-C) or emitter-base (E-B) junctions may also be used. Maximum values for these, as well as the collector-base (C-B) junction capacitance, are

> C-B: $0.2 \, \text{pF/mil}^2$, at zero bias;
> E-B: $0.9 \, \text{pF/mil}^2$, at zero bias;
> S-C: $0.16 \, \text{pF/mil}^2$, at zero bias.

Breakdown voltages range from a few to approximately 20 V.

Thin-Film Capacitors. A capacitor that is superior to the diffused type is the thin-film capacitor. It is nonpolarized, more stable, and exhibits a higher Q than the diffused capacitor. A silicon dioxide thin-film capacitor, with its electrical model, is illustrated in Fig. 16.11. The n^+ diffusion area formed in the collector region serves as one plate of the capacitor, and the metallized aluminum, separated from the diffused silicon by the SiO_2 passivating layer, serves as the second plate. The parasitic elements are diode $D2$ due to the substrate-collector junction and capacitance C_p due to the reverse-biased substrate junction. The bulk resistance R is typically between 5 and 10 ohms.

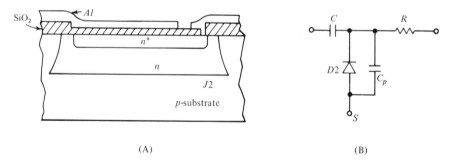

(A)   (B)

Fig. 16.11 Thin-film capacitor for monolithic circuit. (A) Cross-sectional view. (B) Electrical model.

A typical value of capacitance C is $0.25 \, \text{pF/mil}^2$; the value of C_p is $\frac{1}{2}$ to $\frac{1}{10}$ the value of C, depending on the magnitude of the reverse-bias voltage between the substrate and collector regions. The combination of a thin-film capacitor and a monolithic structure is an example of a compatible integrated circuit.

Diffused Resistors

Resistors for monolithics are generally made by diffusing a *p*-type base region into the *n*-island region to a specified depth, length, and width. A diffused resistor and its electrical model (which will be considered later) are illustrated in Fig. 16.12. Resistance *R* is expressed by

$$R = \rho l / A, \qquad (16.2)$$

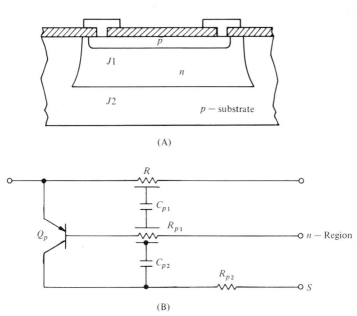

Fig. 16.12 A diffused resistor. (A) Cross-sectional view. (B) Electrical model.

where ρ = resistivity of material, ohm-cm or ohm-mil; l = length; A = cross-sectional area (width × depth). For a given depth d we can define a sheet resistance R_s:

$$R_s = \rho / d, \qquad (16.3)$$

where R_s has the unit of ohms/square of the resistance layer. Substituting (16.3) in (16.2) for ρ, we obtain

$$R = R_s(l/w), \qquad (16.4)$$

where term l/w is the length-to-width ratio.

Example 16.2

Determine the length-to-width ratio for a diffused resistance of 200 ohms. Sheet resistance R_s = 200 ohms/square.

Solution

From (16.4), $l/w = R/R_s = 2000/200 = 10:1$. The 200-ohm resistor can therefore be laid out as a 10 mil by 1 mil area (or a 5 mil by 0.5 mil area) on the substrate. A mask showing the resistance layout is given in Fig. 16.13. Because of the end contact areas, the resistance value is greater than 2000 ohms and correction factors would be employed. The edges of the resistor must be at least 2 mils from the edge of the n-region to allow for the lateral spreading of the p-type impurity.

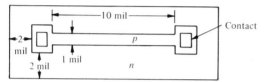

Fig. 16.13   Layout of a diffused resistor.

Values of R_s range from 10 to 500 ohms/square permitting resistances of approximately 100 ohms to 50 K to be realized, in general.

Reference to the model of the diffused resistor (Fig. 16.12B) shows that there exists a number of parasitic elements. Besides the parasitic transistor Q_p, resistances R_{p1} and R_{p2} are the bulk resistances of the n- and substrate regions, respectively; $R_{p1} \approx 70$ ohms and $R_{p2} \approx 5$ ohms. Distributed junction capacitances C_{p1} and C_{p2} (typical values: C_{p1}, 2–5 pF; C_{p2}, 5–20 pF) limit the high-frequency response of diffused resistors.

The absolute tolerances of diffused resistor values are generally poor; $\pm 25\%$ is not too uncommon. If ratios of adjacent resistor values are considered, however, the tolerance for the ratio may be less than $\pm 5\%$. The allowable power dissipation at 25°C for a diffused resistor is about 3 mW/mil². The maximum voltage across a diffused resistor is limited by the breakdown voltage of the collector-substrate junction; a typical value is 20 V.

From solid-state physics, resistivity ρ may be expressed by

$$\rho = 1/q\mu_p N_A, \qquad (16.5)$$

where μ_p = mobility factor of holes; q = charge of an electron; and N_A = number of acceptor atoms. Equation (16.5) shows that resistivity depends on the mobility factor μ_p. The mobility decreases with increasing temperature and results in a positive temperature coefficient for ρ. Furthermore, changes in μ_p also depend on the impurity concentration; the greater the concentration, the less is the change in μ_p. Lower resistance value base-diffused resistors are therefore more stable with temperature. For very low resistance values, emitter diffusion (the resistance is formed at the same time the transistor emitters are being diffused) may be used instead of base diffusion.

Thin-Film Resistors. Compatible thin-film resistors, made by depositing such materials as tin oxide (SnO_2) and nickel-chromium (NiCr) alloy on the silicon dioxide layer, exhibit improved electrical characteristics. Resistance tolerances are $\pm 5\%$, and sheet resistance values of 80 to 4000 ohms/square for SnO_2 and 40–4000 ohms/square for NiCr are obtainable.

16.3 Integrated Field-Effect Transistors

The fabrication of integrated circuits containing field-effect transistors share many of the processing steps in making junction transistors. A cross-sectional view of an insulated-gate FET (IGFET), or metal-oxide semiconductor FET (MOSFET), is illustrated in Fig. 16.14. If one begins with an *n*-type wafer, basically only a single diffusion is required to form two p^+ regions for the source and drain. These devices, however, have a number of limitations such as a low gain-bandwidth product and a high *threshold* voltage. The threshold voltage is the minimum gate voltage required to make the channel between the source and drain conducting.

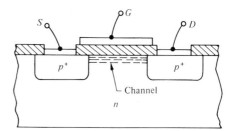

Fig. 16.14 Cross-sectional view of a conventional IGFET (MOSFET).

The recent development of *silicon-gate* technology has contributed greatly to the realization of field-effect transistors possessing superior characteristics over their predecessors. Lower threshold voltages are obtained by using a silicon nitride (Si_3N_4) and silicon dioxide "sandwich" for the dielectric under the gate. A lower threshold voltage is realized because the dielectric constant Si_3N_4 is twice as great as for SiO_2. The lower threshold voltage, of the order of 0.4 V, makes the new IGFET compatible with junction transistors. Another advantage gained from the new technology is an appreciable increase in the gain-bandwidth product of the device.

16.4 Large-Scale Integration

With the considerable success achieved in integrating multistage amplifiers, such as operational amplifiers, workers in the field began investigating the feasibility of integrating more complex functions on a single chip of silicon.

A fully integrated system containing some hundreds of transistors and associated passive components, such as the arithmetic section of a digital computer, would yield a reliable package of small dimensions and at low cost. This evolvement from the integration of single functions to complex functions where all interconnections are made on the chip itself is referred to as *large-scale integration* (LSI).

There are, however, some problems with this approach. Because of imperfections in the silicon wafer and possible subsequent defects arising from diffusion and masking operations, there are always some defective circuits on the wafer. It is pointless to connect circuits in a complex array that are, to begin with, inoperative. Some procedure must be adopted to detect and bypass the defective circuits before the metallized interconnection pattern is formed. To this end, two approaches have received considerable attention: *discretionary wiring* and *fixed interconnections*.

In discretionary wiring, each individual circuit that serves as a basic building block on the chip is tested before being connected to other such circuits. A suitably programmed digital computer keeps track of the good circuits on the wafer. Another program generates instructions for the formation of the interconnection pattern that connects all the good circuits making up the LSI circuit. An obvious disadvantage of discretionary wiring is that extra, or *redundant*, circuits have to be included on the chip to take the place of defective ones. Furthermore, new defects may arise during the metallization which can make the completed unit worthless.

Instead of connecting individual circuits, as is done in the discretionary wiring method, small groups of interconnected circuits, referred to as *polycells*, are used as the basic building blocks in the fixed interconnection method. Each polycell has a useful function by itself. If, in the interconnection of these polycells to form a large-scale integrated circuit the end product is defective, the polycells are salvageable and can be marketed as individual units.

16.5 IC Amplifiers

Based on our discussion of IC technology, the significant properties and limitations of diffused components may be summarized as follows:

1. Resistors have poor absolute tolerances; their relative tolerances, however, are good.

2. The range of component values is restricted.

3. Close matching of components is superior for integrated components compared with discrete components.

4. Good thermal coupling exists between diffused components.

5. In terms of cost per component, it costs approximately as much to

make a diffused resistor, capacitor, or diode as it does to make a diffused transistor.

6. No practical monolithic inductors are possible at this time; thin-film inductors are available.

Because of these factors, the design philosophy for integrated circuits is different from that for discrete circuits. For example, there is nothing to be gained from using fewer transistors and more passive components in a circuit; the difference in cost is negligible. Also, we must design circuits such that the ratios of resistances are significant—not their absolute values. Because of their restricted values, capacitors should be avoided. In this section we analyze IC amplifiers that take advantage of the favorable characteristics of integrated-circuit components while minimizing their limitations.

Diode-Biased Amplifier

As mentioned earlier in the text, establishing and stabilizing the Q-point are necessary steps in the design of an amplifier. Various techniques especially suitable for discrete circuits were examined in Chapter 5. It was shown there that voltage and current feedback stabilization required decoupling and bypass capacitors, respectively, to prevent degradation in the ac signal gain. Nonlinear techniques, however, are well suited for the integrated-circuit amplifier. An example of such a circuit, the *diode-biased* amplifier, is given in Fig. 16.15A.

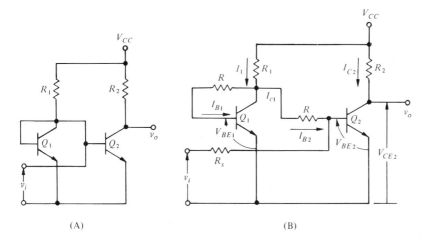

Fig. 16.15 Diode-biased amplifier. (A) Basic circuit. (B) Practical circuit.

Transistor $Q1$, with its collector and base tied together, acts as a forward-biased diode (see Fig. 16.8A) across the base-emitter junction of amplifier transistor $Q2$. Assume the temperature of the IC chip rises; the current gain of transistors $Q1$ and $Q2$ will tend to rise. Because of their close physical proximity on the chip, the chances are good that both transistors will exhibit nearly identical properties. More collector current will therefore flow through $Q1$, and less base current flows in $Q2$. If R_1 is large, the collector current of $Q2$ does not vary significantly and its Q-point is stabilized.

From an ac signal standpoint, however, the circuit is unsatisfactory. Because the collector and base of $Q1$ are tied together, the signal is effectively shorted to ground. A solution to this problem is the circuit of Fig. 16.15B, where resistor R is inserted in series with the base of each transistor. To maintain circuit balance, resistor R is required for both transistors.

Referring again to Fig. 16.15B and assuming identical transistors, we may assume that $I_{B1} = I_{B2} = I_B$; $I_{C1} = I_{C2} = I_C$; $V_{BE1} = V_{BE2} = V_{BE}$; and $h_{FE1} = h_{FE2} = h_{FE}$. Writing a loop equation around the input circuit of $Q2$, we obtain

$$V_{CC} = R_1 I_1 + R I_B + V_{BE}.$$

But $I_1 = 2I_B + I_C$; therefore,

$$V_{CC} = R_1(2I_B + I_C) + R I_B + V_{BE}. \tag{16.6}$$

Also,

$$I_B = I_C/h_{FE}. \tag{16.7}$$

Substituting (16.7) for I_B in (16.6) and solving for I_C yields

$$I_C = (V_{CC} - V_{BE})/[R_1 + (2R_1 + R)/h_{FE}]. \tag{16.8}$$

If $(2R_1 + R)/h_{FE} \ll R_1$, (16.8) reduces to

$$I_C \approx (V_{CC} - V_{BE})/R_1. \tag{16.9}$$

The quiescent collector-emitter voltage for the amplifying transistor $Q2$ is $V_{CE2} = V_{CC} - R_2 I_C$; substitution of (16.9) in this expression yields

$$V_{CE2} = V_{CC} - (R_2/R_1)(V_{CC} - V_{BE}). \tag{16.10}$$

Note that V_{CE2} depends primarily on the ratio of R_2/R_1 which can be held to better than $\pm 5\%$ for diffused resistors. If $R_2/R_1 = \frac{1}{2}$, the quiescent collector-emitter voltage is approximately $V_{CC}/2$, providing an ideal operating point for maximum signal swing before wave clipping appears.

AC Signal Analysis. Models of integrated circuit components (Figs. 16.8.10, 11B, and 12B) contain parasitic capacitances, resistances, diodes, and transistors. A diffused resistor, for example, has distributed capacitance similar to a transmission line. If we were to analyze the signal performance of an IC amplifier at very high frequencies, the parasitic elements must be considered. Because the techniques for analyzing distributed elements are different from lumped element techniques, we shall restrict the analysis to low-signal frequencies where all reactive elements may be ignored.

With h_{re} and h_{oe} neglected, an incremental model of the diode-biased amplifier of Fig. 16.15B is shown in Fig. 16.16A (identical transistors are still assumed). By applying the reduction theorem, the controlled-current source $h_{fe}i_{b1}$ may be removed if resistances h_{ie} and R are divided by $1 + h_{fe}$.

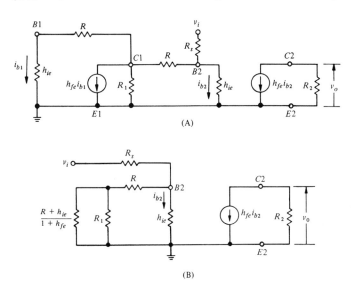

(A)

(B)

Fig. 16.16 Analyzing the diode-biased amplifier at low frequencies. (A) Small-signal model. (B) Simplified model obtained with the aid of the reduction theorem.

The resulting simplified circuit of Fig. 16.16B will be analyzed. Let

$$\left(\frac{R + h_{ie}}{1 + h_{fe}}\right) \bigg/\!\!\bigg/ R_1 = R_B;$$

then

$$i_{b2} = \frac{v_i}{h_{ie} + R_s(R_B + R + h_{ie})/(R + R_B)}. \tag{16.11}$$

A reasonable assumption to make is that $R_B \ll R$; then $(R + R_B) \approx R$, and (16.11) reduces to

$$i_{b2} = \frac{v_i}{h_{ie} + R_s(R + h_{ie})/R}. \tag{16.12}$$

Output voltage v_o is $-h_{fe}i_{b2}R_2$, or

$$v_o = \frac{-h_{fe}v_iR_2}{h_{ie} + R_s(R + h_{ie})/R}.$$

Voltage gain $A_{vs} = v_o/v_i$:

$$A_{vs} = \frac{-h_{fe}}{(R_s/R_2 + h_{ie}/R_2)(1 + R_s/R)}. \tag{16.13}$$

For a given value of h_{fe}, the voltage gain depends primarily on ratios of resistors which can be held to $\pm 5\%$. Because h_{fe} can vary over wide limits, however, overall voltage feedback is necessary to maintain a given voltage gain.

Example 16.3

For the diode-biased amplifier of Fig. 16.15B, $V_{CC} = 20$ V, $R_1 = 8$ K, $R_2 = 4$ K, $R = 10$ K, $R_s = 5$ K, $V_{BE} = 0.7$ V, and $h_{fe} = h_{FE} = 50$. Find (a) the dc quiescent operating point, (b) h_{ie} at room temperature, and (c) the ac voltage gain at low frequencies.

Solution

(a) From (16.9) and (16.10),

$$I_C = (20 - 0.7)/8 = 2.4 \text{ mA},$$

$$V_{CE} = 20 - \tfrac{1}{2}(20 - 0.7) = 10.35 \text{ V}.$$

(b) A reasonable approximation (see Chapter 8) is $h_{ie} = h_{fe}(26/I_E)$ at room temperature; current I_E is expressed in milliamperes. Using $I_E \approx I_C = 2.4$ mA found in (a), one obtains $h_{ie} = 50(26/2.4) = 0.54$ K.

(c) $R_B = (10.54/51)//8 = 0.2$ K (which is much less than $R = 10$ K). From (16.13),

$$A_{vs} = \frac{-50}{(5/4 + 0.54/4)(1 + 5/10)} = -34.5.$$

The Difference Amplifier

The amplifier commonly used in linear IC designs is the *difference*, or *differential*, amplifier of Fig. 16.17. This circuit has been used in discrete form as a dc amplifier and as a phase inverter (see Chapter 10). The two available inputs provide a flexibility not realized with conventional amplifier designs, and the circuit is relatively immune to spurious signals. More importantly, the difference amplifier is ideal for an IC design where the advantages and limitations of diffused components are most effectively utilized. In fact, the difference amplifier is the basic circuit of the operational amplifier, the most used linear IC.

We shall first consider the dc biasing of the difference amplifier. Let $v_1 = v_2 = 0$. If $Q1$ and $Q2$ are assumed identical, $V_{CE1} = V_{CE2} = V_{CE}$ and

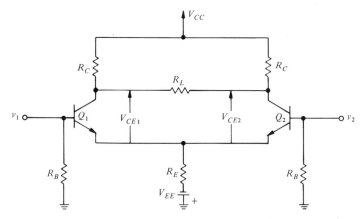

Fig. 16.17 Basic circuit of a difference amplifier.

the current flowing through R_L is zero. Because of *symmetry*, $2I_E$ flows in R_E; therefore, for each half of the circuit, only I_E flows in the emitter resistance. To maintain the same voltage between emitter and ground, R_E is replaced by $2R_E$ in the simplified model of Fig. 16.18. Writing a loop equation for the input circuit yields

$$V_{EE} = [R_B + 2R_E(1 + h_{FE})]I_B + V_{BE}$$

or $\qquad I_B = (V_{EE} - V_{BE})/[R_B + 2R_E(1 + h_{FE})].$

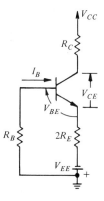

Fig. 16.18 Using symmetry to obtain the Q point of a difference amplifier.

Also,

$$I_C = h_{FE}I_B = h_{FE}(V_{EE} - V_{BE})/[R_B + 2R_E(1 + h_{FE})]. \qquad (16.14)$$

If $2R_E(1 + h_{FE}) \gg R_B$ and $h_{FE} \gg 1$, (16.14) reduces to

$$I_C = \frac{V_{EE} - V_{BE}}{2R_E}. \qquad (16.15)$$

The collector-emitter voltage V_{CE} is

$$V_{CE} = V_{CC} + V_{EE} - R_C I_C - 2R_E I_E. \qquad (16.16)$$

Letting $I_C \approx I_E$ and substituting (16.15) for I_C in (16.16), one obtains upon simplification:

$$V_{CE} = V_{CC} + V_{BE} - \frac{R_C}{2R_E}(V_{EE} - V_{BE}) \qquad (16.17)$$

The quiescent-collector voltage is a function of the ratio of the diffused collector and emitter resistances, which is desirable for monolithic amplifiers.

Common-Mode and Differential-Mode Signals. The difference amplifier may be viewed as a bridge circuit. For identical transistors and $v_1 = v_2$, the bridge is balanced and the net voltage across R_L is zero. If, for example, $v_1 > v_2$, the collector current in $Q1$ increases and the collector current in $Q2$ decreases. The bridge becomes unbalanced and a net voltage appears across R_L and load current flows.

For the condition $v_1 = v_2$, *common-mode* input signals are said to exist; for $v_1 = -v_2$, *differential-mode* signals exist. For an ideal difference amplifier, the gain is zero for the common-mode signals and greater than zero for the differential-mode signals. In general, a signal will contain both common- and differential-mode components. For example, the common-mode signal component may be due to changes in temperature, power supply variations, or noise. These signals must be minimized at the amplifier output. The desired output signal is that due to the differential input signal.

Considering general signals, let

$$v_1 = v_{ic} + v_{id}, \qquad (16.18a)$$

$$v_2 = v_{ic} - v_{id}, \qquad (16.18b)$$

where v_{ic} and v_{id} are the common-mode and differential-mode signal components, respectively. Adding (16.18a) and (16.18b) yields

$$v_{ic} = (v_1 + v_2)/2 \qquad (16.19a)$$

Subtracting (16.18b) from (16.18a) yields

$$v_{id} = (v_1 - v_2)/2. \qquad (16.19b)$$

The gain for the common-mode component will be designated by A_{vc} and that for the differential-mode component by A_{vd}. A figure of merit for the difference amplifier, the *common-mode rejection ratio* CMRR is defined as

$$\text{CMRR} = A_{vd}/A_{vc}. \qquad (16.20)$$

For an ideal difference amplifier, CMRR equals infinity.

AC Signal Analysis of Difference Amplifiers. In analyzing the ac signal performance of the difference amplifier, identical transistors are assumed, and reactive elements are neglected. For common-mode signals the current through R_L of Fig. 16.17 is zero. If one neglects h_{re}, h_{oe}, and the source resistance, because of symmetry, the simplified circuit of Fig. 16.19A may be used. Base current i_b is

$$i_b = v_{ic}/[h_{ie} + 2R_E(1 + h_{fe})],$$

$$v_{oc} = -h_{fe}i_bR_C$$

$$= -h_{fe}R_Cv_{ic}/[h_{ie} + 2R_E(1 + h_{fe})].$$

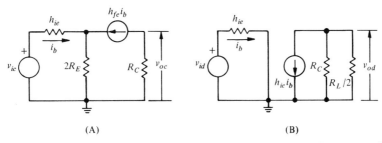

(A)   (B)

Fig. 16.19 Determining the signal gain at mid frequencies for the difference amplifier. Models for (A) common-mode gain and (B) differential-mode gain.

The common-mode voltage gain A_{vc} is

$$A_{vc} = v_{oc}/v_{ic} = -h_{fe}R_C/[h_{ie} + 2R_E(1 + h_{fe})]. \qquad (16.21)$$

If $2R_E(1 + h_{fe}) \gg h_{ie}$ and $h_{fe} \gg 1$, (16.21) becomes

$$A_{vc} = -R_C/2R_E. \qquad (16.22)$$

For all practical purposes the common-mode voltage gain is a function of resistor ratios. If $R_E \gg R_C$, $A_{vc} \approx 0$, which is desired for optimum performance of a difference amplifier. A technique of increasing R_E is its replacement with a transistor connected to approximate a constant-current source; this approach is considered later.

For a differential-mode signal the emitter currents are 180° out of phase and are equal; therefore the net current in R_E is zero. Because of symmetry, the effective load resistance for half the circuit is $R_L/2$. Considering these facts, we obtain the model of Fig. 16.19B. With $(R_L/2)//R_C = R'_L$, the differential-mode voltage gain A_{vd} is

$$A_{vd} = -h_{fe}R'_L/h_{ie}. \qquad (16.23)$$

By substitution of (16.22) and (16.23) in (16.20), an explicit expression for CMRR is obtained:

$$CMRR = 2h_{fe}R'_L R_E / h_{ie} R_C. \tag{16.24}$$

Example 16.4

For the difference amplifier of Fig. 16.17, assume $V_{CC} = V_{EE} = 20$ V, $R_E = R_B = 5$ K, $R_C = h_{ie} = 1$ K, $R_L = 2$ K, and $h_{FE} = h_{fe} = 50$; let $V_{BE} = 0$. Find (a) the quiescent operating point and (b) the values of A_{vc}, A_{vd}, and CMRR.

Solution

The values of $2R_E(1 + h_{FE})$ and $2R_E(1 + h_{fe})$ are 510 K, which is considerably larger than either R_B or h_{ie}; approximate equations may therefore be used.

(a) From (16.15) and (16.17),

$$I_C = V_{EE}/2R_E = 20/10 = 2 \text{ mA},$$

$$V_{CE} = V_{CC} + V_{BE} - (R_C/2R_E)(V_{EE} - V_{BE}) = 20 - 20/10 = 18 \text{ V}.$$

(b) By using (16.22), (16.23), and (16.20), we obtain

$$A_{vc} = -R_C/2R_E = -1/10 = -0.1;$$

$$A_{vd} = -h_{fe}R'_L/h_{ie}; \qquad R'_L = (R_L/2)//R_C = (2/2)//1 = 0.5 \text{ K};$$

$$A_{vd} = -50 \times 0.5/1 = -25;$$

$$CMRR = A_{vd}/A_{vc} = -25/(-0.1) = 250.$$

Practical Considerations. Achieving a high value of CMRR (or a low value for A_{vc}) requires a large value of emitter resistance R_E. A serious problem with this approach is that as the value of R_E is raised, inordinately large bias sources, V_{CC} and V_{EE}, are required. Furthermore, the dc power dissipated in the emitter resistor may rise to excessive values. These deficiencies can be eliminated by simulating a large value of emitter resistance with a "constant" current source.

An example of a circuit approximating a constant current source is found in the commercial (Fairchild μA730) difference amplifier of Fig. 16.20. Transistors $Q1$ and $Q2$ constitute the difference amplifier; $Q5$ and its associated components form the constant current source. Biasing of $Q5$ is provided by the 5.6 and 1.3 K resistors; the 2.1 K emitter resistor stabilizes $Q5$ and raises its output resistance. Transistors $Q3$ and $Q4$ are connected as emitter followers for low output impedance. This circuit is analyzed in the following example.

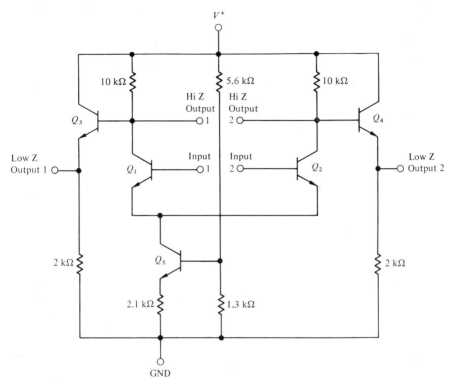

Fig. 16.20 A schematic diagram of the *Fairchild µA730* difference amplifier. (Courtesy of Fairchild Semiconductor).

Example 16.5

For the Fairchild µA730 difference amplifier of Fig. 16.20, determine (a) the quiescent collector and base currents for each transistor, (b) the quiescent collector voltages with respect to ground of $Q1$ and $Q2$ and the emitter voltages with respect to ground of $Q3$ and $Q4$, (c) total dc input power, and (d) A_{vc}, A_{vd}, and CMRR. Assume identical components and $h_{FE} = h_{fe} = 100$, $V_{CC} = 12$ V, $V_{BE} = 0.7$ V; neglect h_{re} and let $1/h_{oe} = 20$ K. Assume that inputs 1 and 2 are connected to suitable sources.

Solution

(a) The Thevenin voltage at the base of $Q5$ is $V_{TH} = 12 \times 1.3/(1.3 + 5.6) = 2.26$ V and $R_{TH} = 1.3//5.6 = 1.1$ K. Therefore,

$$I_{B5} = (2.26 - 0.7)/[1.1 + (101)2.1] = 0.007 \text{ mA},$$

$$I_{C5} \approx I_{E5} = h_{FE}I_{B5} = 100 \times 0.007 = 0.7 \text{ mA},$$

$$I_{C1} = I_{C2} = 0.7 \text{ mA}/2 = 0.35 \text{ mA},$$

and $\qquad I_{B1} = I_{B2} = 0.35 \text{ mA}/100 = 0.0035 \text{ mA}.$

If we neglect I_{B3}, the voltage across the collector of $Q1$ with respect to ground V_{C1} is

$$V_{C1} = 12 - 10(0.35) = 8.5 \text{ V}.$$

Hence, $I_{E3} = (8.5 - 0.7)/2 = 3.9 \text{ mA}.$ $I_{C3} = I_{C4} \approx I_{E3} = 3.9 \text{ mA}.$ $I_{B3} = I_{B4} = 3.9/100 = 0.039 \text{ mA}.$

(b) From (a) $V_{C1} = V_{C2} = 8.5 \text{ V}$ and $V_{E3} = V_{E4} = 8.5 - 0.7 = 7.8 \text{ V}.$

(c) Total dc input power, with the very minute bias currents neglected, is:

$Q3, Q4$: $3.9 \times 12 \times 2 = 93.6 \text{ mW}$		93.6 mW
$Q1, Q2, Q5$: $0.7 \times 12 = 8.4 \text{ mW}$		8.4
	Total	102.0 mW

(d) To determine A_{vc}, we have to find the equivalent value of R_E which, in the case of the constant current source, is equal to the output resistance R_o of $Q5$. It can be shown that, neglecting h_{re} and letting $R_e =$ the emitter resistance of $Q5$, the output resistance is

$$R_o = \frac{1}{h_{oe}}\left[\frac{(1 + h_{fe})R_e + h_{ie}(1 + h_{oe}R_e)}{R_e + h_{ie}}\right]. \qquad (16.25)$$

Substitution of the given values in (16.25) yields $R_o = 460 \text{ K}$. From (16.22),

$$A_{vc} = -10 \times 10^3/(2 \times 460 \times 10^3) = -0.01.$$

Input resistance h_{ie} may be approximated by $100 \times 26/0.35 = 7.4 \text{ K}$. From (16.23),

$$A_{vd} = -100 \times 10/7.4 = -135$$

$$\text{CMRR} = -135/(-0.01) = 13,500 = 83.4 \text{ dB}.$$

Our analysis of the difference amplifier has been idealized in the assumption of identical transistors and resistors. Notwithstanding the excellent matching of components in monolithic circuits, some differences in their values do exist. These differences unbalance the "bridge" and result in the degradation of amplifier performance. Assume that the current gain of $Q1$ is greater than that of $Q2$. With the presence of common-mode signals at the input terminals of the transistors, more collector current flows in $Q1$ than in $Q2$. This produces a net voltage across R_L and the flow of load current, as though a differential-mode signal instead of a common-mode signal was impressed across the transistors. The imbalances, therefore, tend to reduce the CMRR. In a well-designed monolithic difference amplifier, the common-mode rejection ratio is 80 dB or greater.

Circuit imbalances also result in an output voltage without the presence of an input signal. The degree of this undesirable effect is designated by two other figures of merit: the *input-offset voltage* and the *input-offset current*. The input-offset voltage is defined as the dc voltage applied between the input terminals to obtain zero output voltage. Input-offset current is defined as the difference in dc input currents for equal emitter currents. Input-offset voltages and currents of less than 1 mV and 1 μA, respectively, are typical.

Coupling the Difference Amplifier. To realize the full operating advantages of the difference amplifier, the load resistance should be connected between the collector of each transistor. This is referred to as a *floating* connection. For practical reasons, however, the floating connection is seldom used because one side of the load is generally grounded. In some applications the output voltage is taken across the collector of either transistor and ground. A bad feature of this method of load coupling is that the common-mode signal will produce a greater output voltage than if the load were floating.

A better approach is the circuit of Fig. 16.21 where the collector-to-collector output of the difference amplifier $Q1$ and $Q2$ is converted to a single-ended output ($Q4$). Transistors $Q3$ and $Q4$ constitute the diode-biased amplifier that was analyzed earlier in the chapter.

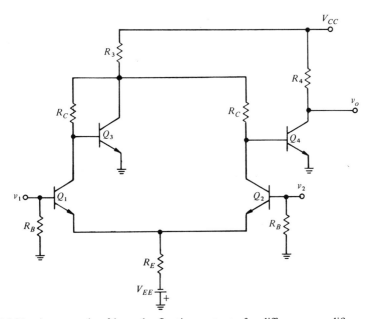

Fig. 16.21 An example of how the floating output of a difference amplifier may be converted to a single-ended output.

16.6   The Operational Amplifier

The operational amplifier (op amp) is used as the basic building block in most applications of linear integrated circuits. With suitable feedback elements (see Chapter 11), they are extremely versatile and can be used as inverting or noninverting amplifiers, integrators, active filters, etc. The operational amplifier exhibits a very high open-loop gain and a high input impedance.

An example of a typical operational amplifier, the RCA CA3010, is shown in Fig. 16.22. It may be viewed as essentially composed of two difference amplifiers (transistor pairs $Q1$, $Q2$ and $Q3$, $Q4$) in cascade. Transistors $Q6$ and $Q7$ act as constant current sources for the difference amplifiers. Diodes $D1$ and $D2$ provide bias stabilization for $Q6$, $Q7$, and $Q9$.

Because the inputs to $Q3$ and $Q4$ are derived across the collectors of $Q1$ and $Q2$ (which is equivalent to one signal instead of the difference of two

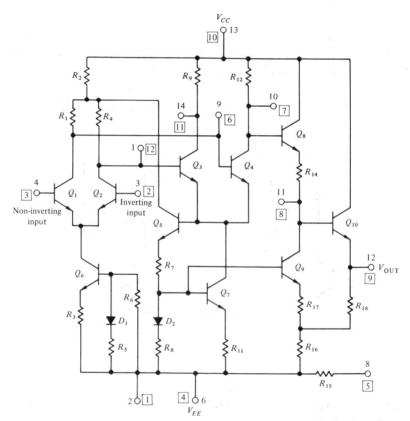

Fig. 16.22   Schematic diagram of the *RCA CA3010* operational amplifier. (Courtesy of RCA Corporation).

signals), the second difference amplifier operates in push-pull. In this operation, $Q3$ and $Q4$ cannot reject common-mode signals and transistor $Q5$, used
as a negative-feedback element, is required. In the absence of common-mode
signals, the voltage at the emitters of $Q3$ and $Q4$ is zero. If a common-mode
signal is present, it is amplified by $Q5$ and developed across R_2 in the correct
phase to reduce the error. Because it acts as a feedback element, $Q5$ also
reduces the effects of power supply variations, noise, etc.

Transistors $Q8$ and $Q9$ form a *cascode amplifier*. It shifts the dc level such
that the output of the emitter follower ($Q10$) is zero in the absence of an input
signal. To analyze the circuit, it is isolated in Fig. 16.23 where V_{B8} and V_{B9}
are the quiescent base-emitter voltages. If the circuit elements are chosen to
satisfy the equation

$$I_{16}R_{16} + R_{18}I_{18} - V_{EE} = 0, \tag{16.26}$$

the output will be equal to zero.

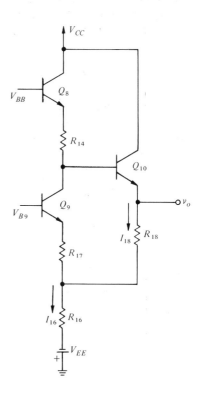

Fig. 16.23 The cascode amplifier.

Emitter resistor R_{18} is returned to the emitter circuit of $Q9$ instead of to
ground to provide positive feedback. If, for example, the output voltage
increases, the emitter voltage of $Q9$ also increases. The base voltage of $Q9$,
V_{B9}, is determined essentially by R_7, R_8, and $D2$ (see Fig. 16.22) and is

relatively constant. Because of these factors, the base current in $Q9$ decreases and the collector and base voltages of $Q9$ and $Q10$, respectively, rise. This results in an increase in the output voltage v_o and is an example of positive feedback. For the RCA CA3010, the cascode amplifier-emitter follower combination voltage gain is about 1.5. Without positive feedback, the gain would be unity or less.

Applications

A commonly used symbol for the operational amplifier, such as the CA3010, is illustrated in Fig. 16.24A. Terminal 1 is the common connection; terminals 2 and 3 are input terminals for output inversion ($-$) or non-inversion ($+$) of the input signal, respectively. External supply voltages V_{CC} and V_{EE} are applied to terminals 10 and 4. The remaining terminals are available for the introduction of frequency, or phase, compensation networks.

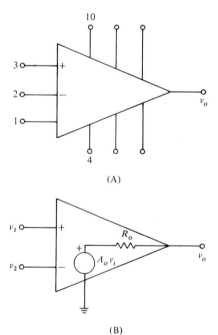

(A)

(B)

Fig. 16.24 Symbols for the operational amplifier. (A) General. (B) Simplified.

A simplified schematic symbol for the op amp, useful in its analysis as a circuit element, is shown in Fig. 16.24B. Voltage source $A_o v_i$ and resistance R_o are the Thevenin controlled source and output resistance, respectively, as mid frequencies. Signal v_1 results in a noninverting output, while signal v_2 yields an inverted output. When used as a difference amplifier, signals v_1

and v_2 are applied simultaneously, and the output voltage is a function of their difference, $v_1 - v_2$.

Owing to production variability, the open-loop gain of an amplifier can vary by more than 2 to 1. For this reason, feedback is introduced externally around the amplifier. In the following discussion, the effects of offset voltage and bias current will be neglected.

Introducing Feedback

Noninverting Amplifier. The circuit for a noninverting amplifier with feedback is illustrated in Fig. 16.25A. The effective input resistance at mid frequencies is represented by R_i. Feedback is obtained with the resistance network composed of R_1 and R_2. Using the results of Chapter 11 with $G = A_o$ and $H = R_2/(R_1 + R_2)$, we obtain

$$A_f = \frac{A_o}{1 + A_o R_2/(R_1 + R_2)}.$$

Because A_o is at least equal to 1000,

$$A_f \approx 1/H = 1 + R_1/R_2. \tag{16.27}$$

The closed-loop voltage gain becomes a function of the external resistances R_1 and R_2, for large values of open-loop gain A_o. As discussed in Chapter 11, the closed-loop gain may be made very stable and relatively independent of the operational amplifier itself.

For large values of A_o the output resistance with feedback R_{of} is approximately equal to zero. The input resistance with feedback, R_{if}, for $R_1 \ll R_2$, is

$$R_{if} \approx (1 + A_o)R_i. \tag{16.28}$$

Voltage Follower. If 100% feedback is used around the noninverting amplifier, the *voltage follower*, or *unity-gain buffer*, of Fig. 16.25B is obtained. The circuit exhibits a higher input resistance than for any other op amp configuration and is equal to (16.28); the output resistance is approximately zero. Because $R_1 = 0$, $H = 1$ and the voltage gain is close to unity:

$$A_f = A_o/(1 + A_o) \approx 1. \tag{16.29}$$

Inverting Amplifier. The operational amplifier used as an inverting amplifier is shown in Fig. 16.25C. As proved in Chapter 11, for very large values of A_o, the closed-loop voltage gain A_f is

$$A_f = -R_2/R_1. \tag{16.30}$$

The input resistance $R_{if} \approx R_1$ and $R_{of} \approx 0$.

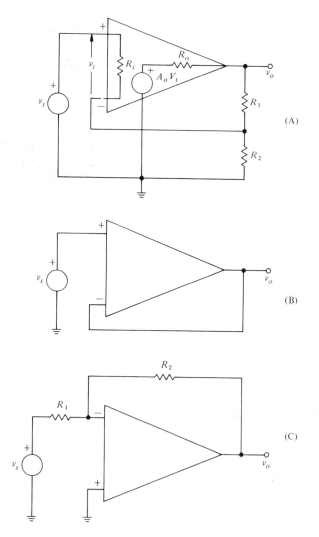

Fig. 16.25 Introducing external feedback. (A) Noninverting amplifier. (B) Voltage follower. (C) Inverting amplifier.

Difference Amplifier. The op amp used as a difference amplifier is shown in Fig. 16.26A. The output v_{o1} due to source v_{s1} ($v_{s2} = 0$) is

$$v_{o1} = -R_2 v_{s1}/R_1.$$

Setting $v_{s1} = 0$, the corresponding output v_{o2} due to v_{s2} is

$$v_{o2} = (1 + R_2/R_1)v_{s2}.$$

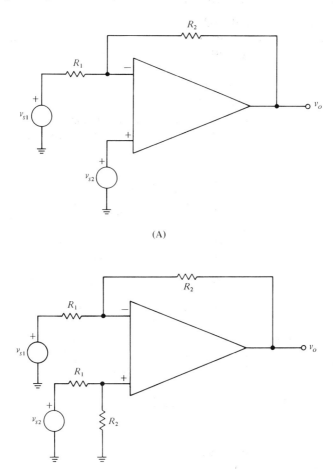

(A)

(B)

Fig. 16.26 The difference amplifier with external feedback. (A) Basic circuit. (B) Improved version.

The total output v_o is equal to the sum of v_{o1} and v_{o2}:

$$v_o = (1 + R_2/R_1)v_{s2} - R_2 v_{s1}/R_1. \tag{16.31}$$

It is desirable to have (16.31) in the form of $v_o = K(v_{s2} - v_{s1})$. This is achieved in the circuit of Fig. 16.26B where a voltage divider, composed of resistances R_1 and R_2, is placed across the noninverting input terminal of the op amp. It can be shown that $K = R_2/R_1$ and

$$v_o = (R_2/R_1)(v_{s2} - v_{s1}). \tag{16.32}$$

Offset Voltage and Current Compensation

As a typical example, the offset voltage (V_{OS}) for the CA3010 op amp at room temperature is approximately 1.1 mV. With the open-loop gain at 1000, the output voltage, with $v_{s1} = v_{s2} = 0$, is $1.1 \times 10^{-3} \times 10^3 = 1.1$ V. This is undesirable, and it therefore becomes necessary to compensate for the offset voltage. Unfortunately, V_{OS} varies with temperature, as illustrated in Fig. 16.27; consequently, perfect compensation is only attainable at one temperature. With an inverting amplifier, a circuit for offset voltage compensation is shown in Fig. 16.28. The potentiometer setting is determined for the condition that $v_o = 0$ with $v_{s1} = 0$.

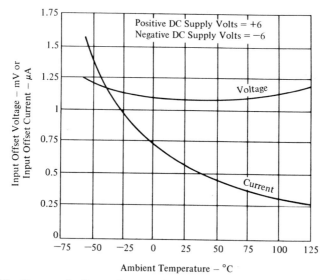

Fig. 16.27 Curves of offset voltage and current versus temperature for the *RCA CA3010* op amp. (Courtesy of RCA Corporation).

Consider now the inverting amplifier with feedback and $v_{s1} = 0$ (Fig. 16.29A). Because of dc bias current I_1, the dc voltage drop across the input to the amplifier, with zero output resistance and $R_1 \ll R_2$, is $-I_1 R_1$. A method of compensating for the bias current is the insertion of resistance R_C between the noninverting input and ground (Fig. 16.29B). The output voltage is

$$v_o = A(I_1 R_1 - I_2 R_C). \tag{16.33}$$

If $I_1 = I_2$, $R_C = R_1$ for perfect compensation ($v_o = 0$). In practice, however, $I_1 \neq I_2$. By taking their difference, an equivalent offset current, $I_{OS} = I_1 - I_2$, is defined. A typical variation of I_{OS} with temperature is also given in Fig. 16.27. Note that I_{OS} varies inversely with temperature.

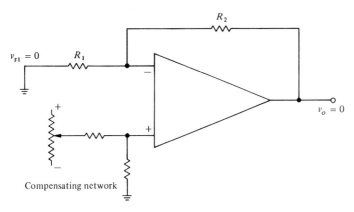

Fig. 16.28 Compensating for the offset voltage V_{OS}.

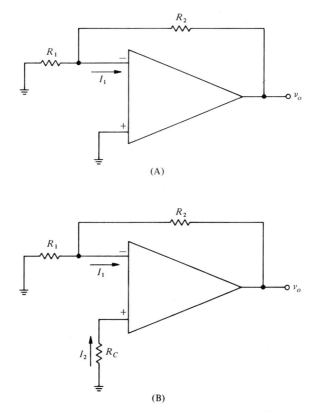

Fig. 16.29 Compensating for the offset bias current. (A) Without compensating resistor. (B) With compensating resistor R_C.

A complete inverting amplifier with feedback and compensation for voltage and current offset is illustrated in Fig. 16.30A. To simplify its analysis, the compensation network is replaced by a dc source, $V_{TH} - V_{OS}$, in series with R_{TH} in Fig. 16.30B. Voltage V_{TH} is the Thevenin voltage of the compensating network. Because perfect compensation is only obtained at a single temperature, to take into account the variation in V_{OS}, it is included in the expression. Resistance R_{TH} is the Thevenin resistance which includes the equivalent resistance of the compensating network in series with R_C.

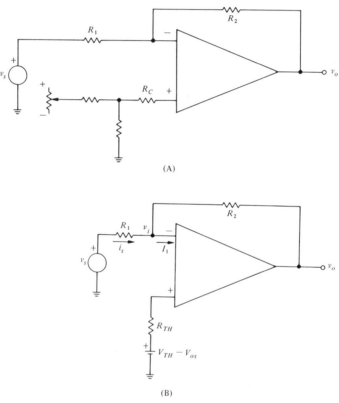

(A)

(B)

Fig. 16.30 Complete inverting amplifier with feedback and compensation. (A) Circuit. (B) Compensating network replaced by a Thevenin equivalent.

Applying superposition and setting $V_{TH} - V_{OS}$ to zero, from Fig. 16.30B, assuming $v_i \approx 0$ one obtains

$$i_s = I_1 - v_o/R_2. \tag{16.34a}$$

Also,

$$v_s = R_1 i_s + R_2(i_s - I_1) + v_o. \tag{16.34b}$$

By substitution of (16.34a) in (16.34b) and upon simplification, v_{o1}, the output due to v_s, is obtained:

$$v_{o1} = (v_s - R_1 I_1)(-R_2/R_1). \tag{16.35}$$

Setting v_s to zero yields

$$v_{o2} = [(V_{TH} - V_{OS}) - R_{TH} I_2](1 + R_2/R_1). \tag{16.36}$$

With $R_2/R_1 \gg 1$, $v_o = v_{o1} + v_{o2}$:

$$v_o = (v_s - R_1 I_1)(-R_2/R_1) + [(V_{TH} - V_{OS}) - R_{TH} I_2](R_2/R_1). \tag{16.37}$$

Assuming $R_{TH} = R_1$ and substituting $I_{OS} = I_1 - I_2$, one can reduce (16.37) to

$$v_o = -R_2 v_s/R_1 + [R_2 I_{OS} + (V_{TH} - V_{OS})(R_2/R_1)]. \tag{16.38}$$

Ideally, the output voltage expressed by (16.38) should be independent of temperature. As seen from Fig. 16.27, however, both V_{OS} and I_{OS} vary with temperature. Because the expression in brackets in (16.38) is equal to zero only at one temperature, it is therefore required to determine the change in output voltage as a function of temperature. This change is referred to as *dc drift*, or *error voltage*. Assuming linear variation and recognizing that $-R_2 v_s/R_1$ and V_{TH} are essentially constant with temperature, we obtain the error voltage V:

$$V = \Delta v_o = \frac{-R_2}{R_1} \frac{\Delta V_{OS}}{\Delta T} \Delta T + R_2 \frac{\Delta I_{OS}}{\Delta T} \Delta T. \tag{16.39}$$

The use of the preceding concepts is explored in the following example.

Example 16.6

Assume that at mid frequencies the open-loop gain of the RCA CA3010 op amp is equal to 1000 and is relatively stable with respect to temperature. Resistance $R_1 = 1$ K, $R_2 = 30$ K, and the rms value of the input signal is 0.1 V. The amplifier is compensated at room temperature (25°C). Determine (a) the output voltage at 25°C; (b) the value of V_{TH} for compensation; the error voltage at 125°C (c) using the curves of Fig. 16.27 and (d) the values of $\Delta I_{OS} \Delta T = -3$ nA/°C and $\Delta V_{OS} = 0.8$ μV/°C which were approximated from the curves of Fig. 16.27.

Solution

(a) At 25°C, the bracketed term in (16.38) is equal to zero. Therefore,
$$v_0 = -30 \times 0.1 = -3 \text{ V}.$$
(b) The compensating network was adjusted for $v_o = 0$ at room

temperature. From Fig. 16.27, at 25°C, $I_{OS} = 0.55\ \mu$A and $V_{OS} =$ 1.1 mV. Substitution of these terms in the bracketed expression of (16.38) yields

$$30 \times 10^3 \times 0.55 \times 10^{-6} + (V_{TH} - 1.1 \times 10^{-3})30 = 0.$$

Solving $V_{TH} = 0.55$ mV.

(c) From Fig. 16.27, at 125°C, $I_{OS} = 0.26\ \mu$A and $V_{OS} = 1.15$ mV. The error voltage $V = 30 \times 10^3 \times 0.26 \times 10^{-6} + 30(0.55 - 1.15)10^{-3} = -10.2$ mV.

(d) From (16.39), $V = -30 \times 0.8 \times 10^{-6} \times 100 - 3 \times 10^{-9} \times 30 \times 10^3 \times 100 = -11.4$ mV.

The results of parts (c) and (d) are in good agreement.

Phase Compensation

In Chapter 11 the use of phase lead compensation to ensure sufficient gain margin for stable operation of a feedback amplifier was examined. Because an operational amplifier exhibits a number of break frequencies, some type of phase compensation is generally required when feedback is used for stable operation. A commonly used network for this purpose is the phase lag network of Fig. 16.31A which is placed effectively in series with the op amp. Taking the ratio of voltage $V_o(j\omega)$ to $V_i(j\omega)$, the transfer function $G(j\omega)$ for the network is obtained:

$$G(j\omega) = \frac{V_o(j\omega)}{V_i(j\omega)} = \frac{R_c + 1/j\omega C_c}{R_A + R_c + 1/j\omega C_c}.$$

Multiplying numerator and denominator by $j\omega C_c$ yields

$$G(j\omega) = \frac{1 + j\omega R_c C_c}{1 + j\omega (R_A + R_c)C_c}. \tag{16.40}$$

With

$$\omega_2 = 1/R_c C_c \tag{16.41a}$$

and

$$\omega_1 = 1/(R_A + R_c)C_c, \tag{16.41b}$$

equation (16.40) may be expressed as

$$G(j\omega) = (1 + j\omega/\omega_2)/(1 + j\omega/\omega_1), \tag{16.42}$$

where $\omega_2 > \omega_1$. A plot of (16.42) is given in Fig. 16.31B.

The effect of the phase lag network on the amplifier response for the case where ω_2 is equal to the first corner frequency of the open-loop gain is shown

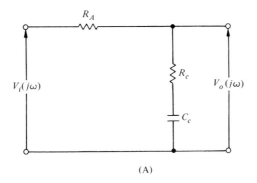

(A)

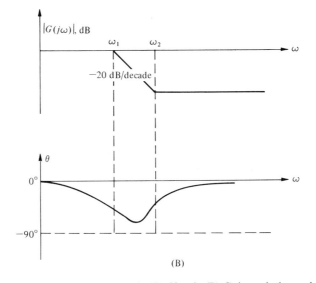

(B)

Fig. 16.31 Phase lag network. (A) Circuit. (B) Gain and phase plots.

in Fig. 16.32. Note that for the uncompensated amplifier the response curve intersects the 0–dB axis with a slope of -60 dB/decade—an unstable condition. For the compensated amplifier, the curve intersects the axis with a slope of -40dB/decade. This means that the loop gain will probably have sufficient gain margin for stable operation. To ensure this, ω_1 could be equal to, or less than, $0.1\omega_2$.

In practical operational amplifiers, resistance R_A could represent an equivalent internal amplifier resistance. The manufacturer, therefore, would give values for the compensating resistor R_c and capacitor C_c for his particular op amp. For the RCA CA3010, a 0.02 μF capacitor (C_c) in series with a 22-ohm resistor (R_c) is sufficient to stabilize the amplifier.

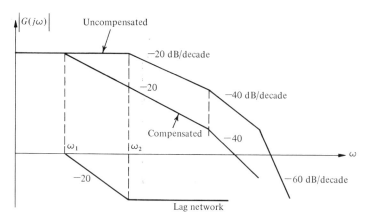

Fig. 16.32   Effect of phase lag network on amplifier response.

16.7   Summary

Integrated-circuit technology is a significant factor in today's design and fabrication of amplifier and digital circuits. In this introductory chapter to the subject, the basic processes used in making monolithic integrated-circuit amplifiers were considered to gain insight into the advantages and limitations of monolithic components. It was seen that good matching of the electrical and thermal properties of transistors is realized, but their absolute tolerances are poor and the range of component values is restricted. Ratios of resistances, however, can be held to good tolerance. Another drawback is the parasitics, owing to the electrical isolation of devices in a chip, associated with the components. Parasitic elements limit the frequency response of an amplifier.

Two basic amplifiers used widely in monolithic circuits are the diode-biased and difference amplifiers. Expressions for their quiescent-operating point and ac signal gain at mid frequencies and balanced operation were derived. Both amplifiers make use of the best features of monolithic circuits in that their performance depends primarily on ratios of resistance instead of their absolute values. High-frequency signal analysis of monolithic circuits would have to consider the device and parasitic elements, which are often distributive in nature.

The IC op amp is the most versatile linear IC component and enjoys wide application. With suitable feedback, it may be used as an inverting, non-inverting, difference, or voltage follower amplifier. By using reactive components in its forward and/or feedback paths, the resulting configuration can function as an integrator, active filter, etc. Because of physical limitations, there exist dc voltage and current offsets in the op amp. These may be compensated for, generally, at a single temperature. Consequently, at other temperatures, the amplifier will exhibit drift.

To ensure stable operation, a compensating network, such as a phase lag network, is generally required. In practice, it often consists of a series RC network specified by the manufacturer.

References

Application of the RCA CA3008 and CA3010 Integrated-Circuit Operational Amplifiers, RCA IC Application Note ICAN-5015, Harrison, New Jersey, 1967.

CHIRLIAN, P. M., *Integrated and Active Network Analysis and Synthesis*, Prentice-Hall, Englewood Cliffs, New Jersey, 1967.

GILES, J. N., *Fairchild Semiconductor Linear Integrated Circuit Applications Handbook*, Fairchild Semiconductor, Mountain View, California, 1967.

HOLLAND, L., ed., *Thin Film Microelectronics*, Wiley, New York, 1965.

KAHN, M., *The Versatile Op Amp*, Holt, Rinehart, and Winston, New York, 1970.

MEYER, C. S., et al., eds., *Analysis and Design of Integrated Circuits*, McGraw-Hill, New York, 1968.

MIDDLEBROOK, R. D., *Differential Amplifiers*, Wiley, New York, 1963.

RCA Linear Integrated Circuits, Technical Series IC-41, Radio Corporation of America, Harrison, New Jersey, 1967.

STERN, L., *Fundamentals of Integrated Circuits*, Hayden, New York, 1968.

VADASZ, L. L., et al., "Silicon-gate Technology," *IEEE Spectrum*, October 1969, pp. 28–35.

WARNER, R. M., JR., and J. N. FORDEMWALT, eds., *Integrated Circuits—Design Principles and Fabrication*, McGraw-Hill, New York, 1965.

Problems

16.1   Assume that, because of carelessness in processing, rectifying diodes are formed at the collector and emitter connections of an *n–p–n* transistor, as shown in Fig. P16.1. Can the transistor be used for normal operation? Why?

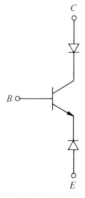

Fig.   P16.1

16.2   In Fig. 16.2B, show how the parasitic transistors should be biased for minimum interaction.

16.3   The circuits of Fig. P16.3 are to be integrated. Draw a complete mask layout for each, showing all components and their connections.

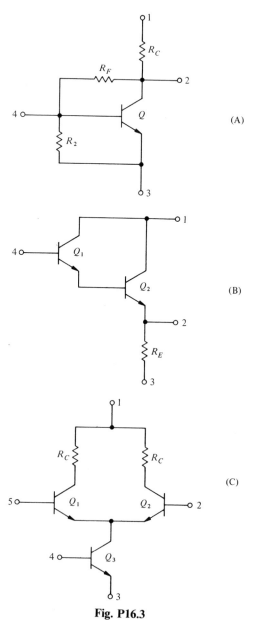

Fig. P16.3

16.4 Using the lumped high-frequency model of an IC transistor shown
      in Fig. 16.7, derive an expression for voltage gain. Load resistance R_L
      is placed across terminals C and E; terminals S and E are connected
      to ground. How do the parasitic elements R_p and C_p affect the mid-
      and high-frequency gain?

16.5 Repeat Example 16.1 for the single-base stripe geometry shown in
      Fig. P16.5. Compare results.

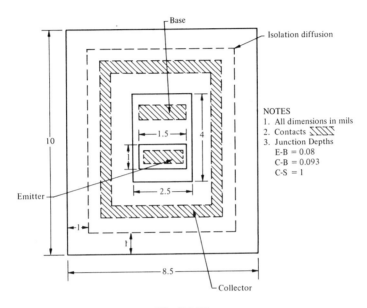

Fig. P16.5

16.6 Show two other connections, in addition to the three of Fig. 16.8, of
      transistors connected as diodes.

16.7 In Prob. 16.6, indicate the capacitances associated with the transis-
      tors connected as diodes, in a manner similar to that shown in
      Fig. 16.8.

16.8 Referring to the model of the diffused capacitor of Fig. 16.10A,
      assume that diodes $D1$ and $D2$ are back biased; $C = 50\,\text{pF}$; $C_p = 5$
      pF; and $R = 10$ ohms. It is connected across a $10\,\mu\text{H}$ inductance
      L, as shown in Fig. P16.8. Calculate the resonant frequency for
      maximum impedance across terminal p and ground.

16.9 Referring to Fig. 16.12, (a) should terminal S be returned to a negative
      or positive voltage? Why? (b) How does the circuit behave at low
      frequencies? Why?

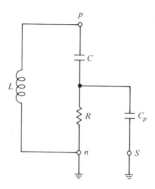

Fig. P16.8

16.10   A 10-in. mask is cut for the following resistance values: 1 K, 20 K, and 50 K. The width of the resistances is 0.1 in., and 0.2 in. is allowed at each end of a resistance for its connection to conductor pads. Lay out the mask for $R_S = 500$ ohms/square.

16.11   Repeat Prob. 16.10 for $R_S = 1000$ ohms/square. Compare results.

16.12   Show how electrical isolation is achieved in the integration of insulated-gate field-effect transistors.

16.13   For the transistors used in the diode-biased amplifier of Fig. 16.15B, assume that for each transistor $V_{BE} = 0.7$ V and $h_{fe} = h_{FE} = 60$. If $R_2 = 5$ K, $R_1 = 2R_2$, $R = 20$ K, and $R_s = 1$ K, find (a) the Q-point; (b) h_{ie} at room temperature; and (c) the signal voltage gain at low frequencies. $V_{CC} = 20$ V.

16.14   For the circuit of Fig. P16.3B, referred to as a *Darlington* emitter follower, show that the input resistance R_i across terminals 4 and 3 is approximately

$$R_i \approx h_{fe}^2 R_E$$

and the voltage gain is approximately unity.

16.15   In Fig. 16.17 assume that $V_{CC} = V_{EE} = 10$ V, $R_E = R_B = 2$ K, $R_C = h_{ie} = 1$ K, $R_L = 4$ K, and $h_{fe} = h_{FE} = 50$. Neglecting V_{BE}, calculate (a) the Q-point; (b) A_{vc}; (c) A_{vd}; and (d) CMRR.

16.16   Verify equation (16.25).

16.17   Repeat Example 16.5 for $V_{CC} = 20$ V. Compare results.

16.18   Verify the operation of the circuit of Fig. 16.21 by drawing signal waveforms at the base and collector of each transistor for (a) $v_1 = v_2 = \sin \omega t$; (b) $v_1 = \sin \omega t$, $v_2 = 0$; and (c) $v_1 = -v_2$.

16.19   Verify equation (16.32).

16.20   Repeat Example 16.6 for (a) $R_1 = 1$ K, $R_2 = 10$ K and (b) $R_1 = 10$ K, $R_2 = 100$ K. Compare results.

16.21 Discuss the operation of each transistor in the Fairchild μA702A IC operational amplifier of Fig. P16.21.

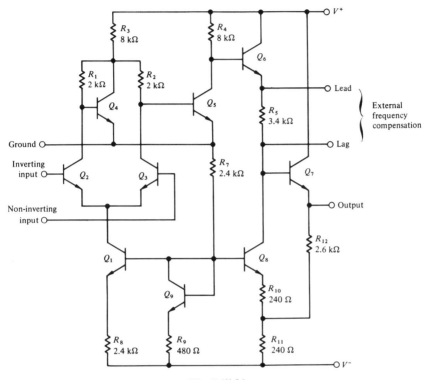

Fig. P16.21

16.22 For an operational amplifier, $A_v = -5000$, $\Delta V_{OS}/\Delta T = 12\,\mu V/^\circ C$, $\Delta I_{OS}/\Delta T = -15\,nA/^\circ C$. The compensation network is adjusted at room temperature. If $R_1 = 1$ K, $R_2 = 20$ K, and $v_s = 100$ mV rms, calculate the output voltage at $125^\circ C$.

16.23 Repeat Prob. 16.22 for $v_s = 5$ mV rms. Compare results. What limits the minimum signal that can be applied to the circuit?

16.24 Repeat Prob. 16.23 for $\Delta V_{OS}/\Delta T = 0.8\,\mu V/^\circ C$ and $\Delta I_{OS}/\Delta T = -0.5$ nA/$^\circ$C. Compare results.

16.25 Design a phase lag network for $\omega_1 = 10$ rad/s and $\omega_2 = 100$ rad/s. Select a reasonable value for R_A.

16.26 Repeat Prob. 16.25 for $\omega_1 = 50$ rad/s and $\omega_2 = 250$ rad/s.

Introduction to Computer Circuit Analysis

In recent years the use of the computer as a tool for solving engineering problems has become widespread. Linear problems that once occupied many people for many days and sometimes months are solved in seconds or minutes. Nonlinear problems, which could not be solved without the use of sophisticated mathematics, are now handled with unprecedented ease and speed. The analog computer, which played an important role in the late 1950s and early 1960s, plays a less significant role in problem solving today as more practical and simpler languages and programs are developed for the digital computer.

One of these programs, originally developed by IBM, is the Electronic Circuit Analysis Program (ECAP). ECAP is a program; it uses a language which can be called "ECAP language." Modifications of ECAP have been developed and used by others. For instance, PCAP is the Princeton University version of ECAP and SENCRAN, an acronym for Software for Electronic Network and Circuit Response Analysis, has been developed by NCR. These programs are basically the same, and they vary only in details.

The object of this chapter is not to examine the differences in these programs, but rather to demonstrate their usefulness and the ease with which they can be learned and applied in the analysis of electronic circuits. ECAP will serve as the basis for our discussion. It might be added that although some knowledge of the FORTRAN language is helpful, in learning ECAP it is not essential.

17.1 Using a Digital Computer for the First Time

The following comments are intended to provide an overall picture of the solution to a problem by means of ECAP or a similar program on a digital computer. In solving an electronics problem on a computer the engineer may follow a similar procedure.

1. The first step is to draw a model of the physical device or network in accordance with the rules of ECAP. The elements in the model may include resistances, inductances, capacitances, independent voltage and current sources, and dependent, or controlled, current sources.

2. From the model the ECAP input statements are written on either the standard coding sheet shown in Fig. 17.1 or ordinary paper. A coding sheet is preferable because it contains 80 columns, as does the IBM card; hence, card punching is made easier.

3. A computer card is punched on a punching machine for each input statement on the coding sheet. An example of an ECAP data card is shown in Fig. 17.2.

4. A general-purpose digital computer accepts programs written in a number of different languages. It therefore becomes necessary at the beginning of the problem to inform the computer of the language used. This is done by submitting to the computer additional punched cards, called *control cards*.

5. The punched cards obtained in steps (3) and (4) are placed in order and sent to the Computer Center. The cards are processed through a card reader, which transfers the information onto magnetic tape. The tape is then read by the computer, which executes the program and stores the results on another tape. At the output, a printer converts the stored solution into a typed form.

It must be emphasized that a computer program is written in accordance with very specific rules that can *never* be violated. For example, if a comma is missing where it should be present, the computer cannot proceed properly with the solution and may either reject the program or garble the results.

The numerical results at the output of the computer are printed in *floating point* form. For this representation the number is printed with a decimal point *even if it is an integer*. The floating point number is treated as a fraction, having values between 0.1 and 1.0, multiplied by a power of 10. To show the exponent the number may be followed by the letter E or D and then a space or a plus sign if the exponent is positive; if the exponent is negative a minus sign is used. Following the sign is a two or three digit number indicating the value of the exponent. If the number is negative a minus sign precedes the number. Table 17.1 provides examples of how floating point numbers are printed out in two different Computer Centers.

Numbers in input statements can be written either in fixed-point (without the decimal) or in floating point, as previously explained. For example, number 123 may be written in an input statement in any one of the following ways:

123

12.3E 01

1.23E 02

12300E − 02

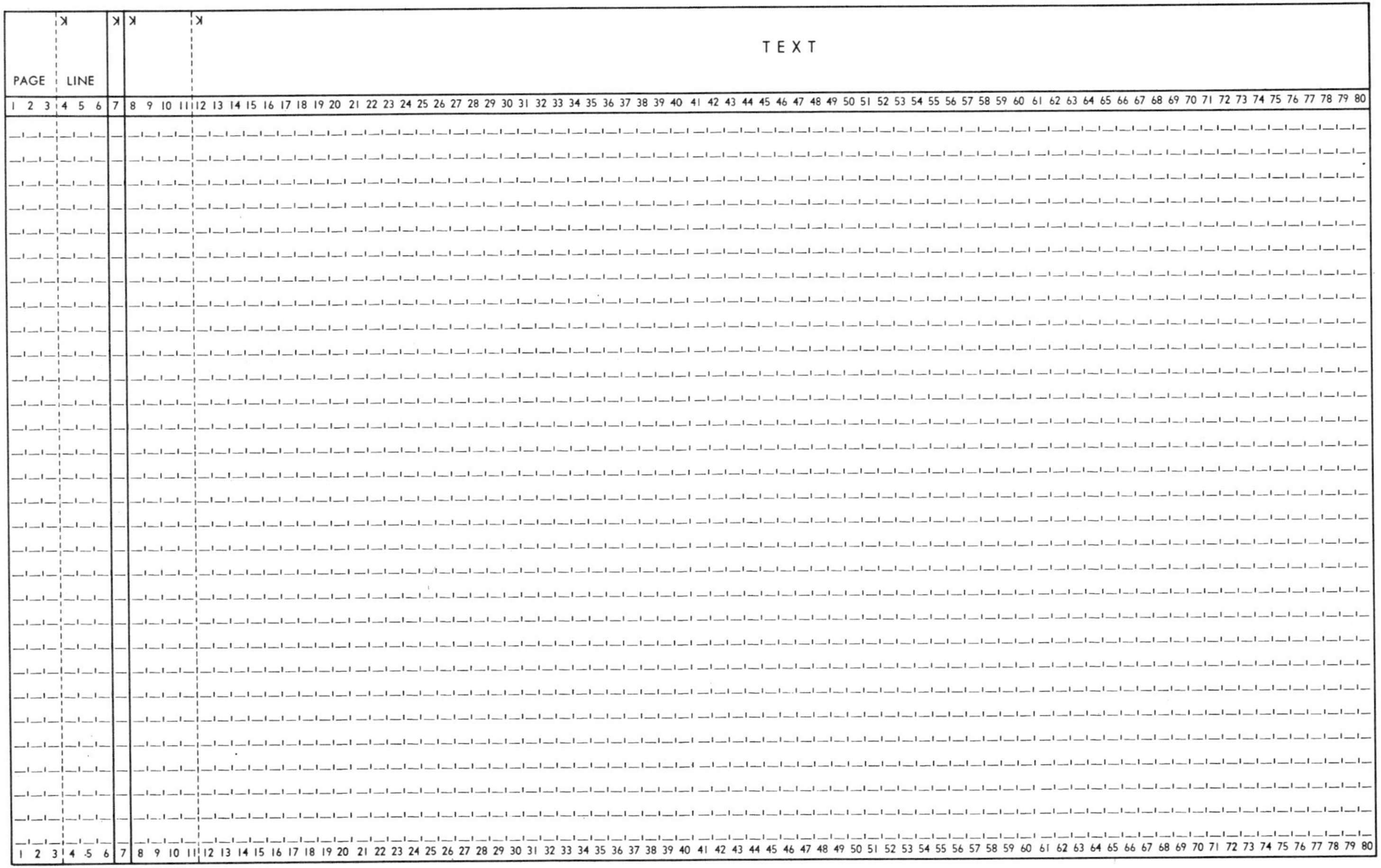

Fig. 17.1 A standard coding sheet.

467

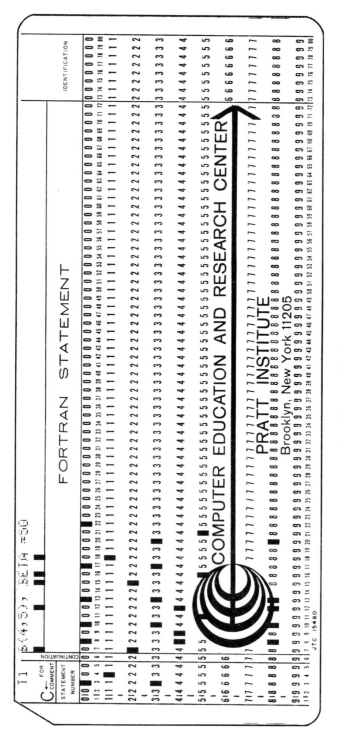

Fig. 17.2 An ECAP data card.

Table 17.1 Examples of Printed out Numbers Used in ECAP

Number	Computer Center 1	Computer Center 2
1125	.11250000E 04	.11250000 + 004
23123	.23123000E 05	.23123000 + 005
−12	−.12000000E 02	−.12000000 + 002
0.15	.15000000E 00	.15000000 + 000
0.011	.11000000E − 01	.11000000 − 001

17.2 Introduction to ECAP

ECAP is a program developed to aid the electrical engineer in the analysis and design of electronic circuits. The problem is fed into the computer in the form of punched cards; each card normally contains a single statement. ECAP has an advantage over a language such as FORTRAN in that it is specifically intended for circuit analysis and design problems. This results in fewer statements and less effort on the user's part to implement the program.

The ECAP program has three distinct parts: dc, ac, and transient response analyses.

Program Elements

The dc steady-state solution of linear electrical networks may be obtained with the aid of the dc program in which the following elements are recognized:

Resistors
Dc voltage and current sources
Dependent current sources

The ac steady-state solution of linear networks excited by sinusoidal sources may be obtained using the ac program which recognizes the following elements:

Resistors
Inductors
Capacitors
Mutual inductance
Sinusoidal voltage and current sources
Dependent current sources

The transient response of linear and nonlinear networks is determined with the transient analysis program. Nonlinear elements are replaced by a switch and linear elements. The following elements are permissible in the transient response program:

Resistors
Inductors
Capacitors
Dc voltage and current sources
Time-varying voltage and current sources
Dependent current sources
Switches

We shall limit our discussion to dc and ac steady-state programs.

A branch cannot be represented by either an ideal voltage or current source. For an ideal voltage source, a low-value resistance is added in series with the voltage source. For an ideal current source, a high-value resistance is shunted across the current source. These resistances are referred to as *dummy elements*, and should be so chosen as not to affect the accuracy of the solution.

Units

The units used for ECAP in this book are

current	amperes
voltage	volts
resistance	ohms
conductance	mhos
capacitance	farads
inductance	henrys
time	seconds
frequency	hertz
phase angle	degrees
power	watts

17.3 The Direct-Current Program

Figure 17.3 defines the *standard branch* used in ECAP which includes all the permissible elements of the dc analysis program (independent current and voltage sources, resistance or conductance, and a dependent current source). The nomenclature used in most cases to represent the nodes, branches, elements, voltages, and currents are defined as

NV = Node voltage
BV = Branch voltage = $NV_{\textcircled{a}} - NV_{\textcircled{b}}$
CV = Element voltage

CA = Element current

BA or BI = Branch current

BP = Element power loss

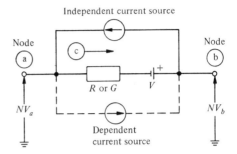

Fig. 17.3 A standard branch.

To illustrate in a simple manner the use of the dc program, we shall analyze the two-mesh network of Fig. 17.4A; the ECAP representation of the network is given in Fig. 17.4B. In this form all branches and nodes are numbered and a chosen direction for current flow must be shown. The ground is taken as the

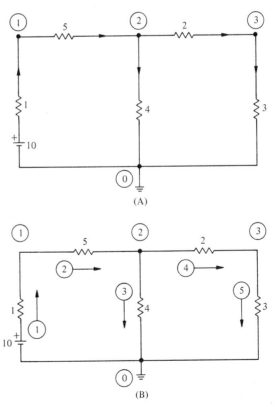

Fig. 17.4 An example of a dc passive network. (A) Circuit. (B) ECAP representation.

reference node and is numbered zero. The node numbers used here are enclosed in circles. The branch numbers are also enclosed in circles and located at the tail of the arrow indicating the direction of current flow.

The input data for the network are given in Fig. 17.5. Attention is directed to the following points:

1. The column numbers correspond to the numbers on an IBM card.
2. The branch designations are punched in columns 1 through 6.
3. Columns 7 and higher order must be used for indicating, consecutively, the connections of the branch with respect to their nodes, the value of resistance of the branch, and the value of the dc sources in the branch. Furthermore, the node numbers in each statement follow the direction of current flow. For example, in branch 1 of Fig. 17.4B current flows from node 0 to node 1. The statement is therefore written as N(0,1). In branch 3 the current flows from node 2 to node 0; consequently the statement reads N(2, 0).

1	2	3	4	5	6	7	8	9	10	11	12	13	14	15	16	17	18	19	20
						D	C	A	N	A	L	Y	S	I	S				
	B	1				N	(	0	,	1	)	,	R	=	1	,	E	=	10
	B	2				N	(	1	,	2	)	,	R	=	5				
	B	3				N	(	2	,	0	)	,	R	=	4				
	B	4				N	(	2	,	3	)	,	R	=	2				
	B	5				N	(	3	,	0	)	,	R	=	3				
						P	R	I	N	T	,		N	V	,	C	A		
						E	X	E	C	U	T	E							

Fig. 17.5 ECAP description of the circuit of Fig. 17.4.

In Fig. 17.5, the first line on the code sheet is labeled B1 for branch 1. Following this is the node designation N(0,1). Although in going from node 0 to node 1 in Fig. 17.4B we "see" the 10-V source before the 1-ohm resistor, the resistance value is always entered before the voltage on the code sheet. Other data entries in Fig. 17.5 should be verified by the reader.

Upon the completion of data, a PRINT statement calling out the solution variables is required. In this example, PRINT, NV, CA means that the values of *all* node voltages and element currents will be printed at the output. The EXECUTE statement orders the computer to execute the program. An END statement may, or may not, be included. The solution (as well as the printed program) to the problem is given in Fig. 17.6.

In general, branches may be numbered in any order. In writing the input data, however, one must use consecutive numbers starting with 1. The maximum number of branches and nodes are limited, depending on the particular computer that is used. Nodes may also be numbered in any order, but consecutive numbers must be used and the reference node is always taken as zero.

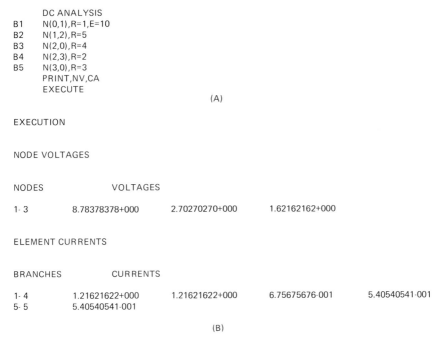

```
        DC ANALYSIS
B1      N(0,1),R=1,E=10
B2      N(1,2),R=5
B3      N(2,0),R=4
B4      N(2,3),R=2
B5      N(3,0),R=3
        PRINT,NV,CA
        EXECUTE
                                    (A)

EXECUTION

NODE VOLTAGES

NODES                VOLTAGES

1- 3        8.78378378+000      2.70270270+000      1.62162162+000

ELEMENT CURRENTS

BRANCHES             CURRENTS

1- 4        1.21621622+000      1.21621622+000      6.75675676-001      5.40540541-001
5- 5        5.40540541-001

                                    (B)
```

Fig. 17.6   Program (A) and solution (B) of Fig. 17.4A.

Representing Controlled Sources

Controlled, or dependent, current sources may be shown either as a current-controlled current source or as a voltage-controlled current source. Consider the circuit of Fig. 17.7A; Fig. 17.7B shows the same circuit with the nodes and branches numbered. Note that the dependent current source is represented by T1. Dependent current sources are always designated by the letter T; their corresponding punched cards are called T cards.

The circuit description is written in Fig. 17.8. The T card must be placed immediately after the card corresponding to the branch to which the source is connected (in this case branch 3). The first number in the parenthesis for a T statement refers to the branch number of the inducing, or controlling current, and the second number refers to the branch across which the source is connected. In our example the controlled source $20i_1$ is a function of current i_1 flowing in branch 1 and the source itself is located across branch 3.

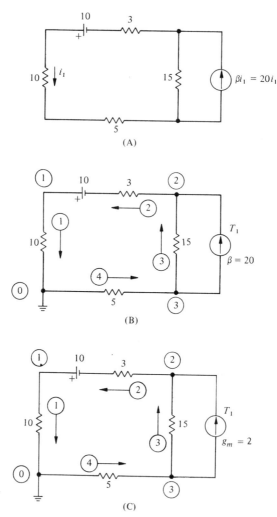

Fig. 17.7 A network containing a dependent source. (A) Circuit. (B) ECAP current-controlled source model. (C) ECAP voltage-controlled source model.

1	2	3	4	5	6	7	8	9	10	11	12	13	14	15	16	17	18	19	20	21	22	23	24	25	26
							D	C		A	N	A	L	Y	S	I	S								
	B	1				N	(	1	,	0	)	,	R	=	1	0									
	B	2				N	(	2	,	1	)	,	R	=	3			E	=	1	0				
	B	3				N	(	3	,	2	)	,	R	=	1	5									
	T	1				B	(	1	,	3	)	,	B	E	T	A	=	2	0						
	B	4				N	(	0	,	3	)	,	R	=	5										
						P	R	I	N	T	,		N	V	,	C	A	,							
						E	X	E	C	U	T	E													

Fig. 17.8 ECAP program for Fig. 17.7.

The statement therefore reads B(1,3). Following this is the value of the coefficient BETA = 20. For a transistor the BETA would refer to the dc current gain h_{FE}. The printed-out solution and program are given in Fig. 17.9.

```
        DC ANALYSIS
B1      N(1,0),R=10
B2      N(2,1),R=3,E=10
B3      N(3,2),R=15
T1      B(1,3),BETA=20
B4      N(0,3),R=5
        PRINT,NV,CA,BV
        EXECUTE
```
(A)

```
EXECUTION


NODE VOLTAGES


NODES                 VOLTAGES

1- 3        -3.74531835-001       -1.04868914+001       1.87265919-001


BRANCH VOLTAGES


BRANCHES              VOLTAGES

1- 4        -3.74531835-001       -1.01123596+001       1.06741573+001       -1.87265919-001


ELEMENT CURRENTS


BRANCHES              CURRENTS

1- 4        -3.74531835-002       -3.74531836-002       -3.74531835-002       -3.74531837-002
```
(B)

Fig. 17.9 Program (A) and solution (B) to circuit of Fig. 17.7A.

The same circuit, where the current-controlled current source has been replaced by a voltage-controlled current source, is shown in Fig. 17.7C. The program is basically the same as for the current-controlled current source model except that the T card would read

$$T1\ B(1, 3),\ GM = 2$$

Determining the Quiescent Operating Point

Let us write a circuit description which will enable ECAP to find the quiescent operating point of the simplified transistor amplifier of Fig. 17.10A with $V_{BE} = 0$. Figure 17.10B shows a piecewise-linear model of the circuit. Notice that in branch 1 a resistor of one ohm is added to complete the branch. This is necessary because a branch cannot be represented by an ideal voltage source alone. The circuit description and solution are given in Figs. 17.11A and B.

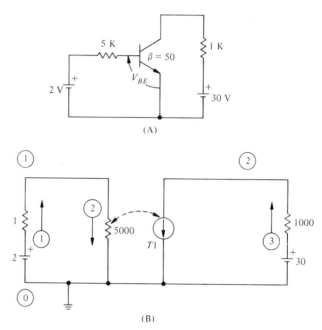

(A)

(B)

Fig. 17.10   Basic transistor amplifier. (A) Circuit. (B) ECAP model.

```
        DC ANALYSIS
B1      N(0,1),R=1,E=2
B2      N(1,0),R=5000
B3      N(0,2),R=1000,E=30
T1      B(2,3),BETA=50
        PRINT,NV
        EXECUTE
```

(A)

Fig. 17.11   ECAP program (A) and solution (B) to circuit of Fig. 17.10A.

EXECUTION

NODE VOLTAGES

NODES   VOLTAGES

1- 2   1.99960008+000   1.00039992+001

(B)

A more complete circuit of a transistor amplifier is shown in Fig. 17.12A, and the piecewise-linear model of the transistor is given in Fig. 17.12B. The complete model of the amplifier used for dc analysis is shown in Fig. 17.12C.

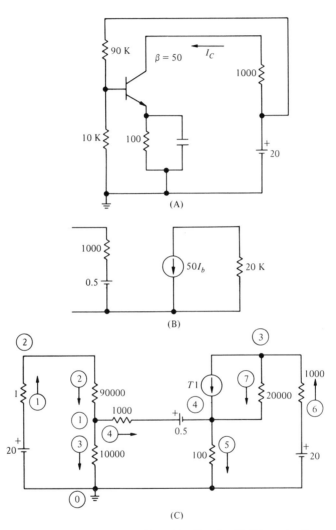

Fig. 17.12 A common-emitter amplifier. (A) Circuit. (B) Piecewise-linear model of transistor. (C) ECAP model.

The program for finding the quiescent point is represented in Fig. 17.13A and the solution in Fig. 17.13B.

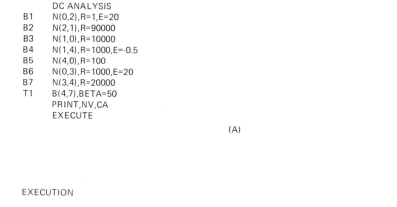

```
      DC ANALYSIS
B1    N(0,2),R=1,E=20
B2    N(2,1),R=90000
B3    N(1,0),R=10000
B4    N(1,4),R=1000,E=-0.5
B5    N(4,0),R=100
B6    N(0,3),R=1000,E=20
B7    N(3,4),R=20000
T1    B(4,7),BETA=50
      PRINT,NV,CA
      EXECUTE
```

(A)

EXECUTION

NODE VOLTAGES

NODES   VOLTAGES

1- 4   1.14770814+000   1.99997905+001   1.45645830+001   5.53011374-001

ELEMENT CURRENTS

BRANCHES   CURRENTS

1- 4   2.09467486-004   2.09467582-004   1.14770814-004   9.46967679-005
5- 7   5.53011374-003   5.43541698-003   5.43541698-003

(B)

Fig. 17.13   ECAP program (A) and solution (B) to circuit of Fig. 17.12A.

17.4   The Alternating Current Program

The preparation and presentation of ECAP input data for ac analysis are very similar to that for dc. The following comments, however, are necessary before we proceed with specific examples.

1. A *frequency card* must be included in every ac analysis problem specifying a nonzero frequency in hertz.

2. Like in dc, a branch must contain only one passive element, that is, one resistor, one capacitor, or one inductor.

3. If the current of a controlled source depends on a branch with an inductance or capacitance, the current source must be represented by a voltage-controlled, and not a current-controlled source.

4. For each source the phase angle must be specified. This is done by writing the phase angle in degrees following a slash which separates the magnitude of the source. For example, a 10-V source at a 30° leading phase angle would be expressed as 10/30°. The output statement is capable of printing phase angles between ±180°.

We shall write an ECAP description for the circuit of Fig. 17.14A to find the incremental voltage gain at 1000 Hz. Assume that the source resistance

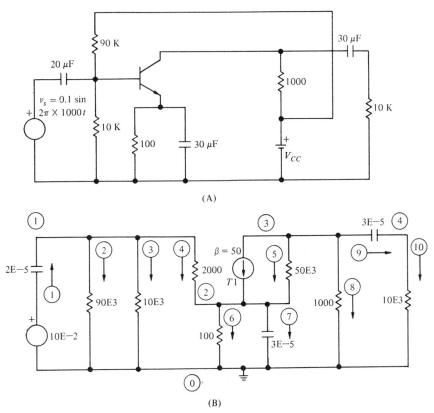

(A)

(B)

Fig. 17.14 Analyzing the ac performance of a transistor amplifier. (A) Circuit. (B) ECAP model.

of v_s is negligible. The incremental parameters for the transistor are: $h_{fe} = 50$, $h_{oe} = 0.02$ mmho, $h_{re} = 0$, and $h_{ie} = 2000$ ohms. The corresponding ECAP model is shown in Fig. 17.14B. Note that floating notation is used in specifying component values. The program and solution are given in Fig. 17.15.

```
        AC ANALYSIS
B1      N(0,1),C=2E-5,E=10E-2
B2      N(1,0),R=90E3
B3      N(1,0),R=10E3
B4      N(1,2),R=2E3
B5      N(3,2),R=50E3
T1      B(4,5),BETA=50
B6      N(2,0),R=100
B7      N(2,0),C=3E-5
B8      N(3,0),R=1000
B9      N(3,4),C=3I-5
B10     N(4,0),B=10E3
        FREQUENCY=1000.
        PRINT,NV,CA
        EXECUTE
```

(A)

EXECUTION

FREQ. = 1.00000000+003

	NODES	NODE VOLTAGES		
MAG	1- 4	9.99477764-002	1.30602295-002	2.19641568+000	2.19641537+000
PHA		2.73042255-001	-7.91864714+001	-1.72225901+002	-1.72195505+002

	BRANCHES	ELEMENT CURRENTS		
MAG	1- 4	6.02277815-005	1.11053085-006	9.99477764-006	4.91999870-005
PHA		6.39205811+000	2.73042255-001	2.73042255-001	7.77073764+000
MAG	5- 8	2.41605718-003	1.30602295-004	2.46179527-003	2.19641568-003
PHA		7.77686215+000	-7.91864714+001	1.08135286+001	-1.72225901+002
MAG	9- 10	2.19641539-004	2.19641537-004		
PHA		-1.72195501+002	-1.72195505+002		

(B)

Fig. 17.15   Program (A) and solution (B) to amplifier of Fig. 17.14A.

17.5   Parameter Modification

After the solution has been obtained for nominal component values, it may be of interest to see results for different parameter values. Only a limited number of parameters may be changed (for the original IBM-1620 ECAP program up to 20 branch parameters may be changed). Following the execution command for the nominal solution, the user enters a card on which is punched MODIFY, followed by the data cards for the modified solution. Any branch that is not modified does not require a card with the modified data.

For example, if in Fig. 17.12A the load and emitter resistors are changed, the modify statements of Fig. 17.16A would be added. If the MODIFY statement appears before the first EXECUTE command, all the modification statements will be processed with the original statements and some computed time may be saved. If more than one change per parameter is required, the MODIFY statement must come after the first EXECUTE statement. Note that after the last piece of data another EXECUTE statement is required.

```
        DC ANALYSIS
B1      N(0,2),R=1,E=20
B2      N(2,1),R=90000
B3      N(1,0),R=10000
B4      N(1,4),R=1000,E=-0.5
B5      N(4,0),R=100
B6      N(0,3),R=1000,E=20
B7      N(3,4),R=20000
T1      B(4,7),BETA=50
        PRINT,NV,CA
        EXECUTE


        MODIFY
B5      R=200
B6      R=1500
        EXECUTE
```
(A)

NODE VOLTAGES

NODES	VOLTAGES			
1- 4	1.14770814+000	1.99997905+001	1.45645830+001	5.53011374-001

ELEMENT CURRENTS

BRANCHES	CURRENTS			
1- 4	2.09467486-004	2.09467582-004	1.14770814-004	9.46967679-005
5- 7	5.53011374-003	5.43541698-003	5.43541698-003	

(B)

NODE VOLTAGES

NODES	VOLTAGES			
1- 4	1:39009097+000	1.99997932+001	1.39342061+001	8.22325601-001

ELEMENT CURRENTS

BRANCHES	CURRENTS			
1- 4	2.06774101-004	2.06774469-004	1.39009097-004	6.77653725-005
5- 7	4.11162800-003	4.04386263-003	4.04386265-003	

(C)

Fig. 17.16 Modification of parameters. (A) Program. (B) Unmodified solution. (C) Modified solution.

```
        DC ANALYSIS
B1      N(0,2),R=1,E=20
B2      N(2,1),R=90000
B3      N(1,0),R=10000
B4      N(1,4),R=1000,E=-0.5
B5      N(4,0),R=100
B6      N(0,3),R=1000,E=20
B7      N(3,4),R=20000
T1      B(4,7),BETA=50
        EXECUTE


        MODIFY
T1      B(4,7),BETA=50(2)100
        PRINT,NV,CA
        EXECUTE
```
                                    (A)

BETA = 5.00000000+001

NODE VOLTAGES

NODES   VOLTAGES

1- 4   1.14770814+000   1.99997905+001   1.45645830+001   5.53011374-001

BETA = 7.50000000+001

NODE VOLTAGES

NODES   VOLTAGES

1- 4   1.26506856+000   1.99997918+001   1.32475385+001   6.83411825-001

BETA = 1.00000000+002

NODE VOLTAGES

NODES   VOLTAGES

1- 4   1.35401931+000   1.99997928+001   1.22493136+001   7.82245977-001

ELEMENT CURRENTS

BRANCHES   CURRENTS

1- 4   2.07175501-004   2.07175261-004   1.35401931-004   7.17733306-005
5- 7   7.82245977-003   7.75068644-003   7.75068644-003
```
                                    (B)

**Fig. 17.17**   Variation in BETA. (A) Program. (B) Solution.
```

Direct-Current Parameter Studies

If a given parameter in a dc problem is to assume many values, it is advantageous to use the following described procedure. Let a given parameter x have an initial value of x_1 and a final value of x_2. Furthermore, assume it takes P steps of equal increments to go from x_1 to x_2. This may be written as

$$x = x_1(P)x_2.$$

For example, in Fig. 17.12A, BETA may vary from 50 to 100. It is desired to calculate the response of the network for values of BETA $= 50$, 75, and 100. Therefore $x =$ BETA, $x_1 = 50$, $x_2 = 100$, and $P = 2$; the statement would be written as

$$\text{BETA} = 50(2)100$$

The complete program and solution are shown Figs. 17.17A and B.

Partial Derivative and Sensitivity Coefficient

In ECAP and its modifications, the dc partial derivatives of the node voltages with respect to the circuit elements are obtainable. This may be used by the engineer as a powerful aid in the analysis and design of circuits. The partials indicate, for instance, circuit parameters with the greatest effect on the node voltages. The sensitivity coefficient is defined as the change of the node voltage relative to 1% change in the circuit parameter value. Both partial derivative and sensitivity parameters are dependent on the particular operating point selected for the problem.

Figure 17.18 shows a simple dc circuit. The node voltage and the partial derivatives are, respectively,

$$V_o = VR_2/(R_1 + R_2),$$

and $$\partial V_o/\partial V = R_2/(R_1 + R_2).$$

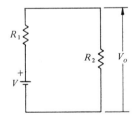

Fig. 17.18 A simple dc passive network.

The partial derivative of V_o with respect to R_2 is

$$\frac{\partial V_o}{\partial R_2} = \frac{(R_1 + R_2)V - VR_2}{(R_1 + R_2)^2} = \frac{VR_1}{(R_1 + R_2)^2}.$$

The sensitivity coefficient with respect to the variation in V is, therefore,

$$1\% \text{ Sensitivity} = (\partial V_o/\partial V) \times 0.01 \times |V| \text{ V.}$$

Table 17.2 shows the units of the partial derivatives with respect to various elements. The sensitivity coefficient will always be in units of volts.

Table 17.2   Units of Partial Derivatives

Partial with respect to	Units of partial derivative
Resistor	volts/ohm
Voltage source	volts/volt
Current source	volts/ampere
BETA	volts

In ECAP programs, partial derivatives may be calculated only for the node voltages. By means of a trick, however, the partial for a branch current may be obtained. In Fig. 17.19A, suppose the partials with respect to the elements

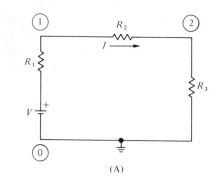

(A)

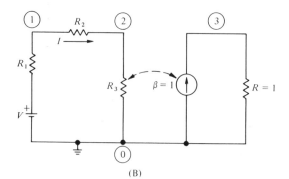

(B)

Fig. 17.19 Obtaining the partial derivative with respect to a branch current. (A) Circuit. (B) Modified ECAP model.

for current I are to be obtained. A dependent current source, as shown in Fig. 17.19B, must be added to the circuit. Because $\beta = 1$ and $R = 1$, the partials and sensitivities at node 3 will be for the current I.

Let us now consider the transistor amplifier of Fig. 17.12A. The partials and sensitivities of the current I_C with respect to the parameters may be calculated. Among these partials are S_v, S_e, and S_h of Chapter 5. Figure 17.20 shows the model, and Fig. 17.21 shows the program and solution. In writing the circuit description one should supply a sensitivity solution card in the input data. Also, on the output specification, the words PRINT, SENSITIVITY must be written as shown in Fig. 17.21A.

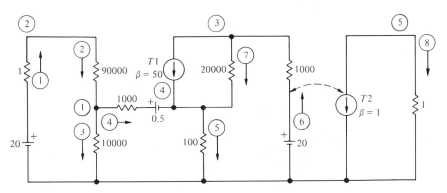

Fig. 17.20 ECAP model of Fig. 17.12A for the calculation of sensitivity coefficients.

17.6 Frequency Response Calculation

The ac analysis program permits the determination of the frequency response of a network. The user should specify the frequency either as FREQUENCY or as OMEGA. The word FREQUENCY or OMEGA indicates whether the frequency is expressed in hertz or in radians per second. Let the frequency F have a smallest value F_1 and the largest value F_2 and P be a multiplicative constant. The frequency F is written as

$$F = F_1(P)F_2.$$

As one can see, the frequency is obtained through logarithmic variation. The different frequencies are obtained for frequencies $F_1, F_1 P, F_1 P^2, \ldots$ until a frequency higher than F_2 is reached. The value of P may be calculated from

$$P = (F_2/F_1)^{1/(1-K)},$$

where K is the number of steps.

In Fig. 17.14A, the frequency response from 100 to 12,800 Hz may be calculated in seven steps by writing

$$\text{FREQUENCY} = 100 \, (2) \, 12{,}800$$

```
*CONTROL,PRINT
        DC ANALYSIS
B1      N(0,2), R=1,E=20
B2      N(2,1),R=90000
B3      N(1,0),R=10000
B4      N(1,4),R=1000,E=-0.5
B5      N(4,0),R=100
B6      N(0,3),R=1000,E=20
B7      N(3,4),R=20000
T1      B(4,7),BETA=50
B8      N(5,0),R=1
T2      B(6,8),BETA=1
        SENSITIVITY
        PRINT,SENSITIVITY
        EXECUTE

EXECUTION
```

(A)

PARTIAL DERIVATIVES

NODE VOLTAGE WITH RESPECT TO RES. IN BRANCH   1

NODE NO.	PARTIALS	SENSITIVITIES
1	-0.82422064-005	-0.82422064-007
2	-0.20946711-003	-0.20946711-005
3	0.66894336-004	0.66894336-006
4	-0.68305948-005	-0.68305948-007
5	0.66894336-007	0.66894336-009

PARTIAL DERIVATIVES

NODE VOLTAGE WITH RESPECT TO RES. IN BRANCH   2

NODE NO.	PARTIALS	SENSITIVITIES
1	-0.82421369-005	-0.74179232-002
2	0.22358134-008	0.20122321-005
3	0.66893772-004	0.60204395-001
4	-0.68305372-005	-0.61474834-002

PARTIAL DERIVATIVES

NODE VOLTAGE WITH RESPECT TO RES. IN BRANCH   3

NODE NO.	PARTIALS	SENSITIVITIES
1	0.40644502-004	0.40644502-002
2	0.45160056-009	0.45160056-007
3	-0.32987368-003	-0.32987368-001
4	0.33683471-004	0.33683471-002
5	-0.32987368-006	-0.32987368-004

(B)

Fig. 17.21 Determination of sensitivity factors. (A) Program. (B) Solution.

PARTIAL DERIVATIVES

NODE VOLTAGE WITH RESPECT TO RES. IN BRANCH 4

NODE NO.	PARTIALS	SENSITIVITIES
1	0.57435082-004	0.57435082-003
2	0.63816048-009	0.63816048-008
3	0.30241851-003	0.30241851-002
4	-0.30880017-004	-0.30880017-003
5	0.30241851-006	0.30241851-005

PARTIAL DERIVATIVES

NODE VOLTAGE WITH RESPECT TO RES. IN BRANCH 5

NODE NO.	PARTIALS	SENSITIVITIES
1	0.33382049-002	0.33382049-002
2	0.37090753-007	0.37090753-007
3	0.17839065-001	0.17839065-001
4	0.37091161-002	0.37091161-002
5	0.17839065-004	0.17839065-004

PARTIAL DERIVATIVES

NODE VOLTAGE WITH RESPECT TO RES. IN BRANCH 6

NODE NO.	PARTIALS	SENSITIVITIES
1	-0.15624010-004	-0.15624010-003
2	-0.17359818-009	-0.17359818-008
3	-0.52600809-002	-0.52600809-001
4	-0.17360009-004	-0.17360009-003
5	0.17533609-006	0.17533609-005

PARTIAL DERIVATIVES

NODE VOLTAGE WITH RESPECT TO RES. IN BRANCH 7

NODE NO.	PARTIALS	SENSITIVITIES
1	-0.20138007-005	-0.40276014-003
2	-0.22375315-010	-0.44750629-008
3	0.22599316-004	0.45198633-002
4	-0.22375561-005	-0.44751122-003
5	0.22599316-007	0.45198633-005

PARTIAL DERIVATIVES

NODE VOLTAGE WITH RESPECT TO RES. IN BRANCH 8

NODE NO.	PARTIALS	SENSITIVITIES
1	0.	0.
2	0.	0.
3	0.	0.
4	0.	0.
5	-0.54354170-002	-0.54354170-004

(B)

Fig. 17.21(B) continued.

PARTIAL DERIVATIVES

NODE VOLTAGE WITH RESPECT TO RES. IN BRANCH   4 TO BRANCH   7
NODE NO.   PARTIALS   SENSITIVITIES
   1   0.54440836+001   0.27220418-002
   2   0.60489145-004   0.30244573-007
   3   -061094808+002   -0.30547354-001
   4   0.60489811+001   0.30244905-002
   5   -0.61094708-001   -0.30547354-004

PARTIAL DERIVATIVES

NODE VOLTAGE WITH RESPECT TO GM, BRANCH   6 TO BRANCH   8
NODE NO.   PARTIALS   SENSITIVITIES
   1   0.   0.
   2   0.   0.
   3   0.   0.
   4   0.   0.
   5 -0.54354170+001   -0.54354170-004

PARTIAL DERIVATIVES

NODE VOLTAGE WITH RESPECT TO VOLTAGE SOURCE IN BRANCH   1
NODE NO.   PARTIALS   SENSITIVITIES
   1   0.39348031-001   0.78696062-002
   2   0.99998933+000   0.19999787+000
   3   -0.31935143+000   -0.63870286-001
   4   0.32609042-001   0.65218084-002
   5   -0.31935143-003   -0.63870286-004

PARTIAL DERIVATIVES

NODE VOLTAGE WITH RESPECT TO VOLTAGE SOURCE IN BRANCH   4
NODE NO.   PARTIALS   SENSITIVITIES
   1   -0.60651576+000   -0.30325788-002
   2   -0.67389891-005   -0.33694945-007
   3   -0.31935462+001   -0.15967731-001
   4   0.32609368+000   0.16304684-002
   5   -0.31935462-002   -0.15967731-004

PARTIAL DERIVATIVES

NODE VOLTAGE WITH RESPECT TO VOLTAGE SOURCE BRANCH   6
NODE NO.   PARTIALS   SENSITIVITIES
   1   0.28744823-002   0.57489645-003
   2   0.31938337-007   0.63876674-008
   3   0.96774193+000   0.19354839+000
   4   0.31938688-002   0.63877376-003
   5   -0.32258075-004   -0.64516149-005
       END
                              (B)

Fig. 17.21(B) continued.

The calculated values will be at frequencies 100, 200, 400, 800, 1600, 3200, 6400, and 12,800 Hz.

Figure 17.22 shows an ECAP model for the two-stage amplifier of Examples 9.2 and 9.3 in Chapter 9. An ECAP program and condensed solution for the frequency response of the circuit are given in Fig. 17.23A and B. The plot of $A_i = i_L/i_s$ as a function of frequency obtained from these results is presented in Fig. 17.24 for two different values of emitter bypass capacitors. One observes that, based on the ECAP solution, the dominant lower and upper half-power frequencies of 260 Hz and 47 kHz, respectively, are obtained. Based on the approximate calculations of Chapter 9, we have found the respective values of 180 Hz and 49 kHz.

Comparing these results reveals that the upper half-power frequencies are in good agreement, whereas the lower half-power frequencies are appreciably different. The reason for the different values in the lower half-power frequency is that the next lower break frequency (see Fig. 9.17 and associated numerical results) is very close to 180 Hz. Because of its influence, if a point-by-point plot were made, one would observe that the actual lower half-power frequency is closer to the computer value of 260 Hz than to 180 Hz.

At the high end, the next break frequency is more than a decade greater than the dominant frequency (see Fig. 9.24). Because of this wide separation, it has little influence on the dominant upper half-power frequency. This accounts for the good agreement between the computer value (47 kHz) and that calculated in Chapter 9 (49 kHz).

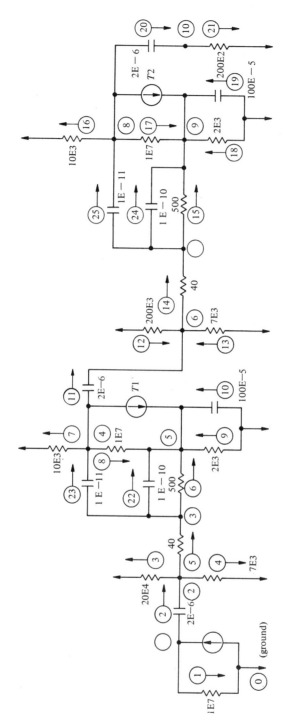

Fig. 17.22 ECAP model of a two-stage amplifier considered in Chapter 9.

```
BEGIN NEW PROBLEM OR MODIFICATION . . .
      1:   C        V KLIMAYTIS
      2:   C        TWO STAGE AMPLIFIER
      3:            ACANALYSIS
      4:   B1       N(1,0),R=1.E7,I=1.
      5:   B2       N(1,2),C=2.E-6
      6:   B3       N(0,2),R=200.E3
      7:   B4       N(0,2),R=7.E3
      8:   B5       N(2,3),R=40.
      9:   B6       N(3,5),R=500.
     10:   B7       N(0,4),R=10.E3
     11:   B8       N(4,5),R=1.E7
     12:   B9       N(0,5),R=2.E3
     13:   T1       B(6,8),BETA=50
     14:   B10      N(0,5),C=100.E-7
     15:   B11      N(4,6),C=2.E-6
     16:   B12      N(0,6),R=200.E3
     17:   B13      N(0,6),R=7.E3
     18:   B14      N(6,7),R=40.
     19:   B15      N(7,9),R=500.
     20:   B16      N(0,8),R=10.E3
     21:   B17      N(8,9),R=1.E7
     22:   T2       B(15,17),BETA=50.
     23:   B18      N(0,9),R=2.E3
     24:   B19      N(0,9),C=100.E-7
     25:   B20      N(8,10).C=2.E-6
     26:   B21      N(10,0),R=200.E2
     27:   B22      N(3,5),C=1.E-10
     28:   B23      N(3,4),C=1.E-11
     29:   B24      N(7,9),C=1.E-10
     30:   B25      N(7,8),C=1.E-11
     31:            FREQUENCY=10000
     32:            PRINT,NV,CU
     33:            MODIFY
     34:            FREQUENCY=1(2)1.E6
     35:            EXECUTE

NO ERRORS IN ABOVE INPUT
```

(A)

Fig. 17.23   Obtaining the frequency response of the model of Fig. 17-22. (A) Program.
(B) Condensed solution showing sample calculations.

CP67USERID   KLIMAYTI   12/02/70   14.47.26

FREQ = 9.9999961E 03

NODE VOLTAGES:
```
MAG   1-  4   5.0485156E 02   5.0357642E 02   4.6706470E 02   2.1926445E 04
PHA          -9.6665716E 00  -8.7740231E 00  -9.5225334E 00   1.6146074E 02
MAG   5-  8   7.4829071E 01   2.1814277E 04   2.0278762E 04   1.3333860E 07
PHA          -9.0253342E 01   1.6232999E 02   1.6077260E 02  -1.0261475E 01
MAG   9- 10   3.2469656E 03   1.3333859E 07
PHA           8.0035553E 01  -1.0238675E 01
```

ELEMENT CURRENTS:
```
MAG   1-  4   5.0485149E-05   9.9995023E-01   2.5178830E-03   7.1939468E-02
PHA          -9.6665716E 00   4.8573059E-04   1.7122595E 02   1.7122595E 02
MAG   5-  8   9.2643386E-01   9.2193276E-01   2.1926441E 00   4.6094543E 01
PHA           7.0295644E-01  -3.0337650E-01  -1.8539215E 01  -3.0251437E-01
MAG   9- 12   3.7414525E-02   4.7016449E 01   4.4012817E 01   1.0907137E-01
PHA           8.9746552E 01   1.7974658E 02  -1.7942661E 02  -1.7669968E 01
MAG  13- 16   3.1163244E 00   4.0961990E 01   4.0028656E 01   1.3333857E 03
PHA          -1.7669968E 01  -1.7801411E 02   1.6998630E 02   1.6973849E 02
MAG  17- 20   2.0000994E 03   1.6234818E 00   2.0401272E 03   6.6669263E 02
PHA           1.6998647E 02  -9.9964340E 01  -9.9643917E 00  -1.0238675E 01
MAG  21- 24   6.6669263E 02   2.8963368E-03   1.4066707E-02   1.2575370E-01
PHA          -1.0238675E 01   8.9696609E 01   7.1648071E 01  -1.0001363E 02
MAG  25- 25   8.3904991E 00
PHA          -1.0027498E 02
```

FREQ = 2.0000000E 00

NODE VOLTAGES:
```
MAG   1-  4   4.0362148E 04   6.3393867E 03   6.3369102E 03   2.9863195E 04
PHA          -8.0736221E 01  -6.5808678E-01  -6.6367859E-01  -1.7987068E 02
MAG   5-  8   6.3059609E 03   4.6904063E 03   4.6885742E 03   2.1074227E 04
PHA          -7.3392600E-01  -9.9792725E 01  -9.9798294E 01   8.3910294E 01
MAG   9- 10   4.6656719E 03   9.4646406E 03
PHA          -9.9868561E 01   1.4722374E 02
```

ELEMENT CURRENTS:
```
MAG   1-  4   4.0362105E-03   9.9935818E-01   3.1696945E-02   9.0562707E-01
PHA          -8.0736221E 01   2.2838891E-01   1.7934186E 02   1.7934186E 02
MAG   5-  8   6.3815832E-02   6.3814759E-02   2.9863186E 00   3.1872196E 00
PHA           1.3363128E 01   1.3359118E 01   1.2927115E-01   1.3374166E 01
MAG   9- 12   3.1529789E 00   7.9242998E-01   7.3940599E-01   2.3452032E-02
PHA           1.7926601E 02  -9.0733871E 01  -9.8906052E 01   8.0207230E 01
MAG  13- 16   6.7005813E-01   4.7214586E-02   4.7213972E-02   2.1074219E 00
PHA           8.0207230E 01  -8.5768539E 01  -8.5772476E 01  -9.6089600E 01
MAG  17- 20   2.3581715E 00   2.3328362E 00   5.8630568E-01   4.7323209E-01
PHA          -8.5760498E 01   8.0131393E 01   1.7013138E 02   1.4722374E 02
MAG  21- 24   4.7323209E-01   4.0096008E-08   4.5489778E-06   2.9665408E-08
PHA           1.4722374E 02   1.0335905E 02   8.9990417E 01   4.2275076E 00
MAG  25- 25   2.2364405E-06
PHA          -6.7643557E 00
```

Fig. 17.23(B)

```
FREQ =  8.0000000E 00


NODE VOLTAGES:
MAG   1-  4   1.2108332E 04   6.3262344E 03   6.3237539E 03   2.7433957E 04
PHA          -5.8509735E 01  -3.4820242E 00  -3.5043955E 00  -1.6484650E 02
MAG   5-  8   6.2927969E 03   1.4333355E 04   1.4327730E 04   7.0037813E 04
PHA          -3.7854443E 00  -1.0981966E 02  -1.0984206E 02   1.0692868E 02
MAG   9- 10   1.4257602E 04   6.2709836E 04
PHA          -1.1012318E 02   1.3337254E 02


ELEMENT CURRENTS:
MAG   1-  4   1.2108327E-03   9.9936801E-01   3.1631187E-02   9.0374821E-01
PHA          -5.8509735E 01   5.9196021E-02   1.7651793E 02   1.7651793E 02
MAG   5-  8   8.7545812E-02   8.7537527E-02   2.7433949E 00   4.3739700E 00
PHA           4.1354675E 01   4.1344955E 01   1.5153467E 01   4.1366653E 01
MAG   9- 12   3.1463985E 00   3.1631031E 00   2.2642546E 00   7.1666777E-02
PHA           1.7621451E 02  -9.3785431E 01  -1.0627736E 02   7.0180237E 01
MAG  13- 16   2.0476217E 00   1.9837046E-01   1.9836044E-01   7.0037823E 00
PHA           7.0180237E 01  -6.4971100E 01  -6.4982788E 01  -7.3071274E 01
MAG  17- 20   9.9100800E 00   7.1287985E 00   7.1666451E 00   3.1354904E 00
PHA          -6.4971268E 01   6.9876755E 01   1.5987674E 02   1.3337254E 02
MAG  21- 24   3.1354904E 00   2.2000575E-07   1.6832157E-05   4.9853406E-07
PHA           1.3337254E 02   1.3134491E 02   1.0168982E 02   2.5017136E 01
MAG  25- 25   4.1200023E-05
PHA           1.0922271E 01




FREQ =  1.6000000E 01


NODE VOLTAGES:
MAG   1-  4   8.4773867E 03   6.2844180E 03   6.2819180E 03   3.3881707E 04
PHA          -4.2599594E 01  -7.0158606E 00  -7.0606012E 00  -1.4721777E 02
MAG   5-  8   6.2509414E 03   2.5116820E 04   2.5106816E 04   1.8637413E 05
PHA          -7.6227293E 00  -1.1163528E 02  -1.1168004E 02   1.2676169E 02
MAG   9- 10   2.4983023E 04   1.8086550E 05
PHA          -1.1224229E 02   1.4072675E 02


ELEMENT CURRENTS:
MAG   1-  4   8.4773847E-04   9.9937612E-01   3.1422105E-02   8.9777452E-01
PHA          -4.2599594E 01   3.2897379E-02   1.7298410E 02   1.7298410E 02
MAG   5-  8   1.3770252E-01   1.3768351E-01   3.3881702E 00   6.8807802E 00
PHA           5.5932449E 01   5.5917938E 01   3.2782181E 01   5.5933670E 01
MAG   9- 12   3.1254702E 00   6.2841282E 00   3.9941196E 00   1.2558407E-01
PHA           1.7237724E 02  -9.7622681E 01  -1.0458446E 02   6.8364670E 01
MAG  13- 16   3.5881166E 00   5.5043465E-01   5.5039728E-01   1.8637405E 01
PHA           6.8364670E 01  -4.8672882E 01  -4.8693802E 01  -5.3238251E 01
MAG  17- 20   2.7500153E 01   1.24915C9E 01   2.5115646E 01   9.0432730E 00
PHA          -4.8686066E 01   6.775766CE 01   1.5775763E 02   1.4072675E 02
MAG  21- 24   9.0432730E 00   6.9207266E-07   3.9120307E-05   2.7665974E-06
PHA           1.4072675E 02   1.4591791E 02   1.1684563E 02   4.1306183E 01
MAG  25- 25   2.0172335E-04
PHA           3.0641327E 01
```

Fig. 17.23(B) continued

FREQ = 3.2000000E 01

NODE VOLTAGES:
MAG 1- 4   7.1395938E 03   6.1250703E 03   6.1224883E 03   5.3789984E 04
PHA   -3.3567993E 01 -1.3812674E 01 -1.3902136E 01 -1.3866634E 02
MAG 5- 8   6.0914141E 03   4.6146105E 04   4.6126668E 04   6.2409231E 05
PHA   -1.5026297E 01 -1.1891287E 02 -1.1900238E 02   1.3355817E 02
MAG 9- 10   4.5892602E 04   6.1932319E 05
PHA   -1.2012685E 02   1.4064594E 02

ELEMENT CURRENTS:
MAG 1- 4   7.1395910E-04   9.9940515E-01   3.0625358E-02   8.7501031E-01
PHA   -3.3567993E 01   2.2631925E-02   1.6618729E 02   1.6618729E 02
MAG 5- 8   2.4761194E-01   2.4756366E-01   5.3789978E 00   1.2372968E 01
PHA   6.1022598E 01   6.0997742E 01   4.1333618E 01   6.1008820E 01
MAG 9- 12   3.0457067E 00   1.2247510E 01   7.5290051E 00   2.3073053E-01
PHA   1.6497365E 02 -1.0502628E 02 -1.0507333E 02   6.1087021E 01
MAG 13- 16   6.5923004E 00   1.8657551E 00   1.8656139E 00   6.2409225E 01
PHA   6.1087021E 01 -4.4056320E 01 -4.4096130E 01 -4.6441788E 01
MAG 17- 20   9.3217224E 01   2.2946289E 01   9.2272491E 01   3.0966141E 01
PHA   -4.4051827E 01   5.9873108E 01   1.4987308E 02   1.4064594E 02
MAG 21- 24   3.0966141E 01   2.4887804E-06   1.1561351E-04   1.8755192E-05
PHA   1.4064594E 02   1.5099771E 02   1.2631549E 02   4.5903839E 01
MAG 25- 25   1.2856554E-03
PHA   3.9611923E 01

FREQ = 6.4000000E 01

NODE VOLTAGES:
MAG 1- 4   6.2343164E 03   5.5912969E 03   5.5884141E 03   8.8973438E 04
PHA   -3.6164032E 01 -2.5829422E 01 -2.6008148E 01 -1.4776808E 02
MAG 5- 8   5.5568281E 03   7.9795CCCE 04   7.9755500E 04   2.1026100E 06
PHA   -2.8255569E 01 -1.3743712E 02 -1.3761584E 02   1.2186253E 02
MAG 9- 10   7.9305000E 04   2.098559CE 06
PHA   -1.3986397E 02   1.25420C3E 02

ELEMENT CURRENTS:
MAG 1- 4   6.2343176E-04   9.9949670E-01   2.7956493E-02   7.9875702E-01
PHA   -3.6164032E 01   2.1088954E-02   1.5417053E 02   1.5417053E 02
MAG 5- 8   4.4183886E-01   4.4168013E-01   8.8973427E 00   2.2075699E 01
PHA   5.4691101E 01   5.4646591E 01   3.2231857E 01   5.4656830E 01
MAG 9- 12   2.7784138E 00   2.2345306E 01   1.4260733E 01   3.9898252E-01
PHA   1.517444CE 02 -1.1825554E 02 -1.1157584E 02   4.2562836E 01
MAG 13- 16   1.1399502E 01   6.3058138E 00   6.3053169E 00   2.1026105E 02
PHA   4.2562836E 01 -5.6875534E 01 -5.6953964E 01 -5.8137421E 01
MAG 17- 20   3.1505444E 02   3.9652496E 01   3.1890405E 02   1.0492793E 02
PHA   -5.6951752E 01   4.0135986E 01   1.3013597E 02   1.2542003E 02
MAG 21- 24   1.0492793E 02   8.8805054E-06   3.7010550E-04   1.2677591E-04
PHA   1.2542003E 02   1.446465BE 02   1.1927252E 02   3.3046021E 01
MAG 25- 25   8.5195005E-03
PHA   2.9741440E 01

Fig. 17.23(B) continued

FREQ = 1.2800000E 02

NODE VOLTAGES:
```
MAG   1-  4   4.7757930F 03   4.3355000E 03   4.3316367F 03   1.1868175F 05
PHA          -4.7783417F 01  -4.2258118E 01  -4.2613953E 01  -1.7347757E 02
MAG   5-  8   4.2972188E 03   1.0774269E 05   1.0764788E 05   5.6258890E 06
PHA          -4.7101517E 01  -1.6796074E 02  -1.6831651E 02   9.3040222E 01
MAG   9- 10   1.0679363E 05   5.6231730E 06
PHA          -1.7280580E 02   9.4820724E 01
```

ELEMENT CURRENTS:
```
MAG   1-  4   4.7757919E-04   9.9967915E-01   2.1677498E-02   6.1935717E-01
PHA          -4.7783417E 01   2.0272013E-02   1.3774185E 02   1.3774185F 02
MAG   5-  8   6.7970920E-01   6.7915702E-01   1.1868179E 01   3.3947830E 01
PHA           3.9399918E 01   3.9329575E 01   6.5223827E 00   3.9341141E 01
MAG   9- 12   2.1486101E 00   3.4560272E 01   2.4821136E 01   5.3871357E-01
PHA           1.3289842F 02  -1.3710150E 02  -1.2564122E 02   1.2039253F 01
MAG  13- 16   1.5391817E 01   1.6885818E 01   1.6884430E 01   5.6258887E 02
PHA           1.2039253E 01  -8.6208237E 01  -8.6364456E 01  -8.6959671F 01
MAG  17- 20   8.4365820E 02   5.3396790E 01   8.5888452F 02   2.8115845E 02
PHA          -8.6363312E 01   7.1941557E 00   9.7194138E 01   9.4820724E 01
MAG  21- 24   2.8115845E 02   2.7310511E-05   9.7764330E-04   6.7896303E-04
PHA           9.4820724E 01   1.2932957E 02   9.4978149E 01   3.6355143E 00
MAG  25- 25   4.5384265E-02
PHA           1.9596472E 00
```


FREQ = 2.5600000E 02

NODE VOLTAGES:
```
MAG   1-  4   2.9730781F 03   2.7116587E 03   2.7052571E 03   1.0583513F 05
PHA          -5.8900482E 01  -5.5507889E 01  -5.6206177E 01   1.5652930F 02
MAG   5-  8   2.6594246E 03   9.6531875F 04   9.6308938E 04   9.9589190E 06
PHA          -6.5125793E 01   1.599C1C6F 02   1.5920285E 02   5.8195175E 01
MAG   9- 10   9.4678500E 04   9.9577160E 06
PHA           1.5027869E 02   5.9085663F 01
```

ELEMENT CURRENTS:
```
MAG   1-  4   2.9730750E-04   9.9984646E-01   1.3558291E-02   3.8737977F-01
PHA          -5.8900482E 01   1.4588375E-02   1.2449205E 02   1.2449205F 02
MAG   5-  8   8.4058654E-01   8.393C689F-01   1.0583514E 01   4.1958038E 01
PHA           2.3167892E 01   2.3082947E 01  -2.3470642F 01   2.3093811E 01
MAG   9- 12   1.3297119E 00   4.2776688E 01   3.5521271E 01   4.8265946F-01
PHA           1.1487410E 02  -1.5512582E 02  -1.4441309E 02  -2.0098907E 01
MAG  13- 16   1.3790271E 01   2.9897537E 01   2.9894714E 01   9.9589160E 02
PHA          -2.0098907E 01  -1.2119023F 02  -1.2150233E 02  -1.2180472E 02
MAG  17- 20   1.4937397E 03   4.7339249E 01   1.5228989E 03   4.9788550E 02
PHA          -1.2150179E 02  -2.9721268E 01   6.02787C2E 01   5.9085663E 01
MAG  21- 24   4.9788550E 02   6.7501C38F-05   1.7391159E-03   2.4042758E-03
PHA           5.9085663E 01   1.1308295E 02   6.5754059E 01  -3.1502380E 01
MAG  25- 25   1.6049176E-01
PHA          -3.2347626E 01
```

Fig. 17.23(B) continued

FREQ = 1.0240000E 03

NODE VOLTAGES:
```
MAG  1-  4   9.4407715E 02   8.8375269E 02   8.6346289E 02   4.1046984E 04
PHA         -5.2429596E 01  -4.9356583E 01  -5.1370972E 01   1.3682764E 02
MAG  5-  8   7.2772095E 02   3.8397789E 04   3.7542559E 04   1.3303939E 07
PHA         -8.3487915E 01   1.3982851E 02   1.3779124E 02   1.5113518E 01
MAG  9- 10   3.1636152E 04   1.3303838E 07
PHA          1.0565794E 02   1.5336147E 01
```

ELEMENT CURRENTS:
```
MAG  1-  4   9.4407689E-05   9.9994242E-01   4.4187605E-03   1.2625039E-01
PHA         -5.2429596E 01   4.2875744E-03   1.3064337E 02   1.3064337E 02
MAG  5-  8   9.2019635E-01   9.18147C3E-01   4.1046972E 00   4.5904648E 01
PHA          6.1901693E 0C   6.0625467E 00  -4.3172318E 01   6.0665188E 00
MAG  9- 12   3.6386037E-01   4.6821381E 01   4.3334167E 01   1.9198895E-01
PHA          9.6512039E 01  -1.7348788E 02  -1.6982150E 02  -4.0171448E 01
MAG 13- 16   5.4853983E 00   3.9951309E 01   3.9938324E 01   1.3303938E 03
PHA         -4.0171448E 01  -1.6353979E 02  -1.6478777E 02  -1.6488644E 02
MAG 17- 20   1.9955854E C3   1.5818C71E C1   2.C354624E 03   6.6519165E 02
PHA         -1.6478760E C2  -7.4342010E 01   1.5657948E 01   1.5336147E 01
MAG 21- 24   6.6519165E 02   2.9536686E-04   2.6959542E-03   1.2848124E-02
PHA          1.5336147E C1   9.60625C0E 01   4.6659286E 01  -7.4787781E 01
MAG 25- 25   8.5727954E-C1
PHA         -7.5022354E C1
```

FREQ = 2.0480000E 03

NODE VOLTAGES:
```
MAG  1-  4   6.4127563E 02   6.1912695E 02   5.8976270E 02   2.8224547E 04
PHA         -3.6189972E 01  -3.3286865E 01  -3.5420135E 01   1.4695151E 02
MAG  5-  8   3.6563916E 02   2.72C566CE 04   2.5953758E 04   1.3528108E 07
PHA         -8.6880600E 01   1.4977768E 02   1.4753961E 02   5.7514830E 00
MAG  9- 10   1.6085027E 04   1.3528082E 07
PHA          9.6061142E C1   5.8627949E 00
```

ELEMENT CURRENTS:
```
MAG  1-  4   6.4127555E-05   9.9994820E-01   3.0956357E-03   8.8446736E-02
PHA         -3.6189972E 01   2.1696188E-03   1.4671310E 02   1.4671310E 02
MAG  5-  8   9.2479271E-C1   9.226C683E-01   2.8224545E 00   4.6128036E 01
PHA          3.1165962E 0C   2.8939543E 00  -3.3048431E 01   2.8960571E 00
MAG  9- 12   1.8281960E-01   4.705C293E 01   4.3872025E 01   1.3602829E-01
PHA          9.3119354E 01  -1.7688C58E 02  -1.7494359E 02  -3.0222275E 01
MAG 13- 16   3.8865232E 00   4.0654633E 01   4.0611420E 01   1.3528105E 03
PHA         -3.0222275E 01  -1.7166762E 02  -1.7416228E 02  -1.7424850E 02
MAG 17- 20   2.0292178E C3   8.0425110E 00   2.C698135E 03   6.7640381E 02
PHA         -1.7416217E C2  -8.3938812E 01   6.C611639E 00   5.8627949E 00
MAG 21- 24   6.7640381E 02   5.936C336E-04   3.7077512E-03   2.6129305E-02
PHA          5.8627949E C0   9.28939C6E 01   5.6903015E 01  -8.4162231E 01
MAG 25- 25   1.7434168E 00
PHA         -8.4316376E C1
```

Fig. 17.23(B) continued

```
FREQ = 8.1920000E 03


NODE VOLTAGES:
MAG  1-  4   5.0850073E 02   5.0666846E 02   4.7037061E 02   2.2216148E 04
PHA         -1.1410247E 01  -1.0333454E 01  -1.1207486E 01   1.6171483E 02
MAG  5-  8   9.1411682E 01   2.2079371E 04   2.0543840E 04   1.3423303E 07
PHA         -8.9941895E 01   1.6276297E 02   1.6123470E 02  -7.7717505E 00
MAG  9- 10   3.9901563E 03   1.3423302E 07
PHA          8.2492935E 01  -7.7439213E 00


ELEMENT CURRENTS:
MAG  1-  4   5.0850053E-05   9.9995011E-01   2.5333427E-03   7.2381198E-02
PHA         -1.1410247E 01   5.7641300E-04   1.6966653E 02   1.6966653E 02
MAG  5-  8   9.2634827E-01   9.2261583E-01   2.2216148E 00   4.6128662E 01
PHA          8.3180368E-01  -1.3424838E-03  -1.8285126E 01  -4.6542892E-04
MAG  9- 12   4.5705829E-02   4.7051254E 01   4.4020920E 01   1.1039686E-01
PHA          9.0058060E 01  -1.7994188E 02  -1.7910767E 02  -1.7236969E 01
MAG 13- 16   3.1541958E 00   4.0931000E 01   4.0297058E 01   1.3423301E 03
PHA         -1.7236969E 01  -1.7768556E 02   1.7243423E 02   1.7222824E 02
MAG 17- 20   2.0135100E 03   1.9950771E 00   2.0538062E 03   6.7116479E 02
PHA          1.7243440E 02  -9.7507004E 01  -7.5070229E 00  -7.7439213E 00
MAG 21- 24   6.7116479E 02   2.3744369E-03   1.1675369E-02   1.0370815E-01
PHA         -7.7439213E 00   8.9998611E 01   7.1861237E 01  -9.7565689E 01
MAG 25- 25   6.9196053E 00
PHA         -9.7788406E 01



FREQ = 1.6384000E 04


NODE VOLTAGES:
MAG  1-  4   4.9891479E 02   4.9836670E 02   4.6157056E 02   2.1036332E 04
PHA         -6.7557497E 00  -6.2012482E 00  -6.7376127E 00   1.5796686E 02
MAG  5-  8   4.5506500E 01   2.0957598E 04   1.9454508E 04   1.2896883E 07
PHA         -9.1045044E 01   1.5850847E 02   1.5662131E 02  -1.8122223E 01
MAG  9- 10   1.9168726E 03   1.2896882E 07
PHA          7.2309784E 01  -1.8108307E 01


ELEMENT CURRENTS:
MAG  1-  4   4.9891460E-05   9.9995041E-01   2.4918341E-03   7.1195245E-02
PHA         -6.7557497E 00   3.3629034E-04   1.7379869E 02   1.7379869E 02
MAG  5-  8   9.2672873E-01   9.1858882E-01   2.1036329E 00   4.5927460E 01
PHA          4.9248737E-01  -1.0796003E 00  -2.2033081E 01  -1.0786562E 00
MAG  9- 12   2.2753246E-02   4.6846039E 01   4.3961243E 01   1.0478795E-01
PHA          8.8954895E 01   1.7895488E 02   1.7987488E 02  -2.1491486E 01
MAG 13- 16   2.9939423E 00   4.1091003E 01   3.8717407E 01   1.2896880E 03
PHA         -2.1491486E 01  -1.7855064E 02   1.6227589E 02   1.6187772E 02
MAG 17- 20   1.9345806E 03   9.5843601E-01   1.9732979E 03   6.4484375E 02
PHA          1.6227617E 02  -1.0769017E 02  -1.7690170E 01  -1.8108307E 01
MAG 21- 24   6.4484375E 02   4.7281459E-03   2.2114262E-02   1.9928569E-01
PHA         -1.8108307E 01   8.8920364E 01   6.8291611E 01  -1.0772404E 02
MAG 25- 25   1.3296472E 01
PHA         -1.0813008E 02
```

Fig. 17.23(B) continued

FREQ = 3.2768000E 04

NODE VOLTAGES:
MAG   1- 4   4.9118799E 02   4.9098389E 02   4.5403491E 02   1.8342207E 04
PHA   -4.9665508E 00 -4.6842318E 00 -5.0964508E 00   1.4636876E 02
MAG   5- 8   2.2464813E 01   1.8285191E 04   1.6939297E 04   1.1270203E 07
PHA   -9.2233719E 01   1.4664940E 02   1.4348363E 02 -3.4471359E 01
MAG   9- 10   8.3760815E 02   1.1270203E 07
PHA   5.6343979E 01 -3.4464417E 01

ELEMENT CURRENTS:
MAG   1- 4   4.9118797E-05   9.9995106E-01   2.4549193E-03   7.0140541E-02
PHA   -4.9665508E 00   2.4365769E-04   1.7531577E 02   1.7531577E 02
MAG   5- 8   9.2761701E-01   9.0693688E-01   1.8342199E 00   4.5345261E 01
PHA   3.6644578E-01 -2.2604065E 00 -3.3631195E 01 -2.2591972E 00
MAG   9- 12   1.1232406E-02   4.6252197E 01   4.3769196E 01   9.1425955E-02
PHA   8.7766235E 01   1.777662CE 02   1.7894740E 02 -3.3350540E 01
MAG 13- 16   2.6121702E 00   4.1509033E 01   3.383638CE 01   1.1270200E 03
PHA   -3.3350540E 01 -1.7905811E 02   1.4631795E 02   1.4552859E 02
MAG 17- 20   1.6906921E 03   4.188C399E-01   1.7245283E 03   5.6351001E 02
PHA   1.4631850E 02 -1.2365598E 02 -3.3656006E 01 -3.4464417E 01
MAG 21- 24   5.6351001E 02   9.3363412E-03   3.8588133E-02   3.4832424E-01
PHA   -3.4464417E 01   8.7739563E 01   5.7031830E 01 -1.2368199E 02
MAG 25- 25   2.3238770E 01
PHA   -1.2447440E 02

FREQ = 6.5536000E 04

NODE VOLTAGES:
MAG   1- 4   4.8133887E 02   4.8124658E 02   4.4421680E 02   1.3217438E 04
PHA   -4.4330521E 00 -4.2889280E 00 -4.6747723E 00   1.3097368E 02
MAG   5- 8   1.0999873E 01   1.3178918E 04   1.2133602E 04   8.0780420E 06
PHA   -9.3224533E 01   1.3113022E 02   1.2513486E 02 -5.5022018E 01
MAG   9- 10   3.0026709E 02   8.0780420E 06
PHA   3.6584030E 01 -5.5018539E 01

ELEMENT CURRENTS:
MAG   1- 4   4.8133865E-05   9.9995196E-01   2.4062330E-03   6.8749487E-02
PHA   -4.4330521E 00   2.1317748E-04   1.7571103E 02   1.7571103E 02
MAG   5- 8   9.2901075E-01   8.881492CE-01   1.3217430E 00   4.4406525E 01
PHA   3.2842642E-01 -3.255847CF 00 -4.9026276E 01 -3.2546234E 00
MAG   9- 12   5.4999329E-03   4.5294678E 01   4.34550C2E 01   6.5894544E-02
PHA   8.6775421E 01   1.767753 9E 02   1.7794173E 02 -4.8869736E 01
MAG 13- 16   1.8827019E 00   4.214534CF 01   2.4259445E 01   8.0780420E 06
PHA   -4.8869736E 01   1.7987357E 02   1.2655286E 02   1.2497792F 02
MAG 17- 20   1.2121646E 03   1.5013355E-01   1.2364241E 03   4.0390186E 02
PHA   1.2655394E 02 -1.4341594E 02 -5.3415955E 01 -5.5018539E 01
MAG 21- 24   4.0390186E 02   1.8285867E-02   5.5748746E-02   4.9947137E-01
PHA   -5.5018539E 01   8.6744110E 01   4.2287994E 01 -1.4344708E 02
MAG 25- 25   3.3313309E 01
PHA   -1.4502174E 02

Fig. 17.23(B) continued

FREQ = 2.6214400E 05

NODE VOLTAGES:
```
MAG  1-  4   4.6931836E 02   4.6928198E 02   4.3237256E 02   4.4856719E 03
PHA         -6.9037533F 00  -6.8669586E 00  -7.5007353E 00   1.2108690E 02
MAG  5-  8   2.6774654E CO   4.4753506E C3   3.7031082E 03   2.4522950E 06
PHA         -9.7051193E C1   1.2118913E C2   9.9751129E 01  -8.6166107E 01
MAG  9- 10   2.2916809E C1   2.4522950E 06
PHA          1.0204152E 01  -8.6165283E 01
```


ELEMENT CURRENTS:
```
MAG  1-  4   4.6931818E-05   9.9995339F-01   2.3464100E-03   6.7040265E-02
PHA         -6.9037533E 0C   3.2323715E-04   1.7313300E 02   1.7313300E 02
MAG  5-  8   9.3110144E-C1   8.6471999E-C1   4.4856715E-01   4.3235703E 01
PHA          5.1086313F-C1  -7.1459274E 00  -5.8913055E 01  -7.1454601E 00
MAG  9- 12   1.3387327E-C3   4.4100479E 01   4.2901077E C1   2.2376966E-02
PHA          8.2948761E 01   1.7294875E C2   1.7325452E 02  -5.8810760E 01
MAG 13- 16   6.3934189E-C1   4.2497482E C1   7.4059944E 00   2.4522955E 02
PHA         -5.8810760E 01   1.7395819E 02   1.0010570E 02   9.3833786E 01
MAG 17- 20   3.7005566E 02   1.1458404E-C2   3.774624CE 02   1.2261476E 02
PHA          1.0010986E C2  -1.6979582F-02  -7.9795837E 01  -8.6165283E 01
MAG 21- 24   1.2261476E C2   7.1213961E-C2   7.8522861E-02   6.0992044E-01
PHA         -8.6165283E 01   8.2854019E C1   3.5152130E 01  -1.6989417E 02
MAG 25- 25   4.0452408E 01
PHA         -1.7615724E C2
```


FREQ = 1.0485760E 06

NODE VOLTAGES:
```
MAG  1-  4   4.2892944E 02   4.2890039F 02   3.9479907E 02   2.1372004E 03
PHA         -2.2573349E 01  -2.2563995E 01  -2.4792038E 01   1.3211011E 02
MAG  5-  8   6.1122179E-C1   2.1360349E 03   9.3399683E 02   5.6977075E 05
PHA         -1.1433266E 02   1.3218355E C2   9.1137604E 01  -1.1250977E 02
MAG  9- 10   1.4452162F 00   5.6977075E C5
PHA          1.6108150E CC  -1.1250955E C2
```


ELEMENT CURRENTS:
```
MAG  1-  4   4.2892934E-05   9.9996036E-01   2.1445018E-03   6.1271485E-02
PHA         -2.2573349E C1   9.4341976E-04   1.5743596E 02   1.5743596E 02
MAG  5-  8   9.4171363F-C1   7.8958941E-01   2.1371996E-01   3.9479248E 01
PHA          1.4816771E C0  -2.4703339E 01  -4.7889847E 01  -2.4703217E 01
MAG  9- 12   3.0561071E-C4   4.0269684E 01   3.9227386E 01   1.0680173E-02
PHA          6.5667236E 01   1.5566727E C2   1.5519260E 02  -4.7816391E 01
MAG 13- 16   3.0514783E-C1   3.8936874E 01   1.8679714E 00   5.6977066E 01
PHA         -4.7816391E C1   1.5537428E C2   9.1226242E 01   6.7490128E 01
MAG 17- 20   9.3346405E C1   7.2260783F-C4   9.5216522E 01   2.8488525E 01
PHA          9.1240341E C1  -1.7838913E C2  -8.8389145E 01  -1.1250955E 02
MAG 21- 24   2.8488525E C1   2.6010633E-01   1.6504878E-C1   6.1534685E-01
PHA         -1.1250955E C2   6.529660CE C1   4.5654709E 01  -1.7877370E 02
MAG 25- 25   3.7595139E 01
PHA          1.5752776E C2
```


Fig. 17.23(B) continued

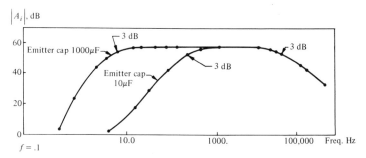

Fig. 17.24 Plots of A_i versus frequency for two different values of emitter capacitance of Fig. 17.22 based on the computer solution.

17.7 Summary

In this chapter the fundamentals of ECAP were presented. ECAP, originated by IBM, and its variations are programs developed to aid the electrical engineer in the analysis and synthesis of electrical and electronic networks. The advantage of ECAP over a language such as FORTRAN is that ECAP is intended specifically for network analysis. This results in fewer and simpler statements and less effort on the user's part to implement the program.

In using ECAP, or its modifications, the engineer first draws a model of the physical device, or network, in strict accordance with the rules of the language. From the model the ECAP input statements are written. Numbers in the input statements can be written either in fixed point or in floating point. The numerical results are always printed in floating point.

Program elements and the ECAP solution of dc and ac steady-state networks were discussed. The sensitivity and frequency response of networks were also studied.

References

IBM, *1620 Electronic Circuit Analysis Program (ECAP)*, User's manual 1620-EE-02X, 1965.

JENSEN, R. W., and M. D. LIEBERMAN, *IBM Electronic Circuit Analysis Program*, Prentice-Hall, Englewood Cliffs, New Jersey, 1968.

LEVIN, H., *Introduction to Computer Analysis*, Prentice-Hall, Englewood Cliffs, New Jersey, 1970.

MULLINS, J., and D. K. PARKER, *SENCRAN (Software for Electronic Network and Circuit Response Analysis)*, The National Cash Register Company, Dayton, Ohio, 1968.

Problems

Note: Once the student has mastered ECAP, it is urged that he be encouraged to write programs for problems selected from the preceding chapters. In the following problems, the objective is to help the student achieve self-confidence and to develop the mechanics of problem solving using ECAP.

17.1   How do the following numbers appear when printed out at a computer center?

$$10, 175, 0.1, 10^3, 1.5, -136.4$$

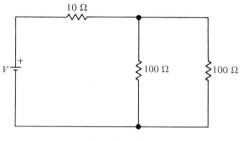

Fig. P17.2

17.2   For the circuit of Fig. P17.2, draw an ECAP model and write a dc ECAP program. All node voltages and branch currents are to be determined. $V = 2$ V.

17.3   Repeat Prob. 17.2 for $V = 15$ V.

17.4   In Prob. 17.2, calculate manually the node voltages and branch currents. Write your answers in the form printed out on a computer. Compare these results with those obtained on the computer.

17.5   Repeat Prob. 17.4 for $V = 15$ V.

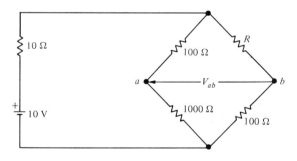

Fig. P17.6

17.6   Referring to Fig. P17.6, (a) draw an ECAP model and write a dc ECAP program for $R = 10$ ohms. Calculate the value of V_{ab}. (b) Modify the program for $R = 100$ ohms and 1000 ohms.

17.7   For the circuit of Fig. P17.7, draw its ECAP model and write a program to solve for the dc node voltages and branch currents.

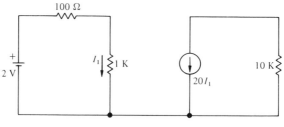

Fig. P17.7

17.8   Repeat Prob. 17.7 for a controlled source of $45I_1$.
17.9   Which of the branches in Fig. P17.9 are acceptable in an ECAP
       program? Modify those that are not acceptable.
17.10 A two-stage transistor amplifier is given in Fig. P17.10. Draw its
       ECAP model and write a program to calculate the quiescent operat-
       ing point for each transistor. Assume identical transistors with
       $h_{FE} = 50$, $h_{IE} = 1\ \mathrm{K}$, $h_{OE} = 0.05\ \mathrm{mmho}$, and $V_{BE} = 0.5\ \mathrm{V}$.
17.11 Repeat Prob. 17.10 for $h_{FE} = 60$.

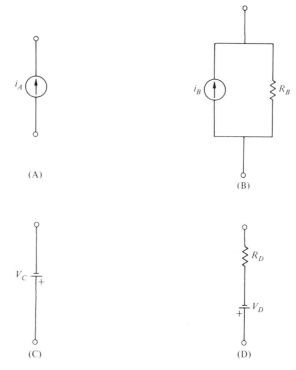

Fig. P17.9

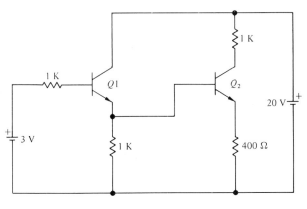

Fig. P17.10

17.12   For the inverting amplifier of Fig. 16.25C, the gain of the operational
amplifier is −4000. Write a program to calculate the gain if $R_2 = 1$ K,
10 K,..., 100 K. $R_1 = 1$ K.

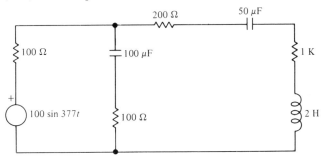

Fig. P17.13

17.13   For the circuit of Fig. P17.13, write the ac program to solve for the
node voltages and branch currents.

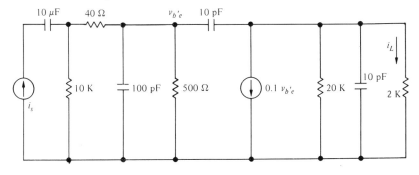

Fig. P17.16

17.14 Repeat Prob. 17.13 for a sinusoidal source of $100 \sin 3770t$.

17.15 Repeat Prob. 17.13 for a frequency range of 10 Hz to 5 kHz in 10 steps.

17.16 Write an ECAP program to determine i_L/i_s at low, mid, and high frequencies for the amplifier of Fig. P17.16.

17.17 Referring to Fig. P17.6, write a program to find the partials and sensitivities of V_{ab} with respect to the 10-V source and to resistance R.

17.18 In Fig. 9.10, both field-effect transistors are identical; $g_m = 0.5$ mho, $C_{ds} = C_{gs} = 5$ pF, $C_{dg} = 0.1$ pF, $r_p = 50$ K, $R_L = R_S = 1$ K, $R_g = 100$ K, and $C_1 = C_S = 10\,\mu$F. Write an ECAP program for calculating the high-frequency voltage gain.

Appendix

m_f	$J_0(m_f)$	$J_1(m_f)$	$J_2(m_f)$	$J_3(m_f)$	$J_4(m_f)$	$J_5(m_f)$	$J_6(m_f)$	$J_7(m_f)$	$J_8(m_f)$	$J_9(m_f)$	$J_{10}(m_f)$
0	1.0000	0.0000	0.0000	0.0000	0.0000	0.0000	0.0000	0.0000	0.0000	0.0000	0.0000
1	0.7652	0.4401	0.1149	0.0196	0.0025	0.0003	0.0000	0.0000	0.0000	0.0000	0.0000
2	0.2239	0.5767	0.3528	0.1289	0.0340	0.0070	0.0012	0.0002	0.0000	0.0000	0.0000
3	-0.2601	0.3391	0.4861	0.3091	0.1320	0.0430	0.0114	0.0026	0.0005	0.0000	0.0000
4	-0.3971	-0.0660	0.3641	0.4302	0.2811	0.1321	0.0491	0.0152	0.0040	0.0009	0.0002
5	-0.1776	-0.3276	0.0466	0.3648	0.3912	0.2611	0.1310	0.0534	0.0184	0.0055	0.0015
6	0.1506	-0.2767	-0.2429	0.1148	0.3576	0.3621	0.2458	0.1296	0.0565	0.0212	0.0070
7	0.3001	-0.0047	-0.3014	-0.1676	0.1578	0.3479	0.3392	0.2336	0.1280	0.0589	0.0235
8	0.1717	0.2346	-0.1130	-0.2911	-0.1054	0.1858	0.3376	0.3206	0.2235	0.1263	0.0608
9	-0.0903	0.2453	0.1448	-0.1809	-0.2655	-0.0550	0.2043	0.3275	0.3051	0.2149	0.1247
10	-0.2459	0.0453	0.2546	-0.0584	-0.2196	-0.2341	-0.0145	0.2167	0.3179	0.2919	0.2075
11	-0.1712	-0.1768	0.1390	0.2273	-0.0150	-0.2383	-0.2016	0.0184	0.2250	0.3089	0.2804
12	0.0477	-0.2234	-0.0849	0.1951	0.1825	-0.0735	-0.2437	-0.1703	0.0451	0.2304	0.3005
13	0.2069	-0.0703	-0.2177	0.0023	0.2193	0.1316	-0.1180	-0.2406	-0.1410	0.0670	0.2338
14	0.1711	0.1334	-0.1520	-0.1768	0.0762	0.2204	0.0812	-0.1508	-0.2320	-0.1143	0.0850

Fig. A.1 Some Bessel-function values

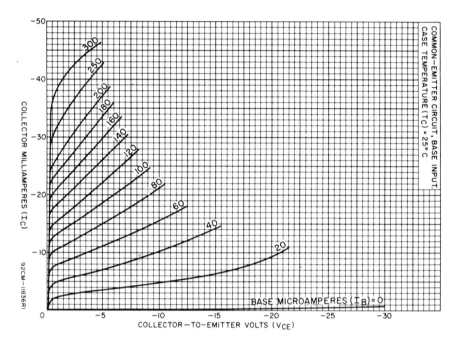

Fig. A.2 Typical collector characteristics for type 2N2614. (Courtesy RCA Corp.).

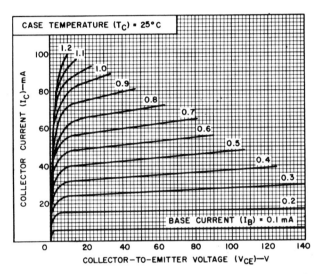

Fig. A.3 Typical output characteristics for types 2N3439, 2N3440, 2N4063, and 2N4064. (Courtesy RCA Corp.).

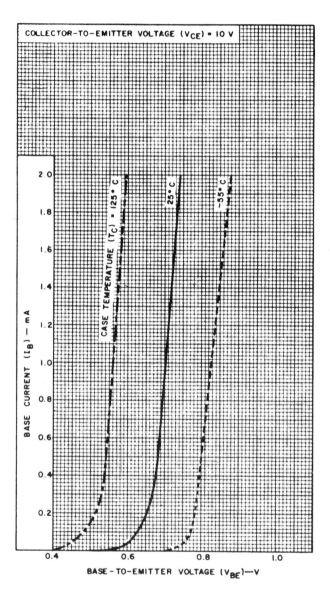

Fig. A.4 Typical input characteristics for types 2N3439, 2N3440, 2N4063, and 2N4064. (Courtesy RCA Corp.).

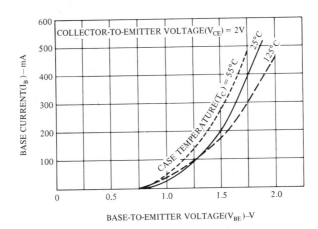

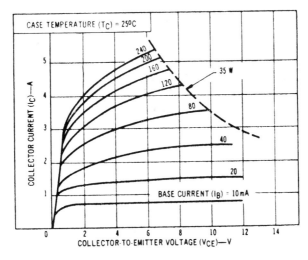

Fig. A.5 Typical input (above) and output (below) characteristics for type 2N3878, 2N3879, and 2N5202. Courtesy RCA Corp.

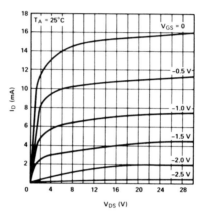

Fig. A.6 Output characteristics E300. (Courtesy Siliconix.)

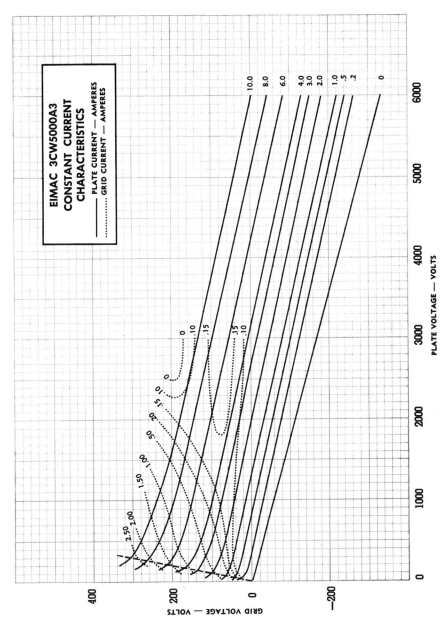

Fig. A.7 Eimac 3W500A3 typical constant current characteristics. (Courtesy Eimac.)

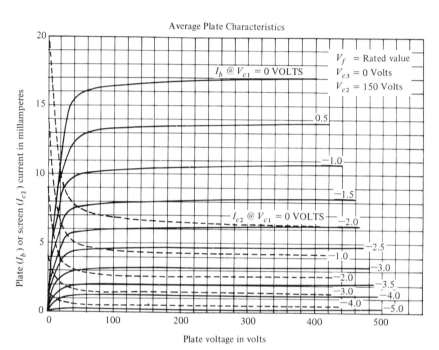

Fig. A.8 Average plate characteristics, 6AU6-A. (Courtesy GE.)

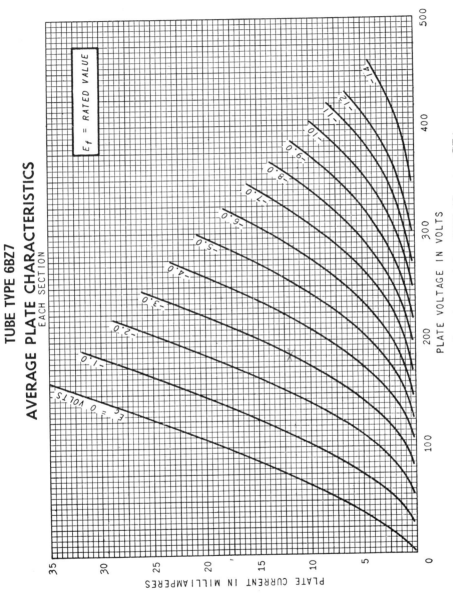

TUBE TYPE 6BZ7
AVERAGE PLATE CHARACTERISTICS
EACH SECTION

Fig. A.9 Average plate characteristics, 6BZ7. (Courtesy GE.)

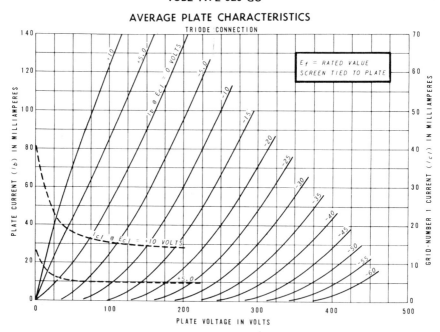

Fig. A.10 Average plate characteristics, 6L6-GC, triode connection. (Courtesy GE.)

Index